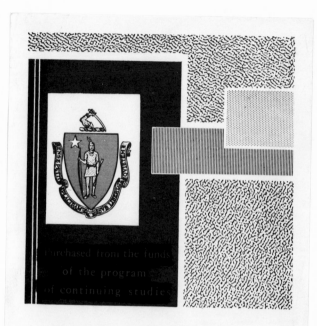

Purchased from the funds
of the program
of continuing studies

FRAMINGHAM
STATE COLLEGE

THE ORIGINS OF
PREBIOLOGICAL SYSTEMS

and of Their Molecular Matrices

"The question of the conditions under which living matter originated on the surface of the earth is still a subject limited largely to speculation. . . . . One of the purposes of the observation reported herein is to add another fact that might have some bearing upon this interesting question.

"One of the most popular current conceptions is that life originated in an organic milieu. The problem to which we are addressed is the origin of that organic milieu in the absence of any life. . . ."

Garrison, W. M., Morrison, D. C., Hamilton, J. G., Benson, A. A., and Calvin, M. (1951). *Science* 114, 416.

The Origins of
Prebiological Systems

and of Their Molecular Matrices

Proceedings of a Conference
Conducted at Wakulla Springs, Florida
on 27–30 October 1963 under the auspices of the
Institute for Space Biosciences
The Florida State University and
The National Aeronautics and Space Administration

EDITED BY

SIDNEY W. FOX

Institute for Space Biosciences
The Florida State University
Tallahassee, Florida
and
Institute of Molecular Evolution
School of Environmental and Planetary Sciences
University of Miami
Coral Gables, Florida

1965

ACADEMIC PRESS NEW YORK AND LONDON

ACADEMIC PRESS INC.
111 Fifth Avenue, New York, New York 10003

United Kingdom Edition published by
ACADEMIC PRESS INC. (LONDON) LTD.
Berkeley Square House, London W.1

LIBRARY OF CONGRESS CATALOG CARD NUMBER: 64-24656

First Printing, 1965
Second Printing, 1967

PRINTED IN THE UNITED STATES OF AMERICA.

Dedicated
To My Favorite
Biological Systems
Including Their
Cooriginator

Larry, Ron, and Tom
and
Raia

LIST OF CONTRIBUTORS

Numbers in parentheses indicate the pages on which the authors' contributions begin.

S. Akabori, *Institute for Protein Research, Osaka University, Osaka, Japan* (127)

J. D. Bernal, *Birkbeck College, University of London, London, England* (65)

M. S. Blois, *Biophysics Laboratory, Stanford University, Stanford, California* (19)

E. Bradley, *Institute for Space Biosciences, The Florida State University, Tallahassee, Florida* (317)

J. M. Buchanan, *Department of Biology, Massachusetts Institute of Technology, Cambridge, Massachusetts* (101)

E. Chargaff,* *Cell Chemistry Laboratory, Columbia University, New York, New York*

T. Dobzhansky,* *The Rockefeller Institute, New York, New York*

S. W. Fox, *Institute for Space Biosciences, The Florida State University, Tallahassee, Florida and Institute of Molecular Evolution, School of Environmental and Planetary Sciences, University of Miami, Coral Gables, Florida* (5, 187, 289, 317, 359, 361)

H. Gaffron, *Institute of Molecular Biophysics and Department of Biological Sciences, Fels Fund, The Florida State University, Tallahassee, Florida.* (437)

K. Grossenbacher, *Department of Soils and Plant Nutrition, University of California, Berkeley, California* (173)

J. B. S. Haldane, *Genetics and Biometry Laboratory, Bhubaneswar, India* (11, 89)

K. Harada, *Institute for Space Biosciences, The Florida State University, Tallahassee, Florida* (187, 289)

(*) Asterisk indicates discussant only.

T. H. JUKES, *Space Sciences Laboratory, University of California, Berkeley, California* (407)

C. A. KNIGHT, *Virus Laboratory, University of California, Berkeley, California* (173)

F. A. LIPMANN, *The Rockefeller Institute, New York, New York* (259)

A. E. MIRSKY, *The Rockefeller Institute, New York, New York* (257)

P. T. MORA, *Macromolecular Chemistry Section, National Institutes of Health, Bethesda, Maryland* (39, 281)

A. I. OPARIN, *A. N. Bakh Institute of Biochemistry, Academy of Sciences, Moscow, U.S.S.R.* (91, 331)

J. ORÓ, *Department of Chemistry, University of Houston, Houston, Texas* (137)

H. H. PATTEE, *Biophysics Laboratory, Stanford University, Stanford, California* (385)

N. W. PIRIE, *Rothamsted Experimental Station, Harpenden, Hertsfordshire, England* (9)

C. PONNAMPERUMA, *Exobiology Division, National Aeronautics and Space Administration, Ames Research Center, Moffett Field, California* (221)

F. H. QUIMBY, *Office of Space Sciences, National Aeronautics and Space Administration, Washington, D.C.* (1)

D. L. ROHLFING,* *Institute for Space Biosciences, The Florida State University, Tallahassee, Florida*

C. SAGAN, *Harvard University and Smithsonian Astrophysical Observatory, Cambridge, Massachusetts* (207)

G. SCHRAMM, *Max Planck-Institut für Virusforschung, Tübingen, Germany* (299)

A. W. SCHWARTZ, *Institute for Space Biosciences, The Florida State University, Tallahassee, Florida* (317)

E. E. SNELL, *Department of Biochemistry, University of California, Berkeley, California* (203)

H. B. STEINBACH, *Department of Zoology, University of Chicago, Chicago, Illinois* (329)

K. STEWART,* *Institute for Space Biosciences, The Florida State University, Tallahassee, Florida*

A. SZUTKA, *Department of Chemistry, University of Detroit, Detroit, Michigan* (243)

J. R. VALLENTYNE, *Department of Zoology, Cornell University, Ithaca, New York* (105)

R. S. YOUNG, *Exobiology Division, National Aeronautics and Space Administration, Ames Research Center, Moffett Field, California* (347)

S. YUYAMA,* *Department of Biological Sciences, The Florida State University, Tallahassee, Florida*

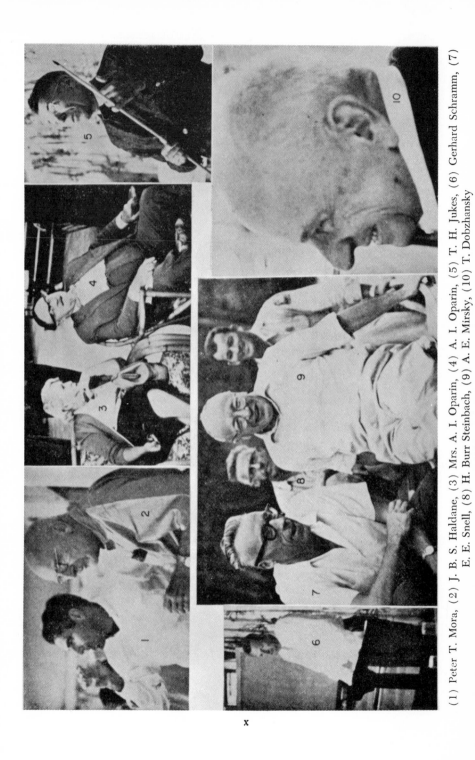

(1) Peter T. Mora, (2) J. B. S. Haldane, (3) Mrs. A. I. Oparin, (4) A. I. Oparin, (5) T. H. Jukes, (6) Gerhard Schramm, (7) E. E. Snell, (8) H. Burr Steinbach, (9) A. E. Mirsky, (10) T. Dobzhansky

x

(3) Mrs. A. I. Oparin, (4) A. I. Oparin, (7) E. E. Snell, (9) A. E. Mirsky, (11) Hans Gaffron, (12) Fritz Lipmann, (13) Richard S. Young, (14) Kaoru Harada, (15) G. Genaux, (16) G. Krampitz, (17) Maynard E. Dockendorf, (18) Anton Szutka, (19) F. H. Quimby, (20) Shiro Akabori, (21) Mrs. Shiro Akabori, (22) Cyril Ponnamperuma, (23) Sidney W. Fox, (24) J. M. Buchanan, (25) K. Stewart, (26) E. Chargaff

xi

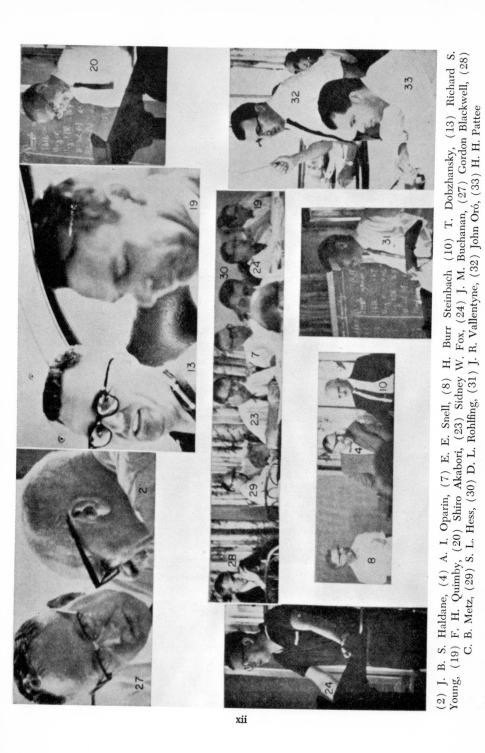

(2) J. B. S. Haldane, (4) A. I. Oparin, (7) E. E. Snell, (8) H. Burr Steinbach (10) T. Dobzhansky, (13) Richard S. Young, (19) F. H. Quimby, (20) Shiro Akabori, (23) Sidney W. Fox, (24) J. M. Buchanan, (27) Gordon Blackwell, (28) C. B. Metz, (29) S. L. Hess, (30) D. L. Rohlfing, (31) J. R. Vallentyne, (32) John Oró, (33) H. H. Pattee

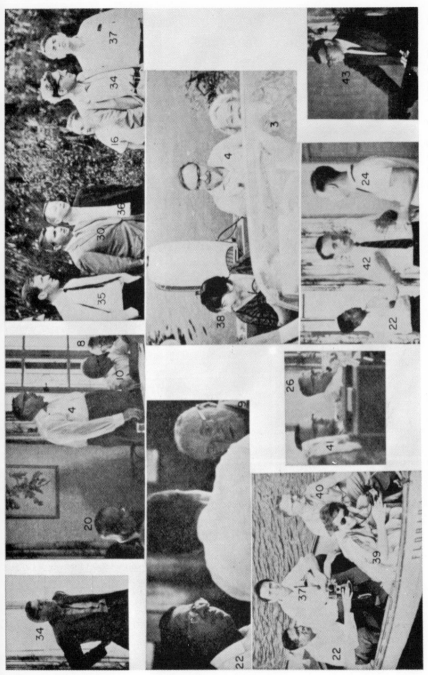

(3) Mrs. A. I. Oparin, (4) A. I. Oparin, (8) H. Burr Steinbach, (9) A. E. Mirsky, (10) T. Dobzhansky, (16) G. Krampitz, (20) Shiro Akabori, (22) Cyril Ponnamperuma, (24) J. Buchanan, (26) E. Chargaff, (30) D. L. Rohlfing, (34) N. W. Pirie, (35) D. Durant, (36) C. R. Windsor, (37) Carl Sagan, (38) Mrs. A. E. Mirsky, (39) Mrs. Karl A. Grossenbacher, (40) Karl A. Grossenbacher, (41) P. D. Hoagland, (42) M. S. Blois, (43) A. W. Schwartz

PREFACE

Conferences on the scientific problems of the origin of life were for a time many. In December 1956, the New York Academy of Sciences and the American Association for the Advancement of Science held a symposium on Modern Views on Spontaneous Generation. In August 1957, a first international conference on the Origin of Life on Earth was organized by the Moscow Academy of Sciences. In March 1958, the American Chemical Society held at its San Francisco meeting a symposium titled Biochemical Origins. This represented the first symposium in which the six participating speakers were individuals who had subjected at least some of their concepts to experimental discipline.

After this 1956–1958 period of conferences, the subsequent formal discussions mostly or entirely involved only one or two speakers. With the emergence of an office of Life Sciences in the National Aeronautics and Space Administration (NASA) in March 1960, the United States supported an agency having as one principal objective the increase of knowledge on how life might have originated anywhere in the universe.

The support by NASA of numerous researches in the subject matter area and other influences converged to suggest that late 1963 was a ripe time for a conference, of limited size, that would permit a workshop type of scrutiny of experiments and interpretations. In particular, a stimulating balance of experimental reports and of armchair theorizing was sought in a locale which could function as a pleasant retreat and be physically limited to twenty-five participants from outside the geographical area of the meeting.

Virtually all of the individuals who had performed experiments and interpreted them in the context of what is usually referred to as "origin of life" were invited to this meeting. Nearly all were able to accept. The invitations to those who had published scholarly conjecture was on another basis. This total group is a much larger number, and some virtue was evident in allowing for an emphasis of fresher points of view.

We were fortunate indeed to enlist especially individuals who have recorded the earliest thinking of the present era. Inasmuch as the primary writing in this field has often been referred to as the Oparin-Haldane theory, it is a matter of historical importance that Professors Oparin and Haldane first met in person at a small conference in Wakulla Springs, Florida in 1963. Another notable feature, in view of the fact that prebiological chemistry has not always been regarded as fully respectable by all conventional biochemists, was the active participation of a number of eminent biochemists who brought rigor to the discussions and sparked new ideas. These could be included only at the cost of not inviting a number of renowned "origin-of-lifers."

If one reads the record closely he will see that a fairly comprehensive outline of biochemical and physiological origins based on experiments has already begun to emerge. Experimental demonstration of the origin of almost all of the amino acids common to protein, the nucleic acid bases, the sugars, ATP, polymerization of amino acids to primitive protein, limited polymerization of mononucleotides, the beginning of organized precellular units with which nature could have experimented, and a way in which catalytic activity could have appeared spontaneously in such units, have been advanced. In the case of some biochemical substances, more than one possible route has been demonstrated experimentally. Even so, it is possible to describe for some individual reactions compatibility in more or less lengthy sequences.

In relating individual reactions to other individual reactions, the experimenter has been attempting to emulate the natural experiments. As Professor Akabori pointed out, the relation of the intellectual treatment at Wakulla Springs of such experiments to nature is most appropriate since the first four letters of Wakulla are those of the Japanese word, *Waku*, which signifies spontaneous life.

The conference is much indebted to Professor Oparin for delivering an historical address in addition to the paper describing some of his latest researches. The special contributions of the session chairmen N. W. Pirie, J. B. S. Haldane, E. E. Snell, J. M. Buchanan, A. E. Mirsky, H. B. Steinbach, and F. H. Quimby are gratefully acknowledged.

Finally, grateful acknowledgment is made to all participants for advice, and particularly to Drs. Hans Gaffron and Richard S. Young. For financial and moral support, the conference was indebted to the National Aeronautics and Space Administration, and to the Eli Lilly Corporation. I should like to thank Dr. and Mrs. D. H. Durant for the preparation of the index.

October, 1964   SIDNEY W. FOX

CONTENTS

Part III

MACROMOLECULES

Part IV

MODELS OF PRECELLULAR ORGANIZATION

THE ORIGINS OF
PREBIOLOGICAL SYSTEMS

and of Their Molecular Matrices

INTRODUCTORY REMARKS

FREEMAN H. QUIMBY

Exobiology Branch, National Aeronautics and Space Administration,
Washington, D.C.

Ladies and Gentlemen: It occurred to me in the light of recent experimental results that the time was ripe for an intensive conference on abiogenesis.

I would normally have begun my remarks with the usual justification, had it not been for the program of the recent centennial celebration of the National Academy of Sciences on October 21–23, 1963. Except for one session in the centennial, and a convocation during which (the late) President (John F.) Kennedy addressed the Academy, the programs constituted essentially a prologue to the subject which brings us together. Two of the sessions in particular constitute an unexpected endorsement of this conference. Without naming the speakers, it is of some significance to note the subjects and their sequence as follows:

One session: origin of elements; history of stars and galaxies; history of the solar system; origin of continents, oceans, and atmospheres; and *origins of life.*

The other session: symmetry and conservation laws; elementary particles; structure of nuclei; *the architecture of molecules;* the *organization of living matter.*

From these topics, we can readily derive the current movement of basic, modern scientific inquiry toward its climax in the nature and origin of living systems.

The beginning of life has an obvious and compelling fascination for all humanity; all wish to know and, I believe, are prepared to pay the price. Research during the last decade indicates the problem is ready to be attacked with mass intellectual artillery. By this I do not mean an experimental steeplechase, but the clarification, expansion, and development of the subject in its most significant aspects.

1

There are perhaps a few points which a general biologist can state concerning the matter at hand which, though largely well known by all of you, may serve as refreshers.

The chemical evolution of living matter seems an inescapable forerunner of the evolution of species, particularly in the light of the molecular similarity of our otherwise divergent terrestrial biota. It is remotely possible that a different form of molecular biology was the original form on the earth and is now extinct; however, it seems obvious enough that the types of chemical compounds which are essential to life today, and some of which are in the ancient sediments, are more readily subject to modern study. The detection and analysis of extraterrestrial life might offer a slightly different kind of chemistry. At least, I hope it does. Otherwise, no one will believe that it is extraterrestrial.

The laboratory synthesis of life, I believe, is not our primary objective. It may never come about anyway. But an adequate materialistic explanation of how life might have begun is intellectually demanding. By crude analogy we may eventually have an adequate explanation of the solar system, but the day is far away indeed when we will be able to make one. This analogy is intentional because the solar system and living systems are comparable in degree of complexity and are associated in origin.

The greatest problems in discussing a topic such as ours, and I suppose this is true for all science, will come from the usual source; namely, ourselves—our disciplinary prejudices, our skepticism of scientists who have not hit the usual quota of home runs, our insistence on being chained to logic or the current body of scientific knowledge, overgeneralizations, twisting or tailoring of data to fit a favorite preconception, defense of the status quo in science, geochemical dogma, our impatience with what we do not know, our frustration with what we cannot know, and, finally, the notion that we must come up with Adam molecules that fit the final product of 1–2 billion years of evolution, the right kinds of protein, DNA, RNA, ATP, 300 or more enzymes, efficient and rapid energy transformation, and all of the other things that pervade our current concepts of terrestrial carbonic biology. I'm not ridiculing these—they are real. I just don't think we should get locked in by the aerodynamics of the 707 while studying the flights at Kitty Hawk.

What are we going to do, for instance, with all this fine and incredible structure should someone by more or less empirical procedures produce little living things, otherwise indistinguishable from other living systems, except that, upon chemical analysis, they do not contain very many of the essential molecular species now dominating the scene of contemporary biology?

Since I suspect that few of my latter remarks have a very high probability of being popular, I would like to close with an attempt at humor. It is a statement made by Dr. Harlow Shapley in 1961: "It is gratifying to be a part of this magnificent evolutionary show, even though we must admit ourselves to be lineal descendants of some rather nauseating gases and sundry streaks of lightning."

This statement is reminiscent of one by the Bishop of Oxford, who turned to Huxley on June 29, 1860, and begged to know whether it was through his (Huxley's) grandmother or his grandfather that he traced his descent from the monkey. Huxley's classical and devastating reply is familiar to all students of Darwinism. The following is one of the versions of a part of what Huxley said in reply to the Bishop's remark: "If this question is treated, not as a matter of sentiment, and if I am asked whether I would choose to be descended from the poor animal of low intelligence and stooping gait, who grins and chatters as we pass; —or from a man, endowed with great ability and splendid position, who should use these gifts to discredit and crush humble seekers after truth— I hesitate what answers I should make."

INTRODUCTORY REMARKS

SIDNEY W. FOX

Institute for Space Biosciences, The Florida State University,
Tallahassee, Florida

We want to thank Dr. Quimby sincerely for those opening remarks of clarification and for setting the stage for the technical subject matter in many ways.

A principal objective of this conference is to promote free discussion. For some of the participants this means freer discussion if it is recorded and for others freer discussion if it is not recorded. I believe we can have it both ways. We can have it both ways because each participant will retain the power, as stated in earlier communications, of final veto on any statement that he might contribute by way of discussion or in the exact presentation of his paper.

Dr. Bernal, who unfortunately is not with us due to a stroke, is, however, well enough so that he has been able to communicate a paper *in absentia.*

We will ask Norman Wingate Pirie to be the first chairman and to introduce the program.

Part I

PERSPECTIVES I

Chairman's Remarks

N. W. Pirie

Rothamsted Experimental Station, Harpenden, Herts., England

The only conceivable reason why I was selected to start is that, except for Haldane and Oparin, I have possibly been thinking about these problems longer than anyone else here; I have probably contributed little, except skepticism, but that is a commodity in rather inadequate supply. So possibly you will excuse a little more of it.

This conference, as you will have noticed, keeps changing its title. I rather liked the original one. "Molecular Matrices" sounded wonderful. I am not altogether pleased with the change. And, as an antidogmatist, I regret the omission of the plural ending from origin; putting it in the singular implies that there was only one. I assume that there is no reason to start with such a limitation. I wonder if it is now too late to get the plural into our final title. To combine skepticism with pedantry, may I also object to "prebiological"? You can have prevital or probiological, take your choice. But you have to use one word or the other. But the word "systems" in the title is fine.

Let me start being chairman. I have the peculiar pleasure of, for once, having Haldane at my feet. I have spent my life sitting with advantage at his feet. He was one of my early teachers, and insofar as I achieve anything, it is almost entirely through the excitement he communicated to me when I was a student. He has gone on communicating excitement. So I introduce him enthusiastically.

DATA NEEDED FOR A BLUEPRINT OF THE FIRST ORGANISM

J. B. S. HALDANE

Genetics and Biometry Laboratory, Bhubaneswar, India

I abandoned molecular biology in 1932. Since then I have worked on genetics of large organisms from *Drosophila* to man, on population genetics, animal behavior, and so on. I am also isolated and can neither keep up with the literature nor discuss molecular biology with colleagues. I shall, therefore, display my ignorance.

Thanks largely to the work of people in this room, we have good reason to think that, during a period when both H_2 and O_2 were fairly scarce in our atmosphere, a large variety of organic compounds, including amino acids and pyrimidine and purine bases, were formed by various meteorological processes, while hydrocarbons, perhaps partially oxidized, came up from below. We know much less about the high-energy phosphoric esters, which are important intermediates in metabolism. Apart from polyphosphates, the simplest such compound known to us is carbamyl phosphate. Has this been looked for (or found) in products from irradiation and discharge?

Most of the substances considered were metastable. Until we know more than I do about their half-lives, it is hard to estimate their concentrations two to three thousand million years ago. Some particular group may have been the limiting factor in biogenesis. Perhaps amino acids, sugars, bases, lipids, and so on were present in adequate amounts, but high-energy phosphates were only rarely so.

I think that we should assume that any small molecules (by small I mean of molecular weights less than 500, say) required were present in the nutrient solution, for two reasons. First, even if a pool on the primitive Earth very rarely contained enough of all of them, the probability of such a pool existing would be far greater than that of the synthesis of an enzyme capable of forming even one of the missing ones. I am told I am a fool to talk about probability. I may confess my folly later on.

11

Second, if we have not committed planetary suicide, some of us, or of the next generation, will try to make a living organism. Their task will be hard enough even if it is made as easy as possible by providing nutrients.

The metabolism of existing organisms is centered around the production of ATP (adenosine triphosphate) and similar compounds. If one of them was there in the primitive environment, such metabolism was unnecessary. At an early stage in evolution, it doubtless became worthwhile to tap the energy of other metastable molecules, as in ordinary anaerobic metabolism, and the necessary enzymes were produced. But I assume that the metabolism of the first organism did, and that of the first synthetic organism will, center around the production of nucleic acids capable of acting as templates for protein synthesis, and of one or more proteins catalyzing the synthesis of nucleic acids and proteins.

In almost all existing organisms (some would say all) the primary specifications for proteins are given by rather stable DNA (deoxyribonucleic acid). This is transferred to the so-called "messenger" RNA (ribonucleic acid) and peptides are then built with the aid of the twenty or so species of soluble RNA, on or more for each amino acid, and the RNA of the ribosomes. However, in the RNA viruses, the specification is carried by RNA. To synthesize new proteins, they presumably use the soluble and ribosomal RNA of their hosts. Thus, they have little title to be called organisms. But there is no reason to think that DNA is involved at any stage in the replication of their RNA. Or is there? Perhaps you can tell me.

Thus, it does not seem necessary to include DNA in our specification for a minimal organism. I suggest that life, by which I mean indefinite replication of patterns of large molecules, can be based on RNA without DNA. The question is how much RNA is needed. A triad of three nucleotides involves six bits of information if all four bases are equally frequent. Similarly, the picking of one amino acid out of twenty involves 4.322 bits, if all amino acids are equally frequent. About half the information in the messenger RNA is redundant, or is believed to be redundant, for peptide synthesis.

If the minimal organism involves not only the code for its one or more proteins, but also twenty types of soluble RNA, one for each amino acid, and the equivalent of ribosomal RNA, our descendants may be able to make one, but we must give up the idea that such an organism could have been produced in the past, except by a similar pre-existing organism or by an agent, natural or supernatural, at least as intelligent as ourselves, and with a good deal more knowledge.

If three consecutive uridine residues are a code for phenylalanine in the messenger RNA, presumably the corresponding s-RNA molecule includes three consecutive adenine residues (AAA) at a particular site. This is quite intelligible. We have very little notion why AAA should unite with phenylalanine in preference to other amino acids.

I suggest that the possibility is still open that, in favorable circumstances, a single RNA chain could suffice to specify a peptide. The study of existing organisms and viruses may be of little help to us here. We shall need information obtained in laboratory experiments, perhaps with synthetic RNA.

If I am right, a key question in this connection is now the reason why the various types of s-RNA fit the amino acids specifically, as it seems that they do. This is a matter of chemistry, clearly a good deal more difficult than the explanation of why adenine pairs with thymine, and so on, but not an insoluble question. The question of how, if at all, RNA can be replicated, may be solved by a study of small RNA viruses, including that of poliomyelitis. We must, however, also ask the following questions: Can proteins be replicated without RNA? Can a protein assemble RNA which specifies it and allows for its reproduction? If either of these possibilities is true, Fox's discoveries are much more important than if RNA necessarily precedes protein in time.

Suppose, then, that we have reduced the amount of RNA needed to specify a protein to the minimum—what protein would be needed? If our culture medium included amino acids, ribose, the four bases, and a source of high-energy phosphate, the following reactions would have to be carried out:

First, formation of nucleotides.
Second, coupling of nucleotides to form chains.
Third, combination of amino acids with ATP or some related substance.
Fourth, coupling of these amino acids to form a peptide chain.

In existing organisms, these reactions are catalyzed by different enzymes. Even in the simplest organisms, it is desirable that an enzyme should not only be efficient but specific, that is to say, should catalyze a limited series of reactions. Otherwise, the control of metabolism would be impossible. I want to suggest that the initial organism may have consisted of one so-called "gene" of RNA specifying just one enzyme, a very generalized phosphokinase, which could catalyze all the above reactions.

It is perhaps not a coincidence that the smallest enzyme at present known is ribonuclease, which might have been evolved at a fairly early stage from this hypothetical primitive enzyme, and perhaps resembles it in its small size. The first enzyme very possibly contained the sequence Asp-Ser-Gly, which is part of the active centers of phosphoglucomutase, trypsin, and chymotrypsin. Ribonuclease contains 124 amino acid residues. If all were equally common, this would mean 540 bits. The number is actually a little less than that. This number could be somewhat reduced if some amino acids were rare both in the medium and in the enzyme. I suggest that the primitive enzyme was a much shorter peptide of low activity and specificity, incorporating only 100 bits or so. But even this would mean one out of 1.3×10^{30} possibilities. This is an unacceptable, large number. If a new organism were tried out every minute for 10^8 years, we should need 10^{17} simultaneous trials to get the right result by chance. The earth's surface is 5×10^{18} cm.^{2} There just isn't, in my opinion, room. Sixty bits, or about 15 amino acids, would be more acceptable probabilistically, but less so biochemically.

I suggest that the first synthetic organisms may have been something like a tobacco mosaic virus, but including the enzyme or enzymes needed for its own replication. More verifiably, I suggest that the first synthetic organisms may be so constituted. For natural, but not for laboratory life, a semipermeable membrane is needed. This could be constituted from an inactivated enzyme and lipids. I think, however, that the first synthetic organism may be much larger than the first which occurred. It may contain several different enzymes, with a specification of 5000 bits or so—about the information on a page of Chamber's 7-figure logarithm tables. This should be quite within human possibilities. The question will then arise: How much smaller may the first natural organism have been?

If this minimum involves 500 bits, one could conclude either that terrestrial life had had an extraterrestrial origin (with Nagy and Braun) or a supernatural one (with many religions, but by no means all). I want, however, to suggest a possible way out, which some of you may think neovitalism, others crass materialism, and all nonsense.

Earlier this year I suggested that a bacterium, an oak tree, or a human mind conserves its characteristic form and activity when not too greatly disturbed, for the same kind of reasons that an atom or a molecule does. It is characterized by a system of energy levels, from one to another of which quantum transitions occur. Those characteristic of the human mind have an energy of about 10^{-19} Ev, a temporal uncertainty of about a second, and a spatial uncertainty of about 1 cm.^{2} For an average cell the temporal uncertainty would be a few millionths of a second, and a good deal less for a primordial organism.

I suggested the following function for this system:

"Any excitation above the lowest energy level would increase the probability of events (such as the oxidation of a molecule or the union of two others), which would serve to bring the cell back towards its lowest energy level. But the details would be unpredictable, and if they could be observed, would suggest the action of a somewhat capricious vital force."

If there is any sense in this view, some RNA configurations may be a great deal more probable than others formed from the same components, and this owing to properties of the whole which, if they are beyond our grasp at present, are, in principle, calculable, like energy levels of a benzene molecule from atomic parameters. Thus, the probability of spontaneous formation of a biologically relevant RNA pattern might be very greatly increased, without any supposition that a vital force or soul was guiding the molecules into the right configuration.

I may be converted in the course of the meeting, but when writing this paper, I am by no means attracted by the theory of a period of many million years of biochemical evolution preceding the origin of life. It seems to me that any half-live systems—for example, catalysts releasing the energy of metastable molecules such as pyrophosphate or sugar— would merely have made conditions less favorable for the first living organisms, by which I mean the first system capable of reproduction. A protein capable of catalyzing such reactions would not multiply in consequence, any more than an enzyme does.

If time permitted, I would have speculated on the next evolutionary steps from the simplest organisms. I think what I would have said would have been something like this. We have very good reason to think that RNA replication is a very chancy process, that RNA viruses produce a very large amount of material which cannot reproduce further. That may not matter if the system is simple enough, if only perhaps three or four proteins are being made, but as soon as one gets to a system consisting of even, let us say, a dozen distinct proteins, it may be worthwhile to have your specification laid down in DNA, even if that requires at least one more enzyme to transfer pattern to the RNA. But I would suggest that the DNA was an adaptation to increase complexity in the system rather than part of the primitive system.

Manuscript received October 27, 1963.

DISCUSSION

Dr. BERNAL: It is a great advantage in a conference like this to start with a model of how life might have originated biochemically. Even if

Haldane knows, as we all know, that it is most unlikely that any model put forward now will resemble the true one, the fact that such a model can be specified in not too implausible terms stirs other workers on, even if only in criticism. Professor Haldane, who is, after all, one of the two pioneers of the modern view of the origin of life as well as one of the founders of modern biochemistry, has in his paper effectively asked a number of questions. I would like to see them added to mine and to others raised at this conference.

I have a few criticisms to make. One, which I will come to later in discussing Dr. Mora's paper, is that we need not be dazzled by probability or, rather, by improbability. By taking the origin in the way I have described, step by step, we will reduce the amount of information required by scores of powers of ten. That they appear so large now may be mainly because we do not know the way of life *was* put together. When we do begin to see this we may appreciate how it may happen by a series of steps, each of which is not highly improbable.

I like particularly Haldane's view that the various events leading to the formation of a specific polynucleotide must be a selection from a number of equally probable alternatives. However, I would go further and suggest that the dice may be loaded and that the crystal lattice energies of some of these configurations may be notably lower than others and, consequently, they will be favored in the production of certain sequences.

On the point he makes about the size of primitive organisms, I am not quite in agreement with him; in his way of thinking the organisms is conceived as an isolate from the environment. The TMV model which he uses is, in fact, only an isolate when it is functionless after the death of the originally infected cell and before the infection of a new one.

I would think rather that the first self-reproducing element in life was not an isolated organism or even an isolated organelle, but something that arose out of and worked in the less organized nonreproducing medium, the highly concentrated part of the primitive soup.

DR. SCHRAMM: One point was the differentiation between DNA and RNA. But that is not necessary, I think. In the beginning we may have something which is more primitive than DNA and RNA, maybe a combination of sugar with some bases which cannot be named RNA or DNA.

DR. HALDANE: I am in full agreement. Let me say I was thinking in terms quite as much of specifications for a synthetic organism, which, I think, will happen in some of your lifetimes, rather than a deduction as to what the first organism was, which I think will require a lot of historical research.

DR. PONNAMPERUMA: In answer to Professor Haldane's question about the formation of carbamyl phosphate, I don't think anybody has reported that so far, but in our work we have been able to make a high-energy phosphate (ATP). As a matter of fact, using the metaphosphate which Dr. Schramm recently used, we have been able to add seven phosphate groups to adenosine.

DR. FOX: I would like to speak to that point, also. In 1961, Harada and I reported on the production of uracil in a thermal milieu in which were present malic acid, polyphosphoric acid, and urea. Professor Haldane asked, I think obliquely, where one might look for carbamyl phosphate. It is very likely, I believe, that carbamyl phosphate was formed in that reaction or that under some minor modification it might be formed from the components of polyphosphoric acid and urea.

DR. ORÓ: It may be added that carbamyl phosphate was synthesized some time ago from cyanate and phosphate [Jones, M. E., Spector, L., and Lipmann, F., *J. Am. Chem. Soc.* **77**, 819 (1955)], and that the formation of this compound under abiotic conditions has been discussed by Jones and Lipmann [*Proc. Natl. Acad. Sci. U. S.* **46**, 423, (1960)]. In discussing the abiotic formation of high-energy phosphate compounds, it has to be taken into consideration that the abundance of phosphorus in the universe is relatively low (less than 0.3%, measured as P_2O_5, in carbonaceous chondrites), and that this element is found in nature mainly in the form of phosphates of alkaline-earth metals.

I very much agree with Professor Haldane's presentation that one of the major problems in terrestrial biopoesis concerns the chemistry of phosphate compounds. From a theoretical point of view a number of candidates can be proposed as primitive high-energy phosphate compounds. There are at least twelve different derivatives of phosphate with monocarbon reactants, such as cyanides, cyanates, urea, isourea, etc., which can be considered as such. And one should not exclude the probable participation in this role of ordinary polyphosphates.

DR. OPARIN: I want to ask Dr. Haldane whether he supposes that this primitive RNA had a fixed sequence of nucleotides or more or less a random sequence, and how does he visualize the formation of the enzymes which reproduced that particular sequence? That's the question.

DR. HALDANE: Well, I would suggest that it had a fairly definite sequence, judging from the example Dr. Zinder was telling me about in New York. It doesn't reproduce itself extremely accurately, but I would suggest that the essential thing would be to have an RNA which would produce some kind of a phosphokinase or perhaps they produced maybe two or three enzymes which in some way would build up these larger molecules on a suitable template in the presence of suitable energy source. I can't say more than that. I think we are all groping very much.

DR. BUCHANAN: Are you assuming that the reproduction of the first RNA molecule was done in the absence of the protein-synthesizing enzyme?

DR. HALDANE: Well, I think the same enzyme could conceivably have done the lot, if it had been a sufficiently generalized phosphokinase. And the essential step in protein synthesis appears to involve these high-energy phosphate bonds.

DR. BUCHANAN: But was the new RNA molecule being duplicated? Is this done in the presence or in the absence of an enzyme?

DR. HALDANE: Oh, in the presence, certainly. And I don't see how it could be duplicated in the absence.

DR. BUCHANAN: I think it might be.

DR. HALDANE: Good luck. I hope so.

DR. SCHRAMM: We investigated the polymerization of nucleotides by metaphosphate ester and we found that the addition of some basic peptides can accelerate the polymerization. Therefore, I think we have not to think about a special enzyme, but something which is similar to the structural protein in the ribosome. That may be the most primitive thing that helps to accomplish the polymerization. The question of enzymes comes later.

MR. STEWART: Dr. Haldane, you had a great deal of information required for the first organism, but for an enzyme you need only the active center plus a carrier. If you have preformed polymers, to which you can add a small active center, you need very little information, even for the ten or fifteen enzymes in your primitive organism—maybe a hundred bits.

DR. HALDANE: I did try to cut it down to a hundred bits in that argument. The hundred bits aren't quite enough. A hundred bits means 13×10^{30} possibilities, and that is not good enough.

DR. FOX: I think it is rather too easy to assume—and in making this statement, I don't necessarily argue for the opposite point of view—that because the first administration of the events in the biochemical history of the cell are under the jurisdiction of DNA and RNA, or under the jurisdiction of RNA, that in the development of prebiological systems RNA and DNA preceded the protein. I believe it unnecessary and perhaps psychologically inhibitory to make this assumption at this time.

RANDOM POLYMERS AS A MATRIX FOR CHEMICAL EVOLUTION

M. S. Blois

Biophysics Laboratory, Stanford University, Stanford, California

Chemical evolutionary reaction mechanisms, by means of which simple carbon compounds under excitation from natural energy sources are converted in part to higher molecular weight substances, in general fall into two categories: homogeneous and heterogeneous. Both in the search for circumstances which would favor chemical evolution in the forward direction (i.e., that of increasing molecular weight and complexity), and perhaps for the better reason that the primitive Earth was essentially a heterogeneous system, a greater interest has attached to the latter category.

As a mechanism for increasing the concentration of organic reactants over that found in the primitive seas, Bernal (1951) has proposed the adsorption of such compounds onto clays and finely divided inorganic particulates. To avoid back reactions, either photolytic or pyrolytic, Kholodnyi (1942), Vil'yams (1950), and others have proposed that newly formed molecular species may have been adsorbed onto mineral particulates. In addition to providing a means of concentration and protection, such adsorption onto mineral surfaces has been proposed as a possible means of catalysis or for the introduction of stereospecificity in an ensuing polymerization. The work of Akabori on the synthesis of glycine polypeptides (1959) from aminoacetonitrile which had been adsorbed on kaolin, together with his subsequent work, has lent experimental support to this view.

It is our purpose here to consider another solid phase which may have been widely present on the primitive Earth but which, instead of being mineral, was organic. This material, the class of random, partially aromatic polymers, occupies an intriguing position in chemical evolution in the sense that while it probably was formed through photopolymeriza-

19

tion on the prebiological Earth, it is still synthesized today by living organisms and is represented apparently in all phyla.

Melanin as a Random Polymer

Melanin is the nonchemical term describing the black or brownish pigments of biological origin which have been considered to be nitrogen-

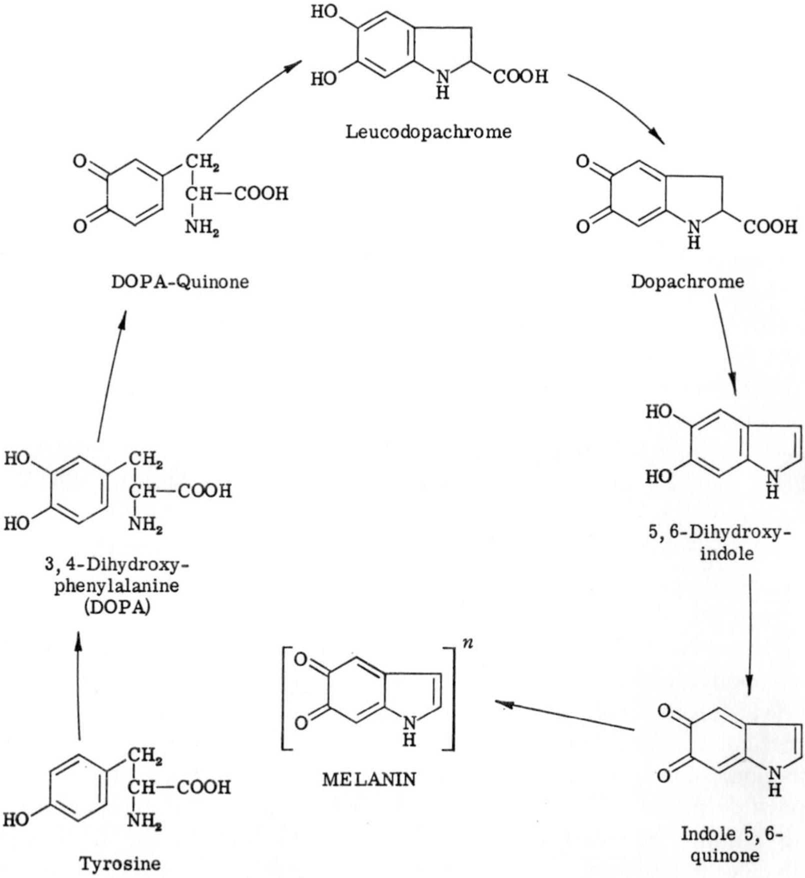

Fig. 1. The Raper-Mason scheme of melanin synthesis.

containing polymers. Being insoluble and nonhydrolyzable, this material has resisted chemical analysis, and unambiguous structural determinations have not been available. What might be termed the classical concept of melanin synthesis is that of Raper (1928) and Mason (1948) and is shown in Fig. 1. This concept of melanin biosynthesis involves a series of stepwise oxidations and reductions leading to the 5,6-indole-quinone which was assumed to undergo condensation and form the polymer. The participation of enzymes has been shown only for the first two steps, and the single enzyme tyrosinase (or the "phenolase complex") has been shown to convert the tyrosine to DOPA, and then to oxidize the latter. Nakamura (1960), however, has shown that the DOPA-oxidase activity extends only to the production of the semiquinone form.

Nicolaus (1962) has reported recently on the results of his studies of

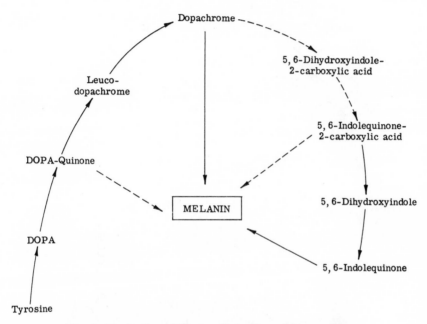

FIG. 2. Nicolaus' modification of the Raper-Mason scheme.

the products of melanin degradation and has cited the evidence for a more complex mechanism for melanin biosynthesis. Instead of the 5,6-indolequinone being the monomer, he has suggested that as many as ten different substituted indolequinones may be involved. The synthetic scheme he has proposed is shown in Fig. 2, but even this, he considers may be oversimplified. The hypothetical structure of melanin given by Nicolaus is shown in Fig. 3.

From the viewpoint of free radical chemistry, the striking thing about the Raper scheme is the series of stepwise redox reactions. It would appear that there must be semiquinone, free radical intermediates be-

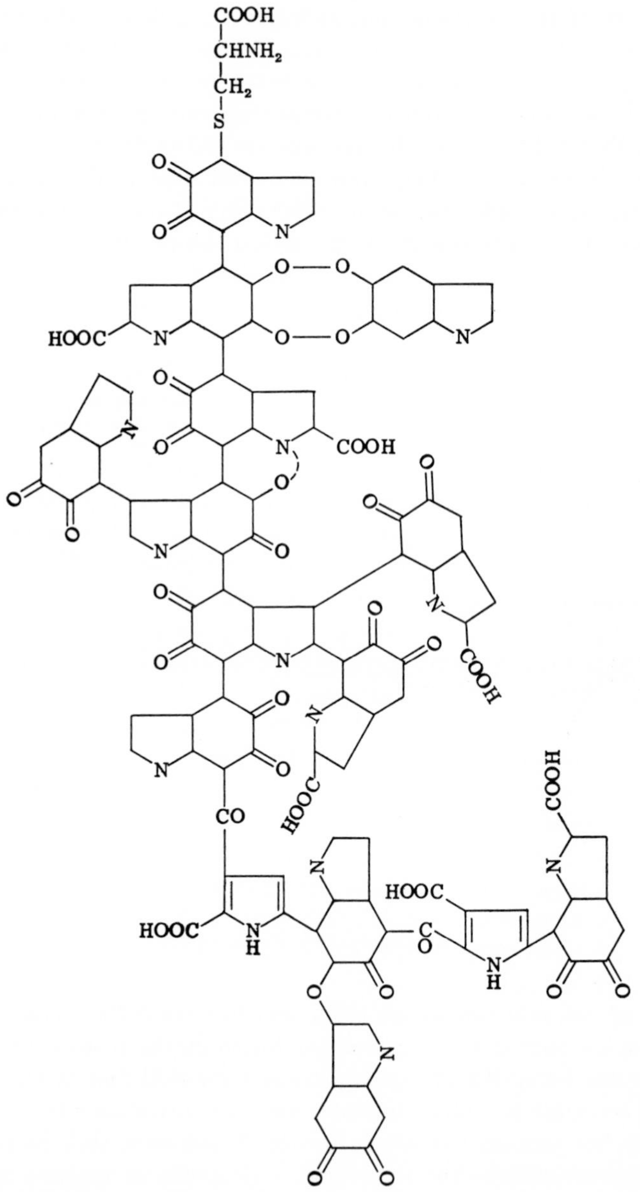

FIG. 3. Hypothetical structure of sepia melanin according to Nicolaus. The cysteine is thought to link the melanin polymer to the protein to form the complete melanoprotein granule.

tween each of the diamagnetic structures from DOPA onward. Wertz *et al.* (1961) have studied the *in vitro* autoxidation of DOPA, and several of the expected semiquinones have been identified by means of electron spin resonance (ESR). In such a heterogeneous system, it would be expected that each of these free radical intermediates could initiate polymerization reactions. From our own ESR studies of melanin (Vivo-Acrivos and Blois, 1958; Blois *et al.*, 1963), there is considerable evidence suggesting that the biosynthesis of melanin may involve such a free radical polymerization. These experimental results show that all natural melanins have trapped free radicals buried inside the polymer, and the properties of these free radicals (including g-value, line widths, hyperfine structure, accessibility to other molecules such as O_2, H_2O, etc., their relationships to the production of photosignals in melanin, the temperature dependence of the spin density) are indistinguishable from those of the polymers prepared synthetically by an autoxidation in which it is known that the polymerization is a free radical one. There is perhaps further evidence against melanin formation by a condensation of quinones in the behavior of resorcinol (1,3-benzoquinol). This compound cannot form a quinone, but does undergo autoxidation to form a polymer, which again is essentially indistinguishable from the polymers formed by the other simple biphenols. For these reasons we have proposed that melanin biosynthesis probably involves a free radical polymerization as shown schematically in Fig. 4. While it is conceivable that within the melanosome—the organelle of melanin synthesis—there is ordering of the monomers in some manner, the ESR evidence and the lack of crystallinity of natural melanins make this possibility appear remote. It is concluded therefore that natural melanin is probably a highly random polymer. Nicolaus has proposed that it consists of some ten different monomers, each of which may be polyfunctional, and some three of four bond types. It is thus a three-dimensional polymer, in which the number of possible structures is very large compared with the number of melanin molecules in existence, from which one concludes that there are probably no two molecules of melanin exactly alike.

Among the class of biological polymers, it would appear that melanin possibly occupies a unique position, by virtue of its mode of synthesis and its highly random structure. The latter feature leads to two interesting biological conjectures: in view of this random structure is it to be expected that melanin would be (1) antigenic and (2) enzymatically hydrolyzed or degraded?

If there are no fixed structural patterns in melanin, how would antibody which had been formed in response to one molecule of melanin "recognize" a second? Or upon what basis would a degradative enzyme perform the same required recognition? The *a priori* assumption that melanins may be nonantigenic and nonhydrolyzable is easy to study but difficult to prove experimentally because of the very nature of negative assertions. Preliminary experiments have been conducted with the following results. Melanin prepared from DL-DOPA with a C^{14} label in

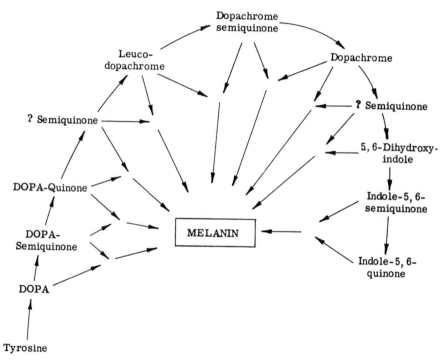

FIG. 4. Hypothetical scheme of melanin synthesis assuming the participation of semiquinone free radicals.

the 2-carbon position, by autoxidation, was administered intramuscularly into rabbits with Freund's adjuvant at approximately monthly intervals for a 3 month period. The "immunizing" doses contained approximately 2–5 mg of melanin. Subsequent search for antibody in the rabbit sera, by means of agglutination, precipitin, agar gel diffusion, and passive transfer into the guinea pig skin, have been negative. At the end of the "immunizing" period the clearance of an intravenous dose of labeled melanin by the experimental animals was found to be no greater than that of the control. As for degradability, a similar labeled melanin was added to a mixed bacterial culture contained in a dialysis bag and this was incubated for several days. Samples of the liquid outside the membrane were taken periodically and there was no evidence of the polymer being broken down to molecules of a diffusible size. Parallel experiments were run in which the labeled melanin was added to the culture and samples were withdrawn periodically during incubation. There was no evidence of a loss of label from the system, which would be expected if the organisms were metabolizing the melanin and converting a fraction to carbon dioxide, or excreting it in diffusible form. In one set of experiments a mixed bacterial culture consisting of *Escherichia coli*, *Proteus vulgaris*, and *Bacillus cereus* was used, and in another a random soil sample was added. There was no evidence of melanin degradation in any of the experiments. It was established in these experiments that these microorganisms have not been killed by the melanin—the possibly toxic monomers having been previously dialyzed out. It is emphasized that these are early results, and the only conclusions possible at present must be very restricted ones. That is, in the rabbit, autoxidized DOPA melanin does not appear to be antigenic, nor does this material seem readily metabolized by the above-cited microorganisms. These two features are of course peripheral to any role such polymers may have played in molecular evolution, but it would be of interest if modern organisms prove not to look upon such substances as foreign macromolecules.

Melanins as a Class of Random Polymer

It was pointed out above that natural melanins, enzyme-synthesized melanins and the melanins prepared by autoxidation have very similar properties as revealed by ESR. The optical absorption properties are also similar, although spectroscopy is not particularly rewarding until the infrared is reached. Figure 5 compares the infrared absorption of a natural melanin with three autoxidized melanins. The close similarity between these four spectra in which the monomers differ widely (even in elemental composition) should perhaps warn us that the apparent congruences should not be overstressed.

However, in view of the earlier assumption that these polymers are highly random and disordered, the spectral similarities of these broad absorption bands would seem to imply that in these samples the numbers and environments of the responsible bonds are, at least in a statistical sense, similar. In Fig. 6 the infrared absorption of two of these samples are compared with the polymer prepared by the ultraviolet irradiation of aqueous phenylalanine in the absence of oxygen. This polymer was a

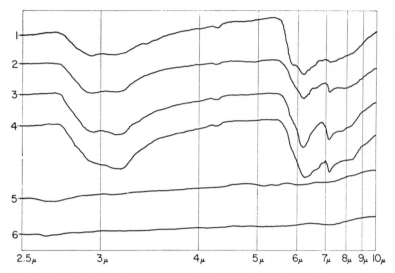

FIG. 5. Infrared absorption spectra of (1) squid (*Loligo opalescens*) melanin; (2) catechol melanin-autoxidized; (3) L-DOPA melanin-autoxidized; (4) hydroquinone melanin-autoxidized; (5) graphite; and (6) charcoal. All samples observed in KBr pellets.

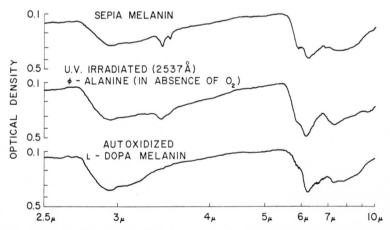

FIG. 6. Infrared absorption spectra of natural melanin, photopolymer from UV-irradiated phenylalanine, and autoxidized L-DOPA melanin. (The small absorptions near 3.5 μ are instrumental artifacts.)

light brown in color as contrasted with the dark black of the two melanins and has been shown to have an ESR similar to that of melanin. It is known, however, that melanins may be reversibly reduced with an accompanying color change from black to brown. We have shown by means of ESR that the color and paramagnetism of natural and synthetic melanins are completely independent of each other and that either may be altered without affecting the other (Blois *et al.*, 1963).

Because this photoproduced polymer of phenylalanine is similar to melanins with respect to insolubility, chemical inertness, infrared absorption and having an electron spin resonance, we believe this to be a member of the class of random, irregular polymers as are the melanins.

Ultraviolet Photoproduction of Polymers[1]

From observations on the photolysis of aromatic amino acids it became apparent that among the secondary reactions, photooxidations played a dominating role. For example, the absorbance changes produced in an aqueous solution of phenylalanine (5×10^{-4} M) by 2532 Å radiation are shown in Fig. 7. In the solution saturated with O_2 and then irradiated while exposed to air, the absorbance increases for a time and then begins to decrease, showing in particular a rapid decrease in absorption at shorter wavelengths. The solution which had been flushed with nitrogen and irradiated under a nitrogen atmosphere showed at first absorbance changes comparable to the preceding but then appeared to approach an equilibrium and did not show the pronounced reversal in absorbance change. In the latter case an insoluble precipitate is found at the end of a run, while in the O_2 system it was noted that, while a similar precipitate was formed, it later disappeared under continued irradiation. The interpretation of these data is this: in both the oxygen and oxygen-free cases the primary photochemical changes are generally similar, and, among these, one of the mechanisms operating is photopolymerization. The polymer itself is stable against ultraviolet irradiation in the absence of oxygen but not in its presence. This has been confirmed in separate experiments.

[1] Note added in proof. In more recent experiments on the photoproduction of polymer from phenylalanine, Kenyon has employed a special grade of oxygen-free, prepurified N_2 as the flushing gas and the results indicate that very small amounts of oxygen are required for polymerization. The N_2 used in the earlier experiments contained oxygen in sufficient amounts as a contaminant to facilitate polymer production, and polymer was not produced when the highly purified N_2 was employed. These more recent data are described in Kenyon and Blois (1964).

M. S. BLOIS

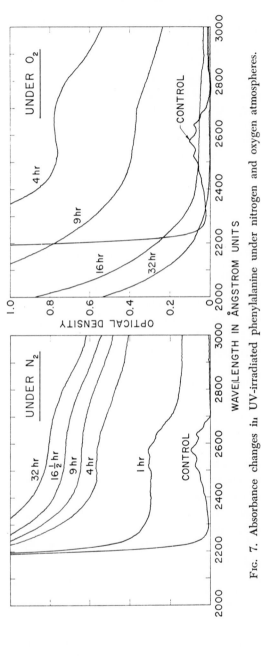

Fig. 7. Absorbance changes in UV-irradiated phenylalanine under nitrogen and oxygen atmospheres.

The results of a similar experiment with aqueous tyrosine ($6 \times 10^{-5}\,M$) are shown in Fig. 8, and although the reversal of absorbance change has occurred in both systems the anaerobic system shows much the greater resistance to photolysis. In both the case of the phenylalanine and of the tyrosine, the persistence of an appreciable absorption at 2200 Å may be evidence for the existence of aromatic compounds, but it is not evidence of polymer formation.

To investigate this, we employed C^{14}-labeled phenylalanine and tyrosine. These compounds were made up in aqueous solution and

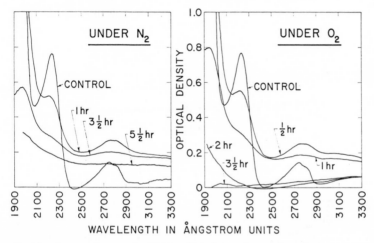

FIG. 8. Absorbance changes in UV-irradiated tyrosine under nitrogen and oxygen atmospheres.

irradiated with 2537 Å with either O_2 or N_2 being bubbled through the solution during irradiation. After the delivery of an amount of radiation which produced the absorbance maxima in the previous experiments, the irradiated solutions were transferred to dialysis bags and the specific activity of the solution inside the bag was determined as a function of time. The curves shown in Figs. 9 and 10 thus indicate the rate of disappearance of the label through the dialysis membrane. Since dialysis was conducted against running water, a small diffusible molecule should leak out at an exponential rate and on the plot shown should be a straight line. It will be noted that both the control phenylalanine and tyrosine diffuse out at the expected exponential rate. For both materials the rate of dialysis is greater for the O_2 system than for the N_2, although as mentioned above the quantity of radiation used was chosen to be in-

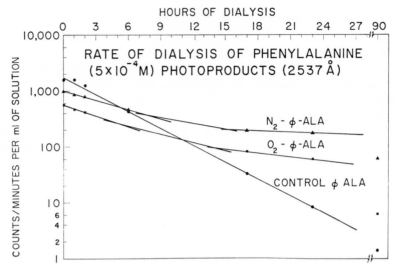

Fig. 9. Rate of dialysis of phenylalanine photoproducts.

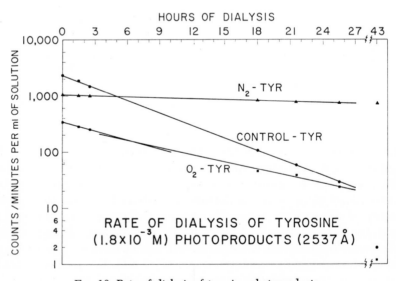

Fig. 10. Rate of dialysis of tyrosine photoproducts.

sufficient to photooxidize completely the polymer formed. The leveling off for each compound suggests that a nondiffusible and presumably polymeric residue remains. The addition of salt produced no alteration in the concentration of the nondiffusible component, which would rule out the possibility of retention of radioactivity by an electrostatically charged but small molecular species.

Studies by Kenyon (1963) on the photoproducts produced by the action of ultraviolet light on aqueous labeled phenylalanine, in the presence and absence of oxygen, are in accord with the preceding results. Aliquots of these solutions were withdrawn periodically during

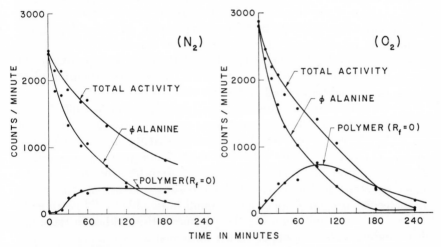

FIG. 11. The kinetics of total radioactivity, phenylalanine, and photopolymer as a function of irradiation time for UV-irradiated C^{14}-phenylalanine.

irradiation and chromatographed. Most of the activity was found to reside in two peaks, one of which remained at the origin ($R_f = 0$) and is considered to represent polymer, with the other representing the surviving fraction of the phenylalanine. The results of these experiments are shown in Fig. 11. It will be noted that, in the presence of O_2, polymer production is greater but with continued irradiation it is photooxidized and soon disappears.

Random Polymer on the Primitive Earth

In order to place these isolated findings in any unified chemical evolutionary scheme, it is at present necessary to assume the pre-existence of aromatic compounds of abiogenic origin. Several mechanisms for their synthesis will be discussed at this conference. For brevity, we shall simply assume their existence on the primitive Earth. In the presence, then, of the reducing atmosphere and of short wavelength solar ultraviolet light, the most stable configuration of these aromatics would seem to be their incorporation into random polymers, having the general features of the present melanin. Because of the chemical inertness and stability of this material against photolysis, it may well have been a thermodynamic trap toward which much of chemical evolution drifted.

As a matrix for further chemical evolution, this material would seem to offer many advantages over simple adsorption of reactants onto minerals. In contrast to the monotony of a mineral lattice, the polymer particles, both on their surfaces and within their porous interiors, would offer an enormous diversity of steric configuration. If one seeks a given combination of stereospecific sites and related functional groups (even to the extent of having metal ions bound thereto) as a prototype for enzymatic behavior, melanin would seem a vastly more promising place to look than would a mineral surface.

Electron spin resonance studies of melanin (Blois *et al.*, 1963) have shown this material to have several properties which might be important in a molecular evolution context. It is known that the unpaired electrons are distributed through the volume of the melanin particles where they are stable against many chemical reagents. Ascorbic acid, for example, cannot penetrate to the unpaired electron sites, and neither apparently can molecular oxygen. Copper ion is found to be able to diffuse directly to these sites and will eliminate the paramagnetism, although there are other binding sites for copper which must first be saturated. Water is able to diffuse close to the unpaired electrons and strongly affects their relaxation times. Melanin particles thus have features resembling both molecular sieves and ion-exchange resins.

At our present level of understanding of chemical evolution, it is always risky to assume that one biochemical molecule is more "primitive" than another. Nevertheless, one wonders whether the question, "Which was the first biological polymer—protein or DNA?" may not have the answer: "melanin."

ACKNOWLEDGMENTS

This work was supported by grant NsG 218-62 of the National Aeronautics and Space Administration.

The results reviewed herein represent the efforts of several individuals: A. B. Zahlan, D. H. Kenyon, L. T. Taskovich, whose contributions are gratefully acknowledged.

Revised manuscript received December 12, 1963.

REFERENCES

Akabori, S. (1959). "The Origin of Life on the Earth," Moscow Symposium, I.U.B. Pergamon Press, London and New York.

Bernal, J. D. (1951). "The Physical Basis of Life." Routledge and Kegan Paul, Ltd., London.

Blois, M. S., Zahlan, A. B., and Maling, J. E. (1963). In preparation.

Cope, F. W., Sever, R. J., and Polis, B. D. (1963). *Arch. Biochem. Biophys.* **100**, 171.

Kenyon, D. H. (1963). Unpublished observations.

Kenyon, D. H., and Blois, M. S. (1964). *Photochem. Photobiol.* In press.

Kholodnyi, N. (1942). *Izv. Akad. Nauk SSSR Arm. Fialiala* **9–10**, 89.

Mason, H. S. (1948). *J. Biol. Chem.* **172**, 83.

Nakamura, T. (1960). *Biochem. Biophys. Res. Commun.* **2**, 111.

Nicolaus, R. A. (1962). Rass. di Med. Speriment. *Anno IX, Suppl.* **1**.

Raper, H. S. (1928). *Physiol. Rev.* **8**, 245.

Vil'yams, V. (1950). *Izbrannye Sochineniya* Vol. I.

Vivo-Acrivos, J. L., and Blois, M. S. (1958). "Informal Discussion on Free Radical Stabilization" (abstracts). Faraday Society, Sheffield, England.

Wertz, J. E., Reitz, D. C., and Dravnieks, F. (1961). "Free Radicals in Biological Systems" (M. S. Blois, et al. eds.), p. 183. Academic Press, New York.

DISCUSSION

CHAIRMAN PIRIE: Thank you, Dr. Blois.

Your paper must have given a great deal of satisfaction to other unskilled chemists who, like me, have always been plagued by the black gunk they got when they were trying to make something that the textbooks said they ought to get. I hadn't realized until I heard your paper that we were really studying the fundamental nature of nature, and the stuff we have been throwing down the sink was a vital part of the whole system.

On a more serious note, in order to start the discussion, I noticed your first structure had cysteine at the top. Do you regard this as an integral part of it?

DR. BLOIS: This figure was taken from Nicolaus' work and refers to a natural melanin, sepiamelanin. Much of our work used diphenols as starting material, and the cysteine would be absent of course.

DR. ORÓ: You say you don't have information with regard to hydrolysis.

DR. BLOIS: The question was whether the photopolymer of phenylalanine could be hydrolyzed to phenylalanine. The polymer is generally resistant in much the same way that melanin seems to be. We have been unable to get the stuff back in solution. We have not succeeded in degrading it. There is, however, no evidence of peptide bonds.

It has been my position that we start with the pre-existence of aromatic molecules as an assumption, hoping that someone would come along with the evidence that this can happen. From the radiochemistry of the unsaturated hydrocarbons, for instance, one is given a little hope that such a mechanism could be found.

DR. CHARGAFF: Since you say you have a random polymer, are you entitled to use melanin in the singular? How can you vouch for the homogeneity of your preparation? Couldn't it be a mixture of nonrandom polymers, each one of a different type?

DR. BLOIS: That is an interesting question. How would one distinguish between a mixture of regular polymers and a random polymer?

DR. CHARGAFF: How would you distinguish between a mixture of different nonrandom polymers and a random polymer? This is a frequent problem in many so-called macromolecules.

DR. BLOIS: Our results say nothing about sequence. The magnetic evidence does suggest that the material is not highly conjugated. It suggests but does not prove that the structure is random. It suggests that the monomers containing the unpaired electrons must offer non-equivalent molecular sites but it doesn't say anything about the structural identity. The best evidence against melanin's being a mixture of different nonrandom polymers is the lack of periodicities as shown by x-ray diffraction.

DR. SZUTKA: Were the IR spectra you presented on melanin and for the synthetic compound, which were beautiful, normalized somehow? If they were not normalized, the ratio of peaks are the same. This could be used as one of the criteria for the identity of your synthetic compound.

DR. BLOIS: I hadn't appreciated the importance of that. There was no normalization. The amount of sample may have varied, though, between the different samples.

DR. SZUTKA: This would not affect the ratio.

DR. BLOIS: No.

DR. SZUTKA: So the ratio was not normalized.

DR. BLOIS: That is right.

DR. CHARGAFF: This is the question I put. While you have a peak there in the first two, it doesn't appear in the rest. You can't quite make it out. It is present in the upper two, but it is not present in the last. That struck me right from the beginning.

DR. SZUTKA: I think here we can speculate a little bit. If you have a larger polymer and if certain groups that are producing that peak, at $3\frac{1}{2}$ μ, for example, are bound tightly, they will not appear or they will appear to a lesser extent. This is what you may also expect in oxidized products.

But the general features of these spectra, I would agree with Dr. Blois, are approximately the same as those of catechol melanin.

DR. BLOIS: They all look very similar. The top one is sepiamelanin. The second one is from autoxidized catechol. Now, catechol has no nitrogen in it, so the polymer must differ in an elemental sense.

DR. CHARGAFF: I would conclude that you cannot conclude much from infrared in this respect.

DR. BLOIS: All I said is that it implies a statistical congruence.

DR. GROSSENBACHER: To get these spectra, you have to dissolve the material in something. To start with you have a granule. You treat it with something, and you get a soluble material. You are assuming you didn't break any molecules in achieving this solubility. Is this assumption justified?

DR. BLOIS: The optical spectra were made using KBr pellets of the melanins, which were dispersed in the solid phase. There was no solubilization.

DR. GROSSENBACHER: Do you have nonrandom polymers in mixed molecules? Unless you can separate the molecules, the question is meaningless. Our only definition of molecules has to be an operational one, and if you can't reduce this material to molecules, then we have no question.

DR. BLOIS: I can describe a concept and an experiment which may bear upon Dr. Chargaff's earlier question.

If melanin is really as random as I have been suggesting it might have two very interesting biological consequences. One question which may be asked is would it be antigenic? If no two molecules are alike, how would an immunological mechanism recognize another molecule if it never sees precisely the same one twice?

We have made some preliminary experiments with Dr. Rosenberg in the Medical Microbiology Department. We have tried to immunize rabbits with synthetic melanin over a period of 3 months, the usual procedures being used. Then by the various techniques—precipitin formation, agglutinin formation, agar gel diffusion, passive transfer to the rabbit's skin, and the rate of loss from the rabbit's blood space of the labeled antigen—we were not able to demonstrate any evidence of antigenicity.

I propose that this may help us distinguish between random molecules, and a mixture of highly uniform molecules.

DR. CHARGAFF: I don't know. I am not enough of an immunologist to know. There are probably many more substances that are nonantigenic than are antigenic. I am not sure I would want to use this argument.

DR. ORÓ: Negative results would tell you very little. If you had positive results, it would not prove anything in your case, either, because it is only a small part of the molecules that are needed to combine with the hapten.

DR. BLOIS: Haptens are micromolecules.

DR. ORÓ: All right, but in nature the micromolecule does not combine with the macromolecule as a whole. It combines with a small part of it. Similarly, antigen and antibody molecules do not combine with each other as a whole or *in toto*. They only do it by their reactive sites, which normally are small parts of the molecule.

Now, let me say that the main thesis of your paper, namely, that primitive random organic polymers may have acted as prototypes of enzymes, appears quite reasonable to me. As a matter of fact, carbonaceous chondrites contain a black polymeric substance which constitutes the bulk of the organic matter present in these meteorites.

We know very little about the structure of this polymer. It may be a highly condensed aromatic system perhaps like a random graphite type compound which has not yet been completely transformed to the ordered stage of graphite. In some respects it may be similar to the polymer you have described. It remains to be seen whether it is capable of any catalytic activity.

DR. PONNAMPERUMA: I would like to ask a question apart from the general discussion on melanin. In your experiment on the irradiation of tyrosine, did you find any other amino acids or peptides, and so on? Did you look for them?

DR. BLOIS: Yes, I should have mentioned that. We did not chromatograph the irradiation products of tyrosine, but in the irradiation of phenylalanine, we identified such intermediates as tyrosine.

DR. PONNAMPERUMA: But you haven't done it with tyrosine?

DR. BLOIS: Not yet.

DR. PONNAMPERUMA: Were there any peptides, or anything like that, formed?

DR. BLOIS: We have never found any evidence for peptide bond formation.

DR. GAFFRON: I would like to come back to the dialysis experiment. One experiment lends itself very nicely to further development. In the case where you irradiate under nitrogen and quickly dialyze afterwards, how does color develop? How soon do you see that the sample becomes discolored, i.e., slightly yellow? Is there nothing to be seen long before the irradiation is stopped?

DR. BLOIS: The dialysis experiment consisted of irradiating an aqueous solution of the material for a characteristic time and then putting it in the dialysis bag. There was then no further irradiation.

DR. GAFFRON: Yes, but under these conditions, did you get any color formation?

DR. BLOIS: The solution being irradiated becomes a faint yellow. As I said, there was some slight opalescence, but no obvious precipitate formation.

DR. GAFFRON: Of course, with 2537 Å you have a lot of energy. I never made anaerobic experiments. With fluorescein as sensitizer you are able to oxidize tyrosine in aqueous solution quite easily with visible light.

DR. BLOIS: And the absorbance moves into the visible.

DR. GAFFRON: The dye sensitized action in visible light might be more selective in its mechanism. It would be very interesting to see whether, in this kind of experiment, you get any polymers with visible light at all.

DR. FOX: I would like to add a few footnotes to these remarks.

First of all, I doubt whether the immunological approach is going to help solve this problem. It has not only the complications that have already been voiced—

DR. BLOIS: These experiments were carried out for their own interest.

DR. FOX: Even so, I think it is perhaps as well to bear in mind that immunological specificity is very often not absolute and, as Landsteiner and others have since shown, departures from antigenic molecules, slight structural departures, result in slight quantitative variations in many cases in the immune response and in the precipitin test. So I don't think there is promise in assessing homogeneity by this procedure.

DR. BLOIS: That was not the reason for doing it. The expectation was that it might not be antigenic, and the thought occurred to us that this might be a reasonable way to make a plasma expander.

It is very nearly a physiological material, and I think if it were to be used as a plasma expander, it would have to be nonantigenic. In this case a negative result is significant.

DR. FOX: I would want also to be very careful about the possibility that there is being formed a diketopiperazine, a cyclodipeptide of phenylalanine, which happens to be a quite insoluble diketopiperazine and diffuses out of the dialysis bag very slowly. If you are sure that there is no insoluble material, this may answer your question rigorously, but we found it essential, especially in thermally polymerizing either phenylalanine alone or with aspartic acid, to convert the products to the soluble sodium salt, and then to dialyze those, and also to filter them before dialysis in order to make sure that none of the phenylalanine diketo-piperazine was present.

We have not worked with the analog from tyrosine, but I suspect its properties may be similar.

Then, I would like to ask a question. You referred to stereospecific sites in the melanin. It wasn't clear to me whether you were thinking of these as stereospecific due to the nature of the folding or conformation of the molecule as a whole, or whether this was stereospecificity that might be derived from a monoconfigurational nature of the monomers.

I wonder if you would like to elaborate on that.

DR. BLOIS: Yes. The thought was simply this: that if one wants to hunt around for primitive catalytic or protoenzymatic mechanisms, in which you might require a specific site here, and a specific site there, and an active atom here, it seems to me that melanin might be a richer place to hunt than a quartz crystal, or any crystal.

DR. VALLENTYNE: What concentrations of the amino acids were you using here for a given dose of absorbed radiation? Was the concentration at all critical?

DR. BLOIS: They are in the order of 10^{-3} or 10^{-4} M.

DR. VALLNETYNE: What happens when you increase it by a factor of 10 or 100? What I am wondering is whether the nature of the reaction is influenced by concentration.

DR. BLOIS: We have not looked into the effects of concentration.

THE FOLLY OF PROBABILITY

PETER T. MORA

National Institutes of Health, Bethesda, Maryland

Probability is a very useful concept when we consider the evolution of the living. We believe that various living forms evolve because of the selection of mutants arising randomly. Probability on the molecular level is pertinent in this context, for example, to explain the appearance of a mutant as a consequence of change in structure of a single nucleotide of the DNA (deoxyribonucleic acid), hit at random by radiation or by a mutagenic chemical such as nitrous acid (cf. Freese, 1963). Probability is useful also when we study *in vitro* the molecular details of this or that biochemical process, cf. the kinetics of an enzyme. The rules of probability are followed in chemical kinetics, and application of statistical consideration is of great value in polymer chemistry (Flory, 1953). What I would like to discuss is the current practice of invoking probability in an attempt to account for the origin of life. In my opinion, this choice is not felicitous and the concept is not sufficient. However, as you might expect, I am unable to suggest in its place an alternate concept, except in the vaguest of outlines.

I shall proceed first by describing the inadequacies and discrepancies which arise when we apply the concept of probability to speculations on the origin of life. Then I shall discuss what I call the semantic confusion in the use of the word *selectivity*, which has at least three different operational meanings. Then I shall discuss some of the limitations in our current scientific approach which might explain why we favor the probability concept. Finally, I will try to say something about a teleological point of view which I believe we should keep in mind in biology, and which might lead us to new approaches or at least which would allow us to reconsider, in a new light, the problems connected with the origin of life. However, I must say that I am unable to be very specific or useful, as you will well see at the end.

39

I. Inadequacies and Discrepancies

A. Order and Macromolecular Structure

In a chemical reaction, such as in the polymerization of monomers, we obtain products, that is polymers, with properties predetermined by the reactivities of the functional groups and by the conditions employed (energy of activation, catalysts, etc.). The feature of the reaction is that we obtain a product in which the arrangements of the monomers and the linkages between them follow the dictates of probability within the confines of the above parameters. The resulting structure may be random or ordered, but not more ordered than what we can expect on the basis of the controlling parameters.

For example, we showed (Mora and Wood, 1958; Mora et al., 1958) that in the polycondensation of glucose at elevated temperature, a polyglucose is produced possessing a high degree of branching. The degree of branching and the frequency of the linkages between the monomers through a particular hydroxyl group is controlled by the relative reactivities of the hydroxyls under the conditions employed in the polycondensation experiment. At higher temperatures, the reactivities of the different nonglucosidic hydroxyls were more alike; therefore, there was a higher probability of more than one linkage being formed on the same monomer, and this led to a higher degree of branching. Similarly, polymers of other sugars, including ribose, deoxyglucose, etc., showed the expected randomness in structure, both in the frequency of the type of linkages and in their distribution, and also in the expected branching, depending on the functional groups of the particular monomers and the reaction conditions employed (Mora et al., 1960; Mora, 1964a). The synthetic polysaccharides had an over-all spherical molecular shape because of the generally high degree of branching.

Contrast these types of structure with the biological polysaccharides. In the latter group, specific linkage and the sequence of the monomers is most important from the point of view of function. The polysaccharides of cell membranes are predominantly linear and all types of biological polysaccharides are characterized by an arrangement of linkage and sequence, befitting their particular functions (cf. the antigenic determinant oligosaccharide sequences) Of course we know that such specific structure is the result of the working of enzymes, which in turn is a reflection of the genetic information transmitted by nucleic acids through cycles of reproduction as selected by evolution.

In the copolymerization of mixtures of 2′,3′-cyclic phosphates of various nucleosides by treatment with diphenyl phosphorochloridate, Michelson

(1959) reported the corresponding copolymers containing a random distribution of the nucleotide units. Only careful copolymerization of protected oligonucleotides, when the pre-existing phosphodiester bonds were not split, led to repeating order of bases (Michelson, 1959). For example, after cyclization of the terminal monoesterified phosphate the dinucleotide adenylyl-3':5'-uridine-3'-phosphate gave oligonucleotides with a defined arrangement of alternating adenylic and uridylic residues (Michelson, 1959). Khorana (1961), by the dicyclohexylcarbodiimide reagent, has produced a series of oligonucleotides with defined base sequence by selecting judiciously the oligonucleotides and the reaction conditions. This chemistry is analogous to the stepwise or controlled polymerizations of amino acid derivatives which were started at Emil Fischer's laboratory and are actively pursued now at the Weizmann Institute and in other laboratories.

My point is that in all of these reactions, be they random copolymerizations such as our work on the polycondensation of sugars with phosphorus and phosphoric acid as catalyst under anhydrous conditions (Mora and Wood, 1958), or Schramm's work using phosphorus pentoxide dissolved in ether (Schramm et al., 1961), or chemically directed selective polymerizations which lead to ordered sequence, the reaction product contains no more than the "information" put in, as defined by physicochemical parameters (Mora, 1964a).

In such chemical experiments we solely bring about random or controlled rearrangement of the interatomic linkages as determined by the reactivities of the atoms or functional groups under the guidance of the level of activation energy and of the catalysts. The products are random mixtures, or regularly repeating structures, and the frequency and the type (structure) of the components including sequence of monomers can be predicted on the basis of probability and chemical knowledge. Such experiments are no more than exercises in organic chemistry. They may pertain to the problem of how the necessary matter for living processes in the form of various molecules and polymers might have accumulated. But when such experiments are motivated by the belief that they pertain to the appearance of the living *processes* through coincidence of multiple similar phenomena, I question such faith.

Order, nonrandomness of a very complicated type as manifested in a specific message in the sequence in macromolecules and a space-time coordinated, as yet very little understood, control process, are essential attributes of living systems as they exist now. But could polymerization processes as ordered or controlled somehow (for example, by surface catalysis) lead to this eventually?

You might say that linear order arose naturally at the macromolecular level, for example by some analogy to the stereospecific copolymerization (Natta *et al.*, 1955). However, consider that in block copolymers there is an orderly repeat of short sequences or structures. This order is more similar to the order of a crystal than to the complex "order" required as information for a self-reproducing system. Furthermore, the repetition of sequences in a linear order is not the way reproduction is achieved now, on the molecular level in nature. Templates and parallel copy of information are characteristic of the biological reproduction mechanism.

The work of Turing made possible the development of simple mechanical models of autonomous sequence computers, and logically equivalent mathematical models of binary feedback shift registers which generate a specific sequence of symbols which repeats itself after a certain period. These models were proposed by Pattee (1961) as one way to account for the natural origin of macromolecular sequence with a high degree of order. However, both the mechanical models and the autonomous computers have to follow a certain set of instructions, and the appearance of the ordered sequence depends on building into the systems a certain amount of information. The order resulting is not more than that expected from the information built into the system, for example, in the molecular properties of the monomers (Mora, 1964a). Whether it could lead through a molecular selection type of process to a persistently self-reproducing functioning system with an internal control is a larger unresolved question (Mora, 1964b).

B. Thermodynamics

What one expects on the basis of probability considerations concerning the distribution of energy or matter is a general tendency toward over-all increase of entropy. Of course local and temporal pockets of low entropy may occur, such as in crystals, when this leads to the lowest energy state, as defined by atomic or molecular parameters. Crystallization results in simple, very uniform, repeating structures, which are inert. These structures do not exhibit any function, and they are not designed by function. The "order" of the living system is different: living structures are organized under the control of living units, under conditions when molecular forces alone may not always favor their formation. Their structure is not a simple repeating order; actually it is far from simple or stable. Living processes are characterized by being in flux, and their complex structural order is designed to allow them to function. Living systems avoid the lowest energy state, whether characterized by disorder or order. An example of avoidance of the low energy state when atomic or molecular parameters alone would lead to order of a different kind (crystallinity) is the experience that to maintain viability of supercooled cells one must prevent crystallization of water or other molecular components. Of course one can obtain crystals of components from a cell homogenate but not from a living cell.

In the thermodynamics of irreversible processes of open systems, it is predicted that during the development toward the stationary, fully developed state, the tendency of entropy production by unit time is to its lowest value (Prigogine, 1962). One may look on the development of a stationary state as analogous to the growing state (Prigogine and Wiame, 1946). It was shown by Prigogine (1962) that, while the entropy content of such a system itself may decrease, frequently it may increase. Actually, the latter would be the case always for isolated systems, if it were not for the fact that such systems cannot be in a stationary non-equilibrium state. Thus, while from the point of view of the thermodynamics of open systems, the behavior of organisms is not contradictory with regard to the change of entropy (Prigogine and Wiame, 1946), it still remains to be explained why living units operate as irreversible processes so that the entropy content decreases *invariably* in the growing state, and why they revert immediately at death to the increase of entropy.

C. Internal Control

Cells exhibit control of their molecular functions, an activity of very large numbers of molecules coordinated in space and time, with the decision somehow coming from inside the cell. This is what Weiss (1962) called the cellular control of molecular activity. Signaling elements (molecules) might come from the outside, although in certain cases it is rather difficult to imagine how this could happen. Consider for example the earliest stages of cellular differentiation of a blastula. When we consider the origin of life, we assume that originally some semblance of control operated from the outside, but at some point the control changed into an essentially internal control, with only signaling elements coming from the outside.

To keep a reaction going according to the law of mass action, there must be a continuous supply of energy and of selected matter (molecules) and a continuous process of elimination of the reaction products. It is assumed that in the prebiological system such control of the flow of matter and energy operated from the outside by a rare fortuitous coincidence, and spontaneously forming phase boundaries and membranes of droplets, etc., separated an inside and an outside phase.

To invoke mechanistic limitations of distribution of matter such as limiting concentrations or reduced diffusion of molecules by membranes, in gels (McLaren and Babcock, 1961), or proposals for cellular control systems through allosteric configurational changes of enzymes paralleling activity changes (Monod *et al.*, 1963), etc., does not solve the problem of the *origin* of an internally controlled process. What I mean is that while membranes, limiting concentrations in gels, etc., are essential to the control of molecular phenomena in the living cells, the argument should not be turned around for the origin of control of cellular activity by molecular processes.

A further assumption is needed. Somehow a control must have developed within an isolated system. Perhaps this can be considered then the beginning of the origin of a living system. Usually what is thought to allow this control to develop is a gradually arising, primitive, selection type of process on a molecular level (Horowitz, 1945; Oparin, 1961). I shall subsequently discuss a semantic confusion in the use of "selectivity" on the molecular and biological level. What I shall attempt to show is that we have a delusion that, because selectivity operates in a certain sense, it may also operate in another.

D. Minimum Requirements

When we consider the minimum requirements necessary for a self-reproducing and mutable system in the light of our current knowledge of molecular biology, we probably have to postulate two kinds of self-reproducing informational macromolecules. One kind is a polynucleotide and the other a protein type. Keep in mind that originally the protein also had to have self-reproducing capacity, since it is not an indestructible molecule. Otherwise, there must have been some kind of direct complementariness between these two types of macromolecules.

If we consider that the earliest primitive self-reproducing systems had something like RNA (ribonucleic acid) as the informational polynucleotide, there may have been need for an "RNA-dependent nucleotide polymerase" but not necessarily so, since the replication of the RNA could have been an uncatalyzed, template-directed, slow process in the early stages. But somewhere we do need at least one other type of macromolecule, a primitive peptide synthetase which reproduced itself, or a translation mechanism, or both. In other words, we need something else, like tRNA, to translate RNA information into polypeptide language (that is, it should produce an amino acid sequence which is directed somehow by the polynucleotide sequence of the RNA), and this tRNA could be produced by the RNA or, if we imagine a primitive polypeptide synthetase, this could be reproduced independently or by the RNA. But still, in its ordering function it must be dependent on the RNA. Or, alternatively, the whole sequence can be turned around, and a primitive protein-type molecule might have been the first informational macro-molecule.

Then there are two more enormously difficult but essential provisions needed: one, a control to keep these systems coordinated in space and time, and another to keep them going. I discussed in a recent article some of the difficulties in trying to account for the very last requirement on the basis of our current molecular orientation (Mora, 1963).

E. Infinite "Escape Clauses"

A further aspect I should like to discuss is what I call the practice of infinite escape clauses. I believe we developed this practice to avoid facing the conclusion that the probability of a self-reproducing state is zero. This is what we must conclude from classical quantum mechanical principles, as Wigner demonstrated (1961). These escape clauses postu-late an almost infinite amount of time and an almost infinite amount of material (monomers), so that even the most unlikely event could have happened. This is to invoke probability and statistical considerations when such considerations are meaningless. When for practical purposes the condition of infinite time and matter has to be invoked, the concept of probability is annulled. By such logic we can prove anything, such as that no matter how complex, everything will repeat itself, exactly and innumerably.

F. Singularity of Origin and Some Insolvable Problems

Living systems on Earth have an underlying unity as manifested by an amazing similarity in their biochemical processes. The same atoms, monomers (nucleotides, amino acids, sugars), and the same type of energy source (ATP: adenosine triphosphate) are utilized by all. This implies that living originated only once, or if more than once then in a sufficiently similar form that it was able to use up the similar constituents through similar pathways, so that it depleted or, so to speak, scavenged away these components from the less adjustable, more primitive anteced-ents. Then we have to ask those questions often brought up by Pirie: Why, for example, did not other polyvalent atoms lead to the appearance of consistently self-reproducing, mutable systems, using other components and other biochemical pathways? We may counter with an argument that dissimilar "living" systems might have appeared which are now extinct. Whether they existed or not, now is unknowable. If they disap-peared spontaneously, they ceased to fulfill the requirement that the existing living system as a whole appears to have, namely that the over-all outcome of persistent reproducibility compensates for the combined effects of the physicochemical dispersion forces and of lethal mutations.

Another futile argument is that the conditions may have changed drastically and many other types of life may have started which are extinct now. This argument removes speculation from the field of physicochemical knowledge by not allowing us to extrapolate backward. My point is that we have no way to prove or disprove such statements, and this efficiently removes them from the domain of science.

Some kind of answer to these questions might come from space exploration. Still, a persistent reproducibility and over-all continuance of a different system would remain in itself an equal puzzle, probably multiplying the puzzle which we have on Earth when we try to account for our living system. However, I admit that such findings would strengthen the argument that, under suitable conditions, persistently self-reproducing and mutable systems automatically appear because of an inherent property of matter; and then beneficial mutations help to overcome somehow the combined effects of deleterious mutations, of the deleterious changes of external conditions, and the randomization tendency of molecules.

I don't know even then if probability or simple chance would be logical and whether we should try to adhere to our present limited knowledge of properties of matter. It could well be that some yet unknown property of matter leads to the living process. However, *if* such a property exists, it is not an inseparable and inherent attribute of matter such as mass or gravitional attraction. The latter are not restricted by time to a certain period, while the manifestation of living processes is peculiar in that it is restricted to matter while the living is alive. You might say, this is invoking the old *vis vitalis*. Consider, however, that our attention in science concerning the properties of matter has been concentrated in the last few centuries on the discipline of physics. In biochemistry, based on this physics, we are able to account fully only for isolated phenomena, which will cease eventually. I cannot reconcile physical principles with the phenomenon of life when considering the whole living unit (Mora, 1963). It is interesting that Niels Bohr concluded that life is a qualitatively different attribute of matter, not subject to current considerations in physics (Bohr, 1933).

II. The Semantic Confusion

Selectivity, as we use the word in biochemistry and in biology, has two different operational meanings. Selectivity in a physicochemical sense means selective reaction of molecules. Molecules may react or not, depending on whether they are in the right energy state, whether they "fit" or not, etc., when they collide. Incidentally, this might be facilitated by certain catalysts, or it might be a very efficient complicated molecular process such as in the case of enzymes.

In chemical processes and in biochemical processes *in vitro,* when such selectivity operates, the end of the reaction is in sight. This selectivity on the molecular level is important in many biochemical processes, for example when biological macromolecules meet. Enzyme-substrate, antigen-antibody interactions, complementariness in building up all kinds of macromolecular structures, and complementariness and selectivity in schemes such as those advanced in the last few years for protein biosynthesis, etc., all are examples of selectivity operating on the molecular level.

It is also well known that biologically preformed molecules or macromolecules carry in themselves the information for the formation of the next level of structural hierarchy and, with this, a functional property. Certain L amino acids in some solvents will form an α-helix; nucleotide bases will stack; complementary polynucleotide strands will anneal into a double helix; virus proteins such as TMV (tobacco mosaic virus) subunits will reassemble; cell-free enzymatic synthesizing or incorporating systems will incorporate monomers into biopolymers with frequency and, presumably, sequence predetermined by a template [for control of sequence, cf. the claimed cell-free synthesis of transforming DNA (Litman and Szybalski, 1963)]. However, all these *in vitro* processes proceed to only one step higher in structural hierarchy. The information is inherent in the molecular parameters of the components preformed *in vivo,* and also in the conditions operating in the *in vitro* process (concentration, temperature, etc.). Furthermore, most importantly, the isolated *in vitro* processes cease and eventually degrade, the components becoming subject to the disruption of the random physicochemical forces (Brownian motion, etc.). These processes do not persist and do not lead to a consistently self-maintaining self-reproducing system, which tends toward more and more complexity as it evolves, as the living system does. They are only parts of such processes and produce only a temporary metastable order or function which will cease and tend to disperse more and more as its complexity increases.

The physicochemical principle of selectivity, even while it operates in the details of *in vivo* processes, cannot be used to account for certain properties of the whole living unit, or for the appearance of the persistently self-reproducing system from molecular components in the prebiotic system (Mora, 1963). Selection, as used by Horowitz (1945) and Oparin (1961) in this last context, includes more than the passive physicochemical principle of selection as outlined above: it includes a tacit assumption of acquisition, of positive action, of building up the improbable and more complex from the more probable, less complex and of actually increasing stability as complexity increases. It also includes an assumption that a function arises through selection of molecules, an internally controlled process with attributes of unexpected persistency and tendency of evolution toward more and more functional complexity.

I believe that this accounting for the appearance of the first persistently self-reproducing unit in a prebiotic system is an unwarranted extension of the meaning of the word selection, used by Darwin in a valid, but different, operational sense. Remember, the Darwinian selection and evolution concept was arrived at empirically, by observing the spectrum of living species and the reproduction and balance of dominance of progenies of the *already living*. Of course, this Darwinian concept of selection is a necessary attribute of the living, which allows it to adjust to the changing milieu. But it is not a sufficient concept. Mutability can occur only when first there is present a persistent reproducibility. Thus, mutability should be considered as a consequence of the persistent reproducibility and not vice versa.

Thus, two operationally different meanings of the word, selectivity— one in the physicochemical sense and the other in the Darwinian sense, each of them valid when used in its proper context—can give an illusion that the word may operate in a third sense. I believe this is the origin of the unwarranted speculation that some kind of molecular selection may account for the appearance of the first persistently self-reproducing, internally controlled, living unit.

To my thinking, to invoke the concept of probability, with the help of some kind of selection intermediary between physicochemical selection, operating on the molecular level, and biological selection in the Darwinian sense, operating in the already living, is not useful or felicitious, and certainly it is not sufficient. As the complexity of the molecular aggregates and of the molecular interactions increases, and indeed very complex interrelationships of molecules are necessary for the simplest known living unit, the probability of the continued existence of these specific interacting systems under the disruptive influence of random physicochemical forces will decrease. The probability will be even lower that an interacting system will function in a certain way so that it will absorb and repair, and the probability that it will reproduce, still lower, and the probability that it will reproduce persistently and that the beneficial changes will be able to overcome the deleterious changes (mutations) even lower. Probability, when followed to its logical conclusion, suggests that the origin and continuance of life is not controlled by this principle. The expression of life and its consequences from which we detect the presence of a living unit is opposite to what we would expect on the basis of purely statistical and probability considerations. I refer to the complex order in structure and in time-space interrelated control processes apparent in the simplest known living units.

III. Limitations in the Scientific Method

1. Currently, in science, we seem to be preoccupied with probability. Of course, probability is a satisfactory and very successful concept in many problems of mathematics and physics. We are also interested in information transfer. One achievement of this combination of interests is the electronic computer. It was thought conceptually possible to design an analog computer having enough information stored in a huge but still finite "genetic tail," to assure its self-reproduction by the organization of matter from the outside (von Neumann, 1951). However, such a finite state automaton would require initially an ordered linear array of external instructions of considerable length, equivalent to a preformed genetic instruction pattern. The possible origin of such instructions was not a part of the problem which was posed by von Neumann; thus these models, be they physical or mathematical, do not pertain to the origin of life.

2. There are certain epistemological limitations inherent in our current thinking in the physical sciences, acquired, I believe, because of the way science developed during the last three or four hundred years.

For practical reasons, we developed a simplifying scientific approach in physics. We follow the dictates of Descartes, that one must divide the difficulties under examination into as many parts as possible, and then study the simplest first and then proceed from the simplest to the more complex (Descartes, 1637). However, complexity is an essential attribute of biological systems: complex interrelations of numerous molecules in time and space are characteristic of them. We have not yet got used to thinking this way; we have yet to develop suitable conceptual approaches. Furthermore, in physics we avoid teleology of any kind, again apparently because of good historical reasons. But a certain type of teleological approach must be pertinent to the study of living systems, since these do have limited, apparently very materialistic, inner-controlled goals, such as self-preservation and reproduction.

3. The cardinal rule in science is that a statement has to be provable;

otherwise we may wade into a metaphysical quagmire. In this last respect, there is always an important limitation present when we speculate about the origin of life. We have not observed the genesis of a living unit and we have not synthesized a persistently self-reproducing mutable unit. As it stands now, speculations on the origin of life are not amenable to the methods of science where statements must be subject to proof. The only justifiable approach is a careful and limited extrapolation backward from existing biochemical knowledge.

Of course, we may resort to some unprovable argument, just to make us feel better, to have an illusion that we are going to be able to see the solution of the problem. One of these assumptions is that when all the biochemical details are known, maybe everything will make sense and the mosaic will show the picture. However, this type of thinking encourages us to avoid exactly those problems of complexity and interrelatedness that are so characteristic of the living. The other argument is that the origin of life is essentially a problem in probability. I hope that I have convinced you that this is an insufficient and actually an unsuitable concept. Furthermore, this appears to me as even a dangerous mental attitude. It leads to a self-satisfied state of mind. We have an illusion that the problem can be explained with existing knowledge (a very natural tendency in scientists) and this lulls us into an attitude of not thinking really about the problem. What other approaches can we take?

IV. New Approaches

Of course, we must retain the principle of provability of a statement. If we start from the fact that living systems are inherently complex and the interrelationships and the complexity are essential, we should think how to bridge the gap between molecular science and controlled interactions of many molecules. We see promising signs of such a new approach in the school of microbial genetics and in the studies of cellular control mechanism, and possibly in certain new developments in quantum mechanics (Tisza, 1963).

But I believe further that we have to have a teleological orientation in our thinking when we ask questions and design experiments prying into the behavior of a whole living unit. Then we might be able to phrase useful prognostic statements to try out by using the criterion of provability.

To be able to ask pertinent questions about the origin of life and to make at least a promising prognostic statement, we must study the simplest existing living cells as they are now, and particularly we must study those attributes of cells that are not likely to arise just from the known physicochemical properties of the components and that are not present in the isolated state. This, of course, includes problems of control of the behavior of the whole cell, especially those which pertain to continuance and persistency in both the individual level and in the progenies. Naturally, it is easier to approach questions in which the existing physicochemical knowledge and thinking can be routinely employed, as in the case in all the research on the details of living processes considered in isolation and clearly on the molecular level. This is fashionable nowadays in biochemistry and in molecular biology. However, it is becoming possible now to approach, even with the present methods of science, some questions which relate to the control mechanisms of whole cells, and to the initiation of reproductive cycles. Now we should go farther, and ask experimentally verifiable questions pertaining to the "urge" of self-maintenance and expansion of the individual living unit, and to the continuance of the living system as a whole as manifested by persistent reproduction (Mora, 1963). Research on these questions may lead to more insight in our thinking about how life may have originated.

Let us think freely. Let us not be afraid to question the sufficiency of principles of physics applied to biology, no matter how successful these principles are in physics, and especially let us not fool ourselves with probability where there is no room for it. Let us even dare to ask whether there is something special in the living, which cannot be treated by physics as we know it, but is still amenable to proof or disproof. By this type of thinking we may be able to devise experiments which may lead to the expansion of knowledge. Who knows, we may be able to throw new light on this old problem.

Revised manuscript received December 16, 1963.

REFERENCES

Bohr, N. (1933). *Naturwissenschaften* 13, 245.
Descartes, R. (1637). "Discourses on Method."
Flory, P. J. (1953). "Principles of Polymer Chemistry." Cornell Univ. Press, Ithaca, New York.
Cf. Freese, E. (1963). In "Molecular Genetics" (J. H. Taylor, ed.), Part 1, pp. 207–269. Academic Press, New York.
Horowitz, N. H. (1945). *Proc. Natl. Acad. Sci. U.S.* 31, 153.
Cf. Khorana, H. G. (1961). "Some Recent Developments in the Chemistry of Phosphate Esters of Biological Interest." Wiley, New York; also (1963). *J. Am. Chem. Soc.* 85, 3821, 3828, 3835, 3841, 3852, 3857.
Litman, R. M., and Szybalski, W. (1963). *Biochem. Biophys. Res. Commun.* 10, 473.
McLaren, A. D., and Babcock, K. L. (1961). *Enzymologia* 22, 365.

Michelson, A. M. (1959). *J. Chem. Soc.* **1371**, 3635.

Monod, J., Changeux, J. P., and Jacob, F. (1963). *J. Mol. Biol.* **6**, 306.

Mora, P. T. (1963). *Nature* **199**, 212.

Mora, P. T. (1964a). "Random Polycondensation of Sugars." This volume, p. 281.

Mora, P. T. (1964b). Remarks on H. H. Pattee's contribution to this volume, p. 402.

Mora, P. T., and Wood, J. W. (1958). *J. Am. Chem. Soc.* **80**, 685.

Mora, P. T., Wood, J. W., Maury, P., and Young, B. G. (1958). *J. Am. Chem. Soc.* **80**, 693.

Mora, P. T., Wood, J. W., and McFarland, V. W. (1960). *J. Am. Chem. Soc.* **82**, 3418.

Natta, C., Pino, P., Corradini, P., Damisso, F., Mantica, E., Mazzant, C., and Moraglio, G. (1955). *J. Am. Chem. Soc.* **77**, 1708.

Von Neumann, J. (1951). *In* "The General and Logical Theory of Automata, in Cerebral Mechanism in Behavior" (L. H. Jefress, ed.). Wiley, New York.

Oparin, A. I. (1961). "Life, its Nature, Origin and Development." Oliver & Boyd, Edinburgh and London.

Pattee, H. H. (1961). *Biophys. J.* **1**, 683: Also, contribution to this volume.

Prigogine, I. (1962). "Introduction to Thermodynamics of Irreversible Processes." Wylie (Interscience), New York.

Prigogine, I., and Wiame, J. M. (1946). *Experientia* **2**, 451.

Rich, A. (1962). *In* "Horizons in Biochemistry." (M. Kasha, and B. Pullman, eds.) p. 103. Academic Press, N. York.

Schramm, G., Grotsch, H., and Pollmann, N. (1961). *Angew. Chem.* **74**, 53; Also contribution to this volume.

Tisza, G. L. (1963). *Rev. Mod. Phys.* **35**, 151.

Weiss, P. (1962). *In* "The Molecular Control of Cellular Activity" (J. M. Allen, ed.). McGraw-Hill, New York.

Wigner, E. P. (1961). *In* "The Logic of Personal Knowledge." Routledge and Kegan Paul, London.

DISCUSSION

DR. BERNAL[1]: Dr. Mora's paper and the discussion to which it gave rise pose the most fundamental questions of the theory of the origin of life that have been raised at this conference or, as far as I know, elsewhere. The fact that it was essentially negative, criticizing the loose use of terms in the discussions that have gone on on the origin of life, was in my opinion most salutary. Taken as a whole, and probably without deliberate intention, Dr. Mora has shown that the principles of experimental science do not apply to discussions on the origin of life and indeed cannot apply in any problem of origin. All one can hope to do in the discussion is to make what Dr. Mora refers to as provable and W. N. Pirie as nonprovable, statements. That does not, in my opinion, mean that such statements are devoid of significance. Questions of origin have a logic of their own. This has not, as far as I know, ever been explicitly analyzed. In the first place, the questions may be wrongly

[1] *In absentia*

put; such a question, for instance, as "could life have originated by a chance occurrence of atoms" clearly leads as our knowledge, and also the limitations of the time and space available, increase, to a negative answer. This answer would seem to me, combined with the knowledge that life is actually there, to lead to the conclusion that some sequences other than chance occurrences must have led to the appearance of life as we know it.

Another probable limitation to a satisfactory theory of the origin of life is that the basic facts are wrong. We may not know enough about organic chemistry, cosmochemistry, or geochemistry to formulate the question correctly. This applies in particular to the first problem which I discussed in my paper, the formation of the small molecules that build up the so-called primitive soup. This becomes a quite different question than it was in Oparin's and Haldane's time, now that the formation of reasonably complex carbon compounds is known to have occurred for at least 4,500 million years in the space around the sun.

A third possible objection is that we are posing questions which *for the time being* cannot be answered. This may be because some essential element is beyond our ken. As Alfven has pointed out, it was quite impossible to find a theory of the origin of the sun's heat before radioactivity had been discovered. The laws of physics as known in 1895 could not contain a clue to this. Admittedly, the missing element may not be of the material kind but simply in the mode of thought, a lack of the necessary logic or mathematics. In many branches of physical science enormous discrepancies have occurred due to the absolute ignorance of the particular mechanism. For instance, until the Frank-Read source had been postulated, the mechanisms of crystal growth and crystal strength were quite inexplicable. Now a Frank-Read source is not a substance; it is a logical consequence of geometrical irregularity in three-dimensional structures. I should be very suspicious of our drawing conclusions from failing to account for any problem of organization which may turn out in the last resort to be due to our own failure to imagine the appropriate geometrical mechanism. This idea is also expressed in Dr. Mora's paper except that he draws a conclusion which is the opposite to the one I would draw. The present laws of physics, I would agree with him, are insufficient to describe the origin of life. To him this opens the way to teleology, even, by implication, to creation by an intelligent agent. Now both of these hypotheses were eminently reasonable before the fifteenth or possibly even before the nineteenth century. Nowadays they carry a higher degree of improbability than any of the hypotheses questioned by Dr. Mora. If he thinks that he has shown conclusively that life cannot have originated by chance, only two rational alternatives remain. The first is that it did not arise at all, and that all we are studying is an illusion. This is the old argument of Parmenides, whose logic led him to believe that the Universe is *One* and that any apparent multiplicity is illusory. The other alternative is that life *is* a reality but that we are not yet clever enough to unravel the nature of its origin which seems to me admittedly *a priori* more probable.

The obstacles that have held up scientific theories in the past, particularly in physics, have been the reluctance or inability to think sufficiently *deeply* to conceive the improbable, even the absurd, such as the coexistence of waves and particles of the quantum theory. In the problem that faces us, it does not seem that *this* is the difficulty, but rather the inevitable *complexity* of the whole situation. In my view, we are not likely to find the way out through a brilliant stroke of genius which finds a *formula* for the origin of life but rather by the continued pursuit of many threads of observation and thought which will successively illuminate more and more of the picture, thus narrowing down the problems until the solution seems obvious.

Dr. Mora laid particular emphasis on the problem of selectivity and on the semantic confusion it has given rise to. I think this criticism is very valuable but that his negative conclusions are not as soundly based as he imagines. For instance, he says that biologically preformed molecules or macromolecules carry in themselves the information for the formation of the next level of structural hierarchy and, with this, its functional property. This statement, to my mind, contains the germ of the solution to the problem of selectivity in the origin of life. All the functional properties of life are in this view immanent in the properties of the next lower level. If he grants that progression from one stage to the next is possible, I cannot see why he stops there. The same argument should reach one stage further and so on down to the atoms.

What we have still to try and understand is the nature of these immanent fractional properties and the structures which give rise to them. As I have stated in my paper, we have taken in the past altogether too limited a view of the kind of ordering that is exemplified by the normal crystal, three-dimensional lattice packing. Among a more complicated molecule, without invoking any new physical principles, two- and one-dimensional packing is also possible, the first giving rise to a normal smectic liquid crystal, the second to one-dimensional crystals which can undergo secondary and tertiary complications—all immanent. This provides the *form* for self-reproduction. What is needed is the *impetus,* the "breath of life," or urge, expressed by Mora in a teleological way, which as far as I can see, might just as well be explained by the physical-chemical activity of high energy phosphates. We need not despair: it may take a long time to achieve and many mathematical logical principles may be involved, but it will not be necessary to appeal to any other physiochemical principles. Instead we may have to add to the known principles the implications of the geometry of complex systems. The question of molecular selection would appear quite insoluble if we did not believe that the material or structure selected had certain intrinsic advantages if only of a thermodynamic or kinetic character. Where the liquid crystal scores and, *a fortiori,* simple biological systems, is in combining low energy in the crystalline form with high probability in the liquid form. A two-dimensional liquid crystal can be modified to form systems of cisternae folded or coiled round to make myelinic figures. The selectivity we look for in the early forms of life is just one stage higher than the selectivity which occurs in the mineral world in which the most fantastic low concentrations of the rare elements can be highly concentrated as mineral crystals.

I do not agree with the criticisms of the limitations of scientific method which Dr. Mora puts forward, but I think he has done a very valuable service in stating them. The contrast between a Cartesian physics with material causes and a teleological biology with final causes which he poses, I think is false. Nevertheless, it contains the truth of the different laws for different levels, an essentially Marxist idea. He said that the cardinal rule in science is that a statement must be provable—but that does not mean that it has to be proved *now.* A good deal of useful work can be done in handling the problem and modifying it so that one can reach a position in which a statement can be proved or, more correctly, disproved.

The teleological method in biology to which Dr. Mora is pleading we should return had been rejected not so much for its inadequacy but for its patent dependence on subjective human feelings. If *we* have an *urge* to live and to reproduce, this can be imputed back to the molecules from which life started and our habits of thinking make this transposition very easy. But such a hypothesis, now intrinsically suspicious, is no longer requisite in the time of molecular biology; there is absolutely no evidence for the occurrence of sensation and thought in such molecular systems nor can there be any *description* of an object toward which an urge may be attributed. On the molecular biological level in existent life forms, a structure is the result of a *prescription.* It is only secondarily by a play-back mechanism that it is related to the original material on the lower level from which it arises. The idea of an urge for self-maintenance was in my opinion put into the descriptions of biological phenomena as an inadmissible and now unnecessary afterthought.

The discussion which took place after Dr. Mora's paper is also of great interest, particularly the contribution of Drs. Oró, Haldane, and Chargaff. Haldane indeed suggests that there may exist orders of complex interactions between atoms other than the orbitals which characterize modern quantum chemical theory. These may indeed be just that missing element which I earlier alluded to as necessary to get further information on origins in terms of physical chemistry. Whether Oro's "super-ordinated systems" are to be considered alive or nearly so may depend on such functions, though I would hardly agree that tobacco mosaic virus could be an example of such a super-ordinated system by itself but only as a part of a much larger system.

The essential point I want to make here is that this discussion is no longer carried out as it was even a few years ago in terms of such general tendencies which may rightly be called, as they were called by Dr. Mora, metaphysical, but in terms of concrete arrangements of atoms in which a few themes recur over and over again: the organic bases, especially the adenine which as Chargaff pointed out is polymerized hydrocyanic acid, the metaphosphate link through oxygen, the lipids and the amino acids, all severally produced automatically without any biological function, which we always find combined together in all the phenomena we choose to call living. Dr. Mora wants to introduce at this point a teleological urge, but the argument is on the level of one carried out centuries ago in India between a Platonic philosopher Meleager and a Buddhist monk in which the latter, claiming that a chariot is made of wheels, body, pole, reins, etc., demands triumphantly "where is the soul of the chariot?"; and receiving no answer says "if the chariot has not a soul, why do we think that human beings have one?".

CHAIRMAN PIRIE: Dr. Mora, you have started people thinking. As for my own point of view, I was surprised at the improbably large number of occasions on which my reaction was almost the precise opposite to yours. Often, when you said "prove," I would have said "disprove," because it appears to me that you can very seldom conduct experiments that prove anything. All you can do is arrange an experiment that will disprove one of the possible points of view. So, if throughout your paper you would say disprove instead of prove, I would have been largely at one with you.

DR. VALLENTYNE: I got the impression that you think there is almost no region between chemistry and biology that is at all explainable; is that really correct?

Dr. Mora: Physical science and biology. I think the gap is too big to bridge. At least I can not.

Dr. Vallentyne: Suppose you took a tobacco plant cell and enlarged it to something the size of the earth, let's say, and considered this as a big ocean full of all sorts of molecules, and then put tobacco mosaic virus in there. Is this living?

Dr. Haldane: You couldn't do that because your qualitative considerations would go wrong. One of the things you have to consider in any form of life is that the transitions which are occurring are of a kind where quantum conditions come in and you just can't use models.

Dr. Oró: You seem to have reached the conclusion that there is some unknown force or property of matter (yet separable from matter) that "leads to the living process." In your presentation you elaborated on the inadequacies of present concepts. Now, would you care to suggest something about the nature of this unknown force or forces that may give an explanation for the existence of living organisms?

Dr. Mora: No. I am very destructive in my attitude. I can't say anything conclusive and constructive and useful. I can only tell you that I consider that the impression of physics on scientists is so strong nowadays that it is difficult to think, without using the same concepts. In my mind, this almost parallels the situation which existed just around the end of the scholastic period, when teleology was so overwhelming that considerations and approaches that physics now uses were very difficult even to think about. For example, it took centuries until the concept of provability or disprovability became an operational concept. It took decades and probably centuries until the principle of starting with the simplest and proceeding from there became an operational concept, and until we liberated ourselves from teleological considerations. The most important thing and often the only thing people were allowed to think about was the reason for everything.

Now, I think we have a somewhat similar but opposite situation where our thinking is so controlled by physical concepts that we can't think of any novel concept. I mentioned to you a few things which might suggest possibly a good way to start, such as control processes pertaining to the simplest whole living unit. How is a cell able to persist longer than you would expect, just on the basis of its being an aggregate of molecules? How does it repair itself, how does it reproduce? Think of the nature of self-maintenance and the over-all "urge" of the living system toward continuance against the disruptive physicochemical forces. We can approach these problems by some kind of research on control mechanisms developed by people such as Monod and Jacob. This might give us new insight. But I really am demonstrating the difficulties in our thinking by showing you that I don't really have any good novel suggestion.

DR. ORÓ: It seems to me that the basic issue in your presentation is a matter of semantics. Perhaps it reflects the scanty efforts that have been made so far to study chemical organic evolution at the molecular level. The discussion would probably be more fruitful if some constructive proposals such as those advanced by Pattee (1961) and Rich (1962) were first considered in detail and discussed. These two proposals show how an increasing degree of organization may be generated at the molecular level, and, in my estimation, they solve some of the inadequacies you have put the finger on.

DR. PONNAMPERUMA: I want to follow up on what Dr. Oró has said. This word "urge" that Dr. Mora has used is simply another term for a chemical tendency. I would like to refer him to a paper written long ago by Pirie on "the meaninglessness of the term, life."

DR. PATTEE: May I just say one word that has nothing to do with the basic argument about whether life can be explained by physics or not. I would like to say a word in defense of probability, since your topic was the "folly of probability."

The concept of probability I don't believe is properly used here, at least the way Laplace and others represent it. The idea is that two models which are sufficiently well defined in order to apply a probability measure may then be objectively compared with probability theory, which is only a mathematical theory. In this sense, probability cannot possibly explain anything. It is an objective way to compare two alternative models. And in this sense, I don't believe it is folly to use probability.

DR. MORA: Maybe, in fact, I used the wrong word. Maybe others just say that the origin of life just happened by some chance or miraculous coincidence or unexpected combination, and I shouldn't use the word "probability." But what I was mainly talking about was that when you try to explain away this sort of singular occurrence on the basis that we have to have so much time and so much material in hand, well, this might be satisfying only to a certain type of mind. I find that it brings up more questions than it answers.

DR. PATTEE: I think we agree that the *chance hypothesis* for the origin of life is unsatisfactory. It is not only conceptually barren, but also untestable empirically. However, if we create an alternative model which is sufficiently well defined to apply probability theory, it may then be correctly applied. It is not the fault of probability theory that a good model hasn't been made yet.

DR. FOX: I would like to point out that some define productive research as that research which produces questions faster than it produces answers.

DR. HALDANE: I would like to suggest that we are not really using physics. In modern physics something very like urge happens if you consider one of the elementary events, let us say the disappearance of an electron and positron to give a photon. You can't calculate what is going to happen, unless you look ahead. In that way physics does bring the future into the calculations. In physics we have practically authenticated that whenever you try to explain a complicated system, whether it is an atom in terms of its electrons or a molecule in terms of its nuclei and electrons, at every stage you are bringing in more new principles of organization. Now we have some links between atoms and molecules, molecular orbitals, and so on, which are part of the system of quantum physics, but were not guessed at until molecules were studied. I have very little doubt that there are far more complicated things of the same general kind in connection with living systems which help them to preserve their structure and function. But I do not think we are bold enough in our physics—a lot of us are thinking in terms of the physics of 1920 rather than the physics of 1963.

DR. MORA: I think there are signs of new approaches in quantum physics. I refer to an article by Tisza in the last winter issue of the *Review of Modern Physics* (35, 151, 1963); which brings up new conceptual approaches in quantum theory to multiplicity and interaction. Where Tisza starts from is really important.

DR. SAGAN: I wonder if the quantity we're really concerned with isn't the time scale of the event in question.

DR. MORA: I say it is an escape clause to use arguments that there must have been infinite time or almost infinite time.

DR. SAGAN: No. The time scale is certainly calculable in principle. For purposes of calculation, we consider a closed system, the parameters of which are known. We then ask how long it takes for a certain event to have occurred (e.g., spontaneous DNA synthesis), and compare that answer with the amount of time available. For example, if it takes much longer than 5×10^9 years, the event is correspondingly unlikely. If it takes much less than 5×10^9 years, such events are likely to have occurred. The use of probability arguments seems to me quite useful and valid.

DR. MORA: I think the essence of the question is: Are we extending time schedules to just suit us—well, just to make us feel good that there could be some way that by chance it actually did occur? We usually do extend both the time scale and the material which is available to make this possible but, I think, when these parameters are so close to the practically infinite, then considerations of chance have no meaning.

Dr. Sagan: I propose that 5×10^9 years is very much less than infinity.

Dr. Mora: I don't know. That is a matter of opinion.

Dr. Szutka: I think that Dr. Mora's paper creates an impression that only chance was responsible for events leading to the living systems. However, it is possible that several parameters were acting and, therefore, increasing the probability that the event would occur. Here I am talking about something like two molecules capable of interacting. There is a probability of their interacting at infinite time, but if there is a suitable force acting upon the two molecules, then the probability of interaction will increase. In addition several parameters that we don't know of may have been acting and perhaps increasing the probability, or improbability, as Professor Haldane would call it, of the occurrence of the event. Couldn't it be possible, Dr. Mora?

Dr. Mora: Yes. I hope I don't give the impression that by pure chance it could have happened just by itself, without there being some particular yet unknown attributes or physicochemical properties in the interacting molecules. I want to give the impression that these types of things could very well have happened spontaneously, but I was arguing against the prevalent considerations that it happened by pure chance, since then we are not looking for the particular conditions.

For example, what you bring up may be the novel molecular parameters I am talking about. I am not talking at all against what you say. It is very useful.

Dr. Szutka: However, in your interpretation there was only time that was primarily discussed—time limitation. This was just my understanding, maybe I was wrong.

Dr. Mora: If you say that there must be other considerations and that it happened within limited time, that is very good. I agree with you. Somehow it had to start. It started.

Dr. Oró: Let me put a question to Dr. Mora. Can you go from a less complex system to a more complex system with the aid of forces which are known to us today?

Dr. Mora: Yes.

Dr. Oró: You can do that?

Dr. Mora: Of course, as we very well know, there are many of these phenomena, for example, DNA annealing, or in every type of molecular reaction involving synthesis. What I am saying is that in these reactions or in these interactions, the original information inherent in the properties of the matter plus the conditions under which these reactions happen control the steps, and the information contains what is necessary for the next step in the hierarchy of both function and structure. But then physicochemical processes eventually cease, and they don't represent the continuous drive for self-maintenance and reproduction, etc., up through several levels of hierarchy so that the total amount of outcome is through the creation of progenies, a continuance of the living system. This is the point, that physicochemical processes eventually cease. But we know very well that there are forces that lead to the more complicated matter. That is what all chemistry is about.

DR. ORÓ: So your conclusion is that actually we do not know the exact mechanism whereby this process takes place.

DR. MORA: That is right.

DR. ORÓ: I would like to state some general considerations concerning the organization of matter in the universe. We have at least five main levels (or elements) of organization which in order of increasing complexity are: (1) elementary particles; (2) chemical elements (nuclides and atoms); (3) molecules; (4) aggregated and gravitational systems; and (5) superordinated organic systems.

Now, if we take the essence of Dr. Mora's thesis, i.e., that we cannot get a higher order or a higher degree of organization that is not contained in the interacting elements and the environment, then we must come to either of two conclusions: (a) that it is not possible to go from elementary particles to elements, from elements to molecules, from molecules to aggregated systems, and from molecules to superordinated organic systems; or (b) that, if it is possible, the information is contained in the interacting elements and the environment. Either one of these two solutions to the problem appears to be satisfactory from a theoretical point of view. But the fact is that the above processes occur in nature. Although we do not know the exact mechanism of the transformation of protons (or hydrogen) into carbon, it occurs in nature, it occurs in stars. The astrophysicists tell us that the proton-proton chain leads to the formation of alpha particles which in turn collide to form carbon, which is certainly an element of higher organization than hydrogen. From carbon, oxygen is formed by a process of alpha-capture, and nitrogen by operation of the carbon-nitrogen cycle. In other words, the synthesis of elements occurs in nature and one cannot deny it. Furthermore, we know that elements go into molecules, for this is the experience of chemists. Chemists know that if they have elements (or atoms) and surround them with an appropriate environment, the atoms are transformed into more or less complex molecules. Again this cannot be denied. This is a fact. So, since these processes occur in nature, then according to (b) the information must be contained in the interacting elements (or species) and their surrounding environment.

If, on the other hand, one applies Dr. Mora's conclusions to the above five systems (or levels of organization), one would have to say that unless we find some unknown force, it would not be possible to go from elementary particles to elements, from elements to molecules, from molecules to aggregated and gravitational systems, and from molecules to superordinated organic systems.

As I understand it, what Dr. Mora probably meant in talking about the folly of probability could perhaps be best illustrated as follows: If from a theoretical point of view and in the absence of pertinent chemical knowledge, one would calculate the probability necessary for five atoms of hydrogen, five atoms of carbon, and five atoms of nitrogen to get together in the right place and form a molecule of adenine, one would obtain such a low probability that one would have to conclude that the formation of adenine is practically impossible unless it is directed by some unknown special force.

The fact is, however, that from hydrogen, carbon, and nitrogen, adenine can be made in significant amounts. Obviously it does not occur in one step. First hydrogen, carbon, and nitrogen react to form hydrogen cyanide, and from hydrogen cyanide in an appropriate environment other more complex molecules are generated which eventually interact to form adenine among other products.

So, if I may conclude with my original statement, the basic issue in your presentation has to do with semantics, or problems of meaning, and it shows how difficult it is to have generally acceptable definitions. I think if we could sit down and arrive together at some definition of probability (and life) then we may conceivably be in agreement. However, from your presentation one gets the impression that a special force or property of matter, yet not an "inherent attribute of matter," is needed to arrive at higher degrees of material organization.

DR. MORA: Let me ask you, first, what you mean by the superordinated organic systems?

DR. ORÓ: Here again we come to a difficult problem of definition. An example of a superordinated organic system would be tobacco mosaic virus.

DR. MORA: Would it have the ability alone to persistently self-reproduce and mutate?

DR. ORÓ: No, unless it was surrounded by the appropriate environment.

DR. MORA: I would like to see what you mean by a superordinated organic system in your fifth level or organization, because I can go along probably all the way to 5 with you. I can go from 1 through 4 by using known principles or what I feel are sensible explanations of chemistry and physics. I would like to know whether the superordinated organic system is another word for what I use the word "living." Otherwise, I could go along with it. I don't propose that probability is useless in physics or in explaining how higher degrees of all kind of material organization may come about in the non-living. But would you mean the living systems in that fifth one?

DR. ORÓ: If you take a tobacco mosaic virus, as such, although it describes the system structurally, it does not describe the system completely for the biologist. You would have to add the corresponding elements (enzymes, metabolic precursors, mutagens, etc.) that would be required by the biologist to make such a system possible.[2]

DR. MORA: Would you add the plant cell?

DR. ORÓ: Not necessarily. As a structural biochemist, one would not have to add anything. As a biologist one would have to add the plant cell or its equivalent. If one would know exactly how to make a tobacco mosaic virus and specifically what other elements to add and environment to provide in order to keep the virus continuously replicating, one would have the design of the first experiment to produce a "living" system. It is obvious from the very fact that we are meeting here today that we do not have the design of such an experiment.

DR. MORA: Then you don't include those groups, systems which we consider now living, into your fifth item.

DR. ORÓ: I include them by extrapolation and have done so in a recent publication (see footnote). For, can you tell me of any other origin of living organisms, which, as we know, are made up of essentially the same elements that make up the rest of the matter of the universe? Can some other origin be reasonably proposed?

[2] For purposes of clarification and in answer to Dr. Mora's question, the following concept taken from J. Oró, "Experimental Investigation of Organo-Chemical Evolution in Current Research in Exobiology" (M. H. Briggs and G. Mamikunian, eds.) Pergamon Press, in press, is offered as an explanation: A superordinated organic system may be defined as an organized arrangement of organic molecules which in an appropriate environment shows one, several, or all properties which are essential to a living organism. It should be taken into consideration that a living organism means different things to investigators in different fields of the life sciences. For instance, a simple virus to the biochemist means an ordered complex of two or more different types of molecules with certain characteristic properties. On the other hand, to the biologist it usually represents a microorganism that has reached a high degree of parasitism.

DR. MORA: No. I think your elements and the matter between those five levels of organization are the ones which lead to the appearance of the living system. And I go along with you if you just stop at TMV and you don't add the plant cell. So long as you do that, that is nicely understandable under the concepts of physics. I have difficulty in seeing further.

DR. GAFFRON: But this difficulty existed in antique times.

DR. MORA: Oh, yes.

DR. GAFFRON: So all we know we know by hindsight. Let's do the experiments little by little. The production of adenine has taken 2000 years to understand. We proceed with the assumption that, although we can't see how, the analysis in detail of future experiments will suddenly give us an intuition as to what we are missing now.

DR. MORA: Yes.

DR. GAFFRON: It is the only way to proceed. Otherwise we have to give up.

DR. CHARGAFF: How much of the adenine do you get? Do you get one molecule of adenine from five HCN?

DR. ORÓ: About a hundred years ago adenine was known as pentameric hydrogen cyanide.

DR. CHARGAFF: Yes, I know. I mean in your experiments.

DR. ORÓ: Yes, in the sense that essentially all the atoms in one molecule of adenine are derived from those originally present in five molecules of HCN.

DR. CHARGAFF: Would you say the probability of forming the other things which HCN goes into is greater?

DR. ORÓ: Sure.

DR. CHARGAFF: Then I don't think you can use this argument.

DR. ORÓ: The yield is small by standards of preparative synthesis, but the fact that the yield is small does not deny that it is possible to synthesize adenine in significant amounts.

DR. CHARGAFF: There is a tremendous gap between what is possible and what is probable.

DR. ORÓ: Right.

DR. CHARGAFF: We continuously jump from one to the other.

DR. ORÓ: The nuclear formation of carbon is supposed to be a highly improbable event, yet carbon is the fourth or fifth most abundant element in the universe. In a more humoristic tone, someone has said that by all probability we should all be dead. But we aren't.

DR. CHARGAFF: But we shall be.

DR. MORA: That is the crucial point.

MOLECULAR MATRICES FOR LIVING SYSTEMS

J. D. Bernal (*in absentia*)

Department of Physics, Birkbeck College,
University of London, London, England

As this conference, which I am very sorry not to be able to attend, will be one of experts in the field of the origin of life and related subjects, I will not attempt any general introduction. I will rather confine myself to asking a number of questions, not because I expect to find immediate answers, but just to see the directions in which current investigations and speculations are going.

The inclusion of such queries in scientific papers was once very prevalent—I only have to mention Newton's "Optics." It seems to me a peculiarly appropriate mode for a subject such as the origin of life, where direct evidence cannot be got and comparative studies are, for the moment, impossible though we may hope to make some in the near future as space travel brings us into some region of different life forms.

We come then to the first question: Are the forms of life necessary or contingent? In other words, wherever we go will we find essentially the same kind of life, though not necessarily in an identical form to what there is on this Earth? I know that on the principle of sufficient reason we might not expect to find anywhere else the kind of life we have here. However, I think we know enough about the basic chemistry of the elements of the periodic table, and there are no others, not to expect a different kind of life, a life based on essentially different elements. This is, firstly, because the life that we have on Earth is based on the commonest elements which exist in the Sun and in all the stars, and secondly because quantum considerations of the energy exchanges of other atoms, such as that of silicon or arsenic, are not such that give rise to the peculiarly easy enzymatic reactions that characterize terrestrial life. In any case, the burden of such a claim rests with the proposer: to put it forward as a base for the possibilities of life at the moment is simply a way of distracting interest from the kind of investigation on the elements we do know and which can quite reasonably be carried out here and now.

It is evident, by the very calling of this conference, that the subject of the origin of life has now become not only a popular one but also one which has got a certain scientific respectability. It has indeed widened and deepened in its investigations. In these days the problem of life no longer becomes the problem of life on Earth but the problem of life inside the solar system or even beyond it. It does attract to itself a small but essential part of the interest which is now devoted to space studies. Not only is there the possibility of being able to determine comparative forms of life on celestial bodies, but also the question arises —which becomes an eminently practical one— of how to preserve these bodies from involuntary contamination by terrestrial forms of life.

At the same time the recent developments of biophysics, biochemistry, and, most of all, of molecular biology have brought to the fore once again the question of origins. The late W. T. Astbury, one of the founders of the subject, understood this when he said: "The line I propose to adopt thus starts from structure, goes on to properties, then seeks out the underlying plan, and lastly tries to delve down into the origin of things."[1]

Any comprehensive biochemical structural plan requires, as it is unfolded, hypotheses of origin to make sense of it. It is as necessary today for biochemistry as hypotheses of an evolutionary tree were for normal systematic biology a hundred years ago.

What can we consider as the most profitable lines of its progress? This is, as I see it, one of the major purposes of the present meeting, and there may be as many lines to follow as there are contributors and, indeed, more. Here I only want to point out those that seem to me to require answers most urgently. We are not concerned any longer with the major proof of whether life has a spontaneous origin or not. What we have to prove is not whether life arose but precisely how it did so. We have to separate out, from between possible forms of the origins of life, the actual one which it followed. These studies are now apparently passing beyond the realm of simple speculation where they started in the Oparin-Haldane hypothesis. Synthetic experimental work is finding its place in them, but the synthetic studies, though completely valid in themselves as parts of chemistry, need to be shown as feasible under conditions which may reasonably be taken as those in which life

---

[1] "Adventures in Molecular Biology" (1952). *The Harvey Lectures* **46**, 3.

originated. By this I want to point out that experimental work may be valid, but irrelevant to the question of the origin of life.

The synthetic approach to the origin of life requires simultaneous satisfaction of the probabilities of the occurrence of the actual constituents from which life originated and of the conditions in which this occurred. The requirements of specialized stellar and nebular astrophysics have also to be met, now that we are no longer limited to the problems of the origin of life on Earth but to the origin of life in general, or at least to the origin of the prelife states of complex carbon and nitrogen compounds.

Any valid theory of the origin of life must account for the existence of compounds not only, so to speak, as living fossils that are found reproduced in life on Earth today, but also as the compounds of carbon found in meteorites and in igneous rocks on Earth.

We have to face another question: Are the two lines of evidence compatible with each other? In other words, are the carbonaceous compounds found in meteorites actually similar to those which are found on earth and which can be deemed to be origins of vital processes there?

The carbonaceous fraction of meteorites is composed of very intractable, high molecular weight materials, and so far the methods to study them, such as have been developed for terrestrial organic compounds of definitely biological origin, are not effectively applicable to them.

We must recognize that the carbonaceous material of meteorites is of an extremely complex and intractable nature. It may not, strictly speaking, contain constituent molecules at all. It may be one simple amorphous mass of carbon, nitrogen, hydrogen, and oxygen like a char. It may exist both in primary and secondary forms. The primary form found in meteorites seems to be associated with relatively low-temperature hydrated silicates, as Kerridge, in particular, has shown in my laboratory. These structures are, however, found in meteorites accompanied by definitely high temperature forms.

There are alternative theories as to the origin of the carbonaceous chondrites. Mueller favors the idea that they are essentially volcanic products, and I have myself given some support to this notion and even proposed a mechanism for the formation of an asteroid in which the carbonaceous meteorites are a sample of intermediate layer, where they may have been formed at moderate temperatures and were finally ejected by a volcanic process. The alternative theory, strongly supported by Wood, is that the carbonaceous chondrites are samples of the original material and condensed from the dust cloud around the early forming Sun, and that the primitive dust particles have been melted by shock waves and then rapidly cooled, as shown by the evidence of the glassy nature of the smaller chondrites. They have an age of about 4.2 thousand million years, and the presence of relatively large quantities of xenon-128 derived from iodine-128, a short-period radioactive element, indicates their formation within a few million years of the original solar dust cloud. The chondrules are embedded in a matrix containing the carbonaceous material and silicates which Kerridge has shown to be similar to serpentines; some of them contain water enriched in deuterium. The most recent evidence from Wood's studies is that the xenon content of the chondrite as a whole is less than that of the chondrules and, consequently, that the interstitial material is still younger. Many chondrites, particularly those which have very little or no carbon, have evidence of subsequent metamorphosis, and there seems to be continuous passage to the definitely remelted achondrites. It is certain, however, that the carbonaceous material with hydrated silicates has not been exposed to temperatures much more than 150°C since their formation, for both the organic material and the hydrated silicates decompose at such temperatures.

The theory of formation from melted dust is not necessarily inconsistent with the volcanic theory, if we take it that the highly carbonaceous chondrites represent the surface of an asteroid which has never been heated and which contains mixtures of material originally deposited there in the asteroid formation and material falling on it later in the form of volcanic dust. This problem can probably be solved within a relatively short time when we obtain samples of the Moon's surface and more samples of meteoric dust, particularly that of the noctilucent clouds.

The question of meteoric carbonaceous material has been already related to various hypotheses on the origin of life. On the basis of hydrocarbon fractions, Nagy and Meinschein have claimed that meteoritic carbon is actually biogenically produced and, therefore, that the original asteroidal sources of these meteorites had life on them. This is still a highly controversial subject, partly intrinsically in the interpretation of the analyses and partly because of the extreme difficulty of explaining how life forms actually arose on celestial objects which could have no hydrospheres. However, it is unnecessary to go into it here but the essential fact is the presence of complex organic naturally occurring compounds which may include the purines and pyrimidines. Their mere existence, however, on meteorites does suggest an important modification of the original Oparin-Haldane hypothesis in so far as it concerns the first method of production of carbonaceous compounds.

A new hypothesis, which I suggested, as to the origin of these is that they started from a condensation of low-temperature gaseous molecules on the surface of a metallic iron and silicate dust. These would consist, in the first place, mostly of ice and also, at lower temperatures, of ammonia and methane or CH_2 radicals. With a slight rise in temperature due to the sunlight penetrating the earlier dust clouds, these condensed layers would evaporate, although it is clear that some of them are still to be found, as witness the ice discovered in noctilucent clouds. However, in some cases—and we have the evidence for that in the carbonaceous materials themselves—incoming radiation, either from solar flares or from cosmic rays, may have polymerized a small portion of this external material and this, having a higher molecular weight, did not evaporate with the ice and condensed gases.

We have evidence of this in the free radicals found by Duchesne in the carbonaceous meteorites. It also fits in very well with the picture of these meteorites being mainly composed of very old high-temperature olivine or enstatite chondrules, in a much softer matrix of carbonaceous material and hydrated silicates. That these are the relics of a more extended hydrated envelope is shown by the amount of deuterium they contain, which is about four times that found on the Earth today and indicates a long period of selective evaporation of water, concentrating the deuterium in the residue.

There is now also quite considerable and rapidly accumulating factual evidence provided by the study of meteoritic dust found in the red clay at the bottom of the ocean or in Arctic and Antarctic ice or by the simple process of catching it in flight on oceanic islands, as has been done by Parkin. In all cases, it seems that the original particles consist of iron-nickel cores which may be oxidized, mostly to magnetite, presumably by the atmosphere or the sea; but the smaller particles may get down slowly to sea level without oxidation and they seem to carry a presumably organic crust capable of being burnt off. Later studies show this dust *in situ* in the so-called noctilucent clouds which were studied by a joint Swedish and American expedition in the summer of 1962.

The clouds themselves seem to be composed very largely of small ice particles. Each one has as its core a minute globule of typical cosmic dust formation of 0.05–0.5 μ diameter. So far, however, no analysis of this has been published in respect to any carbon content.

Studies of this kind will undoubtedly throw much light on the major question of whether there is now a cosmic explanation of the origin of the hypothetical material which was previously called the primitive soup or the first source of free energy for the later chemical alternations which give rise to life. There is, *a priori*, a much greater probability of forming such compounds on a substrate which has a very large area compared with its mass and it may well replace any idea of the formation of primitive carbon compounds in sufficient quantities on the surface of a planet such as the Earth out of the transformation of a carbon-rich reducing primitive atmosphere. According to the meteoritic theory, the minor planets, including the Earth, have been formed from an accumulation of chondritic bodies. It would seem probable that a small proportion of carbon compounds found later on the surface of the Earth, from which in theory life on Earth started, is only a small sample of the material originally composing the body of the Earth, which has worked its way to the surface.

The reason why I am now inclined to pay so much attention to the meteorites in formulating theories on the origin of life—though they have been necessarily left out of account in earlier theories—is that those on the meteorites do represent the only primitive carbon compounds of which we can have knowledge. For what we know of the reworking of the surface of the Earth through continental drift, mountain building, and oceanic rifting, indicates that there can be no immediate comparison with the compounds formed here and that we have to rely on those that have been formed in rather isolated conditions, but of known age, in other parts of the solar system.

At first sight, it would seem that the transfer of the first stages of the origin of life from Earth to sky would make a radical difference to chemical theories of its evolution. In fact, however, this difference is much less than one might expect, for the form of the primitive soup derived by photosynthetic processes from the primitive atmosphere was entirely hypothetical, and the experiments of Miller and others show very well that the same kind of compounds can be formed by a great variety of processes from a great variety of starting elements. A common essential feature is that they are all prebiotic in the biochemical sense. None of the reactions giving rise to such compounds require the presence of enzymes but, at the most, only of very simple catalysts of iron and nickel complexes which are unspecific in their activity.

All the matters that I have dealt with so far belong to what I now call the first of the three stages in the origin of life: the accumulation of highly concentrated compounds of indefinite complexity of carbon, nitrogen, oxygen, and hydrogen. If these are made by any form of radiation, they will represent an equilibrium mixture of the kind found in the various experiments which have been carried out, beginning with those of Miller. They are definitely abiotic and all that they require to move to the next stage is a certain supply of free energy in the form of short-lived radioactivity, energy-rich bonds, or free radicals.

I have described the meteoritic theory—the formation of the basic carbon compounds—in some detail, for it is, on the whole, the theory that I would support today, though not with any sense of certainty because the facts and records are still scattered and rather scanty. The accepted theory—that of photosynthesis of prebiotic molecules on Earth, in the atmosphere, or in the sea—has synthetic plausibility at least qualitatively. Detailed paths of reaction dealing with such compounds as the nitrogen bases, amino acids, and the sugars can be followed from a starting point of formaldehyde and hydrogen cyanide formed in the upper atmosphere. These two substances have been shown to react in a watery medium at low temperatures. The first problem for terrestrial biopoesis here is to devise suitable means for the concentration of the products of these reactions. This demands either that relatively insoluble products are formed or that soluble products are formed in such concentration everywhere that no further enrichment is needed. I think the second is unlikely. As to the first, I have suggested elsewhere a method of concentration, based on the surface action of such compounds, leading to accumulation under wind and wave pressure on shores and in estuaries and to subsequent absorption on mud banks.

Part of the contribution I want to make here to the discussion concerns the second stage, the most obscure and the most speculative. Starting from an equilibrium mixture of carbon-nitrogen compounds, such as can be produced by the action of ionizing radiation acting on small molecules, how did it actually proceed to develop the features we now call those of life? Stage 2, as I see it, whatever the origin in space or the atmosphere of the equilibrium mixture, was played out here on Earth and in particular as part of the Earth's hydrosphere, whether in free water or in mud banks.

In any case, we are from now on entitled to base our arguments not on any geological evidence, but on inferences drawn from biochemistry, particularly the biogenesis of the compounds found in existing life on Earth. Many biochemists consider that life begins with ribonucleic and deoxyribonucleic acids and would consider it a waste of time to examine how these came into existence. Yet to me, less a biochemist than a structural crystallographer, that is just the interesting point. How did the basic elements of molecular reproduction themselves originate?

If neither the structures nor the biochemical functions of life can exist in the absence of this mechanism, we seem to be at a complete impasse, although actually, even in defining the problem more clearly, we are in a better position to attempt a solution. Certainly we shall be saved from having to attempt solutions that are intrinsically impossible or mutually incompatible. We may, however, have taken too particular a view of the reproductive process, imagining it as necessarily occurring only in the form in which we meet it as the nucleic acid-ribosome mechanism. Actually, reproduction is a much more general idea and may possibly be reached in the origin of life by a number of different tracks.

The essential principle of reproduction is implicit in crystallization itself. In other words, it is a mathematical consequence of the interaction of atoms and molecules. To achieve reproduction in the full sense, it is necessary for the object that is to be reproduced to be accessible, not necessarily all at the same time, to the smaller molecules which can unite to form a copy of it. This implies, further, a one-dimensional arrangement such as a linear polymer and, if information is to be carried, a linear heteropolymer. It need be only topologically linear, i.e., coiling and folding may be permitted and, in fact, may be necessary. The topological group formed of the original molecule and its copy must be a finite one, otherwise a three- or two-dimensional infinite crystal will result. The simplest case of this is a twofold group, and the disjunction of the two elements is sufficient to allow for indefinite duplication.

Besides *reproduction* in this sense, there is specific *production*, i.e., the building of molecules one at a time on a form that is not identical to the molecule being built. This is the essence of enzyme action in a general sense. The true properties of reproduction and production provide the sum of what may be called the necessary chemical bases of life; they are probably achievable by a large number of different systems, and it might be worthwhile to explore some examples of what these may be. Life on the present Earth—nucleic acid and protein systems—is fairly obviously a most successful attempt to achieve both these functions.

Such an analysis, even before it can be made in any great detail, inevitably drives us back to the question of how anything analogous to this nucleoprotein mechanism operated in a condition of much simpler structures. It seems to imply by intrinsic mechanism what I had previously considered as most probable from the geological point of view, namely, that life, in the sense of the exchange of metabolites and the using up of free energy, existed before there were definite organisms. Of course, organisms in any sense that we can conceive of now are arrangements of just such microstructures—membranes, organelles, and so forth—that go to make up even the simplest cell or virus.

The effect of the new discoveries is to show that reproduction is not only the occasional division of a complete organism into two or the emergence of a new organism by budding, but is also something which is going on all the time in every kind of organic system. There are not, so to speak, metabolism and reproduction; metabolism is reproduction. This makes the problem of the origin of life several orders more difficult to explain than it was even 10 years ago; for we have to explain not only why cells and organisms but also why organelles and metabolism itself involve a complicated reproductive system.

The purely biochemical functions of a preorganismal equilibrium mass of chemical substances in some kind of mutual and durable inter-action presupposes certain general conditions. First of all, these sub-stances must be reasonably concentrated in certain volumes. These would not, however, have to be permanently localizable; the activities of life may fluctuate over considerably larger volume, rather like the flame front on a smoldering piece of wood. Dynamic but not static function is all that is required. But at that place of dynamic interaction, the concentration must be sufficient to maintain the metabolism; ex-plosions and flames always go out, that is, fail to propagate themselves if the medium is too dilute. This puts a serious—and at first sight im-passable—barrier to the idea of life originating in an extended aqueous medium such as the sea, because its beginnings would have to be some-where and therefore wherever life started, it would be most diluted and least likely to survive in such a medium. Some physical process that will hold things together in an outer medium of fairly high dilution is indicated. This may be exterior, as I had suggested many years ago, by means of adsorption on clay; or interior, on some spontaneously gen-erated polymer, but this depends on the pre-existence or the formation of a colloid of the type of Oparin's coacervates. Whether such a colloid can be made, in conditions that do not permit the reproduction of mole-cules by the nucleic acid process, is one of the major questions we have to ask.

The kind of chemical reactions in such a medium, which must be such as not to involve very large quantum jumps and so preserve quasi-isothermacy, implies some form of catalyst, the subform in the prevital stage, which fills the role filled by enzymes in the vital stage. Now we know that the protein enzymes of today are themselves particular products of the nucleic acid-ribosome cycle.

We are, therefore, obliged to postulate protoenzymes, but there seem to be plenty of sources of these, even in the most normal inorganic hydrosphere environment. They are mostly derived from the transition elements of which the commonest is, of course, iron, but where copper, cobalt, manganese, etc., also have their place.

This seems to be true of some of the most basic metabolic enzymes— the oxidation enzymes, the cytochromes—later on adapted as oxygen carriers in hemoglobin, or as photon traps in chlorophyll. The function, as I see it, of the elaborate and highly specific polypeptide attachments to the protoenzyme is to affect the substrate, making it specific to a particular reaction. That specificity is, in any case, by no means precise, even with existing enzymes. There is usually a range of reactions that they can promote, but there is clearly a biochemical evolutionary advantage in specialization and, therefore, in the multiplication of enzyme types.

The other necessary functional molecules are those that enable energy to be transferred, not necessarily in any specific way, but usually as proton transfer or bond-level promotion. This is what I would call the coenzyme function, and here the organic bases, purines and pyrimidines seem to be outstanding, together with a few nitrogen-free condensed ring systems, such as the flavones. Here polyphosphates undoubtedly also have an important part to play both as energy transferers and as promoters of polymerization.

Everything points to the pyrimidine-purine bases being quite early products of spontaneous or equilibrium arrangement in primitive carbon and nitrogen-hydrogen complexes.

This early part of stage 2, when the simplest biochemical molecules are separating out from the amorphous carbon-nitrogen complex, seems to have occurred in a wet medium and, therefore, on Earth. I find it difficult to imagine, although I have suggested it, that it also occurred underground in asteroids. However, wherever it occurred, the result was a mixture of sugars, vegetable acids, amino acids, and nitrogenous bases from which we must imagine that the second stage of the formation of life—what I have called that of the genesis of prevital areas—took place.

The importance of the nitrogenous bases with sugar-phosphate links as protocoenzymes carries a hint, which I first drew attention to in 1957, that their polymerization, which is remarkably easy, may have given rise first to soluble nucleic acids and then gradually accumulating nucleic acid chains which form the present-day highly polymerized RNA and DNA, and ultimately the genes of elaborate biological systems.

But to give here any consistent, or merely a plausible, picture of the origin of life we have to face much greater difficulties than we had thought earlier we had to face, because it is becoming more and more evident, now that something is known about the mechanism of nucleic acid reproduction and the complicated stages of the production of enzyme proteins, that many more stages must have intervened than we had previously thought necessary. Evidence here must come largely from knowledge of actual biochemistry, particularly of cytobiochemistry, which splits up the activities of the cell and locates them at particular sites in it. The very perfection of these mechanisms, however, makes it more difficult to see how they could have come into existence spontaneously together with their functions.

It is only recently that we are beginning to appreciate how deep are the implications of the discovery of the reproduction of nucleic acids and the production of protein molecules. It is evident that the reproduction applies not so much to the whole organism as to every moment of its metabolism. The reproduction of nucleic acids and the production of protein molecules is essential to all vital processes as we meet them now. We can also say that they are essential to the actual structures of life, to organisms, and to the making of the elaborate subcellular structures now revealed by the electron microscope and followed in detail by the studies of cytobiochemistry that also depend on this nucleic acid-protein cycle.

The clue to this kind of construction was furnished in the first studies of viruses. The tobacco mosaic virus, which I started to work on nearly 30 years ago and described as being formed of subunits, seems to have just such a structure. These long cylindrical virus particles consist of a helical arrangement of protein molecules through which, as Rosalind Franklin showed, is threaded a single strand of ribonucleic acid. The particles of protein can be disaggregated and, under suitable circumstances, the ribonucleic acid destroyed and the protein reaggregated to form a structure very similar to the original but differing in two important respects; first of all, the limiting length of 3000 Å which characterized the virus particles is not respected in the reconstructed particles, which can be apparently of any length—much longer than 3000 Å, for example. Secondly, the peculiar helical arrangement which occurs in the active virus is not reproduced in the reconstructed one: instead of that, it is made of superimposed rings of protein molecules. From this it would appear that the ribonucleic acid thread had some part in the organization of the virus particle.

Nucleic acid, however, is not always required, as is shown by the recently studied structures of the invertebrate blood pigments, the hemocyanins of the Mollusca and Arthropoda. E. F. J. van Bruggen has shown that these are composed of definite shells of noncrystallographic symmetry with a constant number of protein parts. These proteins can be broken down to units of a molecular weight of about 40,000 and be spontaneously aggregated *in vitro* to reform apparently identical native particles. In this case, this is done in the absence of any form of nucleic acid and, therefore, the aggregation is spontaneous and not genetically controlled.

More and more evidence is coming to light to show that this is in general the case for a very large number of organelles and of the membranes which appear to be part of the structure of mitochondria and presumably also of nucleus and cell itself. The protein part of the membrane is particular; the lipid part is a normal lipid double layer which is made by direct two-dimensional crystallization of small molecules. The combination to form all such organelles is not brought about directly by the biological function; it is what might be called a natural liquid crystal formed by the pseudocrystallization of specific molecules.

Now, to get any degree of crystallization whatever, either identical or very nearly identical molecules are needed and this means that the organelles and the viruses depend on the presence of such particles; that is, they depend on the presence of a whole mechanism for, so to speak, mass-producing identical protein molecules. This would seem to imply that the step of producing identical protein molecules is essential and, therefore, earlier than the actual structures that occur in cells.

We are here in face of a general principle of enormous range and power. We might treat all these organelles, even to the complicated viruses such as the T2 bacteriophage with at least six different kinds of protein molecule, as higher forms of crystallization. The three-dimensional lattice formation of normal solid crystals is produced by the identical and what might be called mass-produced atoms themselves, where any inequality between isotope nuclei is masked by an identity of their electronic structure. In these biological paracrystals the identical units are protein molecules, but protein molecules are, as we now know, extremely complex structures, an elaborate heteropolymer of amino acids of at least two or probably three or four stages of folding and curling. These may crystallize in the normal three-dimensional way, but very rarely do so, at least in nature, and it is rather difficult to make them crystallize even in a laboratory. What they seem to prefer is to arrange themselves in noncrystalline or quasicrystalline forms of which the simplest is a secondary polymerization turning a globular protein into a fiber, now known as G-F transformation which has been studied particularly in insulin and actin. The arrangement can also be two-dimensional, as is shown in the formation of membranes, or closed three-dimensional spheres as in some viruses and various cellular organelles.

The principle of this can easily be understood geometrically if we imagine that a protein molecule has a number of points of attachment, each of which can attach itself to a specific part of a similar or different type of protein molecule, thus building the structure automatically. This is a principle which I have called (it is not a very good name) synisomeristic—the putting together of equal parts. This is a central problem of biopoesis today, now that the first problem of how these molecules came to be produced is, in principle, solved. How, from a set of fairly simple chemical substances, can the whole of these complex reproductive and metabolic mechanisms be evolved without the benefit of any preformed structures? For, this is a point I wish to stress very strongly, the existing structures depend absolutely on the pre-existence of identical complex protein molecules. And these can only be formed now by a reproductive mechanism involving nucleic acids.

Now, it is here that we must draw the clearest distinction between the possible and the actual modes of such genesis, the first involving logic and a knowledge of chemistry, the second involving actual information based on substances found in the fossil record or in meteorites, on the one hand, and in the present biochemical structures of life, on the other. Many people have argued and some still do, that the whole of life is a highly improbable process. In fact, it would not be difficult to prove that life could not exist; it would be far easier than to demonstrate that it must exist. But, as we have life and, indeed, are life, we have to accept it and, therefore, to explain it. Thus, the problem has at least one solution that has been very obligingly found for us. How can the new knowledge of the structure and functions of intracellular particles, whether of organisms themselves or of their parasitic viruses, throw light on this previous stage of evolution? I have already indicated how the production of certain protein molecules of identical series can lead to the simplest of these aggregations, such as take part in virus shell production or in respiratory enzymes of invertebrates. The more complicated organelles, particulate or membranous, probably have the same origin.

A universally distributed but still puzzling organelle is that of the cilia or the flagella of the protozoa, not the bacterial flagellae which have a simpler structure. This is now a common object of the electron microscope cropping up in most unexpected places but with extraordinary constancy of structure. Over most of its length it consists of a kind of two-layer cable composed of nine elementary flagellar fibrils arranged in a circle with two somewhat different fibrils at the center. At the base, however, the single sheaths of the subfibrils are seen to be triple and arranged in a set of spirals around an empty center. Further, the base itself is prolonged by nine fibrils of a different character which stretch into the body of the cell. Now, this is more complicated but not so much more complicated than some of the larger bacterial viruses such as T2. The logical deduction of this, although it cannot be proved as yet experimentally, is that the whole ciliary mechanism, including the base, is made from a set of protein molecules which organize themselves in this pattern on account of their intrinsic structure. The simplest organisms which show this structure are the flagellates themselves. It also reappears in all higher animals, though it is not so evident in plants. Sometimes the cilia have their original function of swimming or producing water currents, as in the spermatozoa of animals and of some plants. They are also peculiarly associated with the reproductive process. In a modified form, flagellae or cilia seem to be essential for all cell division. As the centrosomes or polar bodies of mitosis, they seem to initiate cell division and have attached to them the fibers that hold the centromeres or midpoints of the chromosomes and separate them when a cell divides. It is, in fact, the mode of division of the centrosomes that link them to the processes we have discussed earlier in the case of viruses and respiratory pigments.

Now it may well be that what we see in these organelles—endothelial reticulum, mitochondria, ribosomes, Golgi bodies, lysosomes, and centrosomes—are simply, so to speak, living fossils or vestiges of earlier structures.

There is no splitting of the centrosomes; instead, a new centrosome appears in the neighborhood of the old one and usually oriented at right angles to it. If the hypothesis of structural formation put forward here is correct, this would imply the existence of a series of specific nucleic acids, ribose or deoxyribose, in the immediate neighborhood of the centrosome. These synthesize, from the normal cell materials, the specific proteins for different parts of the ciliary base, very much as a virus protein is synthesized in a cell from its own nucleic acid. The difficulty here, which is only part of a general difficulty in connection with cell division and differentiation, is the timing of this operation. For a long time the ciliary base exists without dividing and then it divides and then again it stops dividing. It does not have an uninterrupted run of divisions like a virus. Experiment or observation may clear up this point.

We may imagine that the building up of simple structures and organelles preceded the development of an actual cell. All the particular proteins synthesized at present in the cell may not have been used for their present purposes in the first place. They may originally have had quite a different chemical and enzymatic function. This kind of biochemical evolution was necessary to form the first cells, but it probably continued well after them. We will take as an example the evolution of muscle. Evolution of contractile mechanisms cannot be followed easily in its first stages in the development of so-called smooth muscle which contracts slowly, but it is very apparent in striated muscle, where the structure is regular enough to be carefully analyzed. However, since the appearance of Metazoa (that is, some time early in the Pre-Cambrian, at least a thousand million years ago), when animals moved by tentacles or by jointed limbs, by free swimming tails or fins, they must have employed striated muscle of the same character as we find today in corresponding orders of Mollusca, Arthropoda, and Chordata.

The reason for violent movement involving such muscles is that the timing of the action is an essential part of it. They are in modern parlance "real time" machines. This is because they involved, for the first time in evolutionary history, the dynamic aspects of movement, that is, movement in which the inertia of the moving part, or occasionally with larger animals the weight of the moving part, is important. But the interesting point is that all striated muscle is built on an almost identical pattern in the existing and presumably in the earlier phyla. This system is only now beginning to be understood. It contains at least two elements—a hexagonal network of myosin and another of actin—which slide past each other by what can be described as a marvelous contrivance of vernier-operated crossbars. An interesting point is that this ingenious device seems to have been invented, so to speak, only once and has been taken over by all the different phyla. This can only be because the actual structures themselves are made of simple protein molecules of myosin and actin which, by the process I have called synisomerism, fit themselves together into the whole striated muscle structure. Now, this elaboration, as I have said, must have occurred fairly early in macroevolutionary history, but cannot have occurred in early biochemical history, for the requirement of regular dynamic motion could not have existed in a unicellular animal of a small size. Its prototype is probably to be found in ciliary motion, which seems to be of a protomuscular nature. What this implies is that ready-made types of protein can be later utilized to form new dynamic structures for which organisms had previously no need without invoking any further biochemical evolution.

Such adaptations of preformed molecules of protein and lipids can probably be made to account for many of the characteristic features of the cellular organelles of today. In their great multiplicity of forms, organelles, nuclei, and cytoplasm have something in common. Much of their complexity is in the form of the membranes that divide parts of the cell and form the boundaries of mitochondria, nuclei, Golgi apparatus, etc. From the provisional knowledge we now have it would appear that, if only elementary surface tension forces were acting, most primitive biological systems would be simply spherical in shape. In order to produce any internal rigidity there must be the production of some internal fiber network such as that, for instance, which sustains the vitreous humor of the eye. To establish any shape other than the sphere, a relatively unstretchable rigid membrane is required which would impose the cylindrical shape. The greatest varieties of shape can be produced from complicated membranes, which apparently exist in all cells, and by infolding or complication in a stricter sense to form such structures as endoplastic reticulum, Golgi apparatus, and the cristae of mitochondria. Here again it seems that the type of membrane is almost standardized and works for all the different structures named. The folding of the membranes themselves, as observed in cells of higher organisms and in some protozoa but not in bacteria, is a strong indication that in all these cases we are dealing with hypertrophied cells. The object of the folding is a means to secure a larger surface for the same volume. It points backward toward the origin in a much smaller system when all membranes were spherical or approximately so. These are found now only in some very simple bacteria, cocci, or in the organisms that stand at the boundary between virus and bacteria, the so-called mycoplasmas of which the organisms of bovine pleuropneumonia are best studied. These are complete organisms, actually smaller than some viruses, about 500 Å across, but they contain a complete set of enzymes and nucleic acids, about 300, and can be grown on artificial media. The difference between these and viruses is that the virus is an obligatory parasite on the nucleic acid mechanism of the host, whereas the bovine pleuropneumonia organism can manage only on the particularly highly specialized products of the host (complicated hormones, vitamins, etc.) but needs no nucleic acids. It is fully responsible for its own duplication.

Whether the mycoplasmas in any sense represent early organisms would be difficult to show because, on account of their size, it would be hard even to recognize such organisms in fossil form. Most of the structure of present-day mycoplasmas may be due to their obligatory parasitism; in other words, they are degenerate rather than primitive. At any rate, it gives an idea as to what such a primitive organism might be like and something of its size.

There are other aspects of the conditions for early life that are very often overlooked, that is, the physical-chemical conditions and particularly the relations to the medium. This will, in general, be water with a moderate concentration of ions. I was able to show about 20 years ago, by a quantitative study of the arrangement of TM virus particles in various concentrations of salts and of various pHs, that such large molecules interact with each other to form regular structures even at distances up to about 4000 Å apart in the medium. They were able to maintain equilibrium distances and consequently regular structures of such dimensions. It is in this way, for instance, that the particles of the large tipula virus arrange themselves in true crystals at some 3500 Å spacing which can be measured precisely, as A. Klug has done, by the color of the reflection from their different faces, in the so-called blue virus. Similarly, the spacing of myosin and actomyosin threads in muscle are maintained equidistant, and consequently quasicrystalline, in a medium which is at least 85% water.

Now, whereas the cells in higher organisms in most cases are much bigger than the viruses and mycoplasmas, their inner parts are not much farther separated than in much smaller cells. Indeed, the folding complication of which I have spoken is such that no part of a cell is out of range of the long-range forces from other parts through the cell fluid, the exception being, of course, for large vacuoles, which are themselves examples of membranes stretched into spheres by osmotic forces. Electron microscope studies of cells show that endothelial membranes are not necessarily symmetrical, having a rough side containing ribosomes and a smooth side without them. In fact, the whole cell can be considered as a topologically highly complex system of channels which divide the cell substance into two phases with different concentrations of proteins and other large molecules, the one which might be called the *endoplasm* and the other the *endolymph*.

Such considerations must also be taken into account in the very first stages of the formation of cells or organelles. They imply the existence of particles, essentially polymer particles, of the order of several tens or even hundreds of Ångstroms in dimension, and, in adequate concentrations, they give rise to coacervates or nondissociating bodies in the interstices of which smaller molecular particles such as protein molecules may be concentrated. There has been far too little study of these substances or these states of matter. We cannot expect to begin to understand the origin of organisms, that is, the end of the second stage of the genesis of life, without much more experimental work, some of which must be of a physicochemical or colloid chemical nature.

It is only in this way that we will be able to find out how the earlier stages of life actually took place, long before the formation of organisms, and whether it required the presence of adsorbed molecular layers on clay particles or interleaved in clay or iron hydroxide crystals, as I suggested many years ago. All examples of microstructures drawn from existing life serve as pointers to its origin. On the one hand, they may let us see some of the general principles that seem to regulate not only life here but life under any circumstances; on the other, they may point to the particular features which distinguish life on earth.

As for the former, one general, almost philosophic, point that has emerged from the study of recent molecular biology has been that practically all of the manifestations of structure or function are the result of what might be properly called *prescription*. A strand of DNA does not contain anything which might be called a description of the structure to be made or the activity to be carried out; specific behavior patterns are apparently genetically built-in in a large number of animals. Instead of that, they result from the carrying out of specific instructions and the ends are implicit in those instructions. They have to be realized or made explicit by a long series of indirect moves. Our anthropomorphic or, perhaps more properly speaking, technomorphic view of things has always been one in which an object to be made or an action to be carried out is envisaged or imagined as being made or executed in advance. We work by plans; even though the actual person carrying out the instructions may not be fully aware of what the plan is, he knows that someone has made a plan. Apparently nature does not work this way. It is not in that strict sense creative, although it may be so in a far deeper sense. In fact, when we consider the whole question of self-evolution of chemical or structural patterns in life, we realize that the notion that the pattern should exist in advance as a kind of idea is a logical impossibility. The operations that would be required to make the pattern of an organism imply and are included in the operations to carry out the prescription itself.

What we still have to learn is how prescription is modified by what happens to the finished organism. The whole question of the inheritance of acquired characters is likely to be reformulated in the light of the new biomolecular knowledge and possibly shown to be meaningless.

The idea of prescription can also be used in an evolutionary sense, especially as applied to biochemical evolution in the early stages of prelife and life. In an assembly of molecules interacting with each other in a medium that ensures a general if rather slow communication between the different parts, causal chains starting by what would be properly called chance can produce results which affect all the reacting molecules. To use a molecular analogy to the Darwinian evolutionary concept of survival of the fittest, those chains that lead to economy of materials or of free energy will be favored (Horowitz's principle). This should enable us to grasp, if somewhat vaguely at this stage, the limiting conditions in which life can grow and exist.

It is dangerous to try to generalize from one example such as life on this Earth, even if it has been worked out in great detail. Nevertheless, it would seem that certain general chemical properties would be required for any such self-containing process. It has to maintain its form, at any rate with not too rapid change, and has to maintain its activity; in other words, its thermodynamic open-system property by which its entropy can be kept approximately constant by the input of free energy. These conditions further imply some form of maintaining structures by molecular reproduction, also required to produce any kind of structure that can be formed spontaneously by a modification of crystallization. This, in turn, implies the preservation of information, repeated copying with rarely permissible variations, some kind of information storing and transmitting mechanism. Geometrical requirements indicate that this must be essentially of a one-dimensional kind, that is, through a polymer chain. This condition is fulfilled in our form of life by the nucleic acids. It is possible that in other forms of life another form of polymer could take on the same properties, for instance, the link between two phosphate-carrying bases might not be through the phosphate. In the same way, the protein maintains its chemical properties by folding up the heteropolymer chain. Once the chain is standardized in the order of its links, its folding up appears to be simply a matter of physicochemical minimal energy considerations. This would hold for almost any kind of heteropolymer that had hydrophilic and hydrophobic bases attached to it.

These considerations already throw doubt on the notion that the way life has evolved here is the only one. This would seem to me highly unlikely a priori, but the limits in which other solutions can be found may be very closely bounded. We can even define life in physical-chemical-evolutionary terms as a form of dynamic realization of the inherent properties of the quantum states of atoms. Life, as we know it on earth, is one single process, basically on a chemical level, though multiple in its morphology and activity. It is also genetically continuous and has apparently lasted throughout the major part of the Earth's history. It is self-maintaining and self-changing. It is conceivable, though there is no evidence for it, that the oneness of life on Earth came after the extinction or the blending of various prevital forms. If it did so, it must have been at a very early stage in its development. This, however, does not imply the oneness of life in the Universe: other radically different solutions may exist. When I say other solutions, I do not mean the kind of variations that exist between one organism and another or even one phylum or another on Earth, but differences in the features that all the phyla have in common—the presence of nucleic acids, proteins, enzymes, etc., in the formation of cells and of metaorganisms, metazoa, metaphyta, including organs of reproduction and possibly sex, though sexless life is conceivable and even achieved for long periods of time by certain groups of organisms. In certain organisms, particularly animals, further developments—sensation and movement, for example—will naturally follow, with the possibilities of communication and hence of societies. These may be, in the Aristotelian sense, part of the *essence* or total possibilities of life, but not of the *substance* of life or the minimum of these necessary for mere existence.

There are many other possibilities of variation, different bases, for instance, for nucleic acids, different types of protein or of carbohydrate, different lipid arrangements, but it seems difficult to imagine that the major roles of chemical elements and their simpler compounds can be varied very much. Those of iron and of other transition metals and of sulfur and phosphate are likely to be important in any form of life. Under different atmospheric and hydrological conditions, the balance may be weighted in favor of other types of systems of reactions. So I think we may rest on the idea that life on Earth is not unique but that it represents a fair sample of what life might be everywhere.

The oneness of terrestrial life is a function of the finite but connected nature of the surface of the Earth—of the hydrosphere, in short. The biosphere, which is part of the hydrosphere, at some period achieved that unity and has never been able to lose it since. Radically new forms of life cannot now originate on Earth except in laboratories. The possibilities of different forms of life depend on its existence on several noncommunicating biospheres. Such different forms may evolve on a limited number of different planets in the same or in different solar systems. On purely chemical or physical grounds, any conceivable form of life would require a liquid water environment, that is, the biosphere on any planet would evolve as part of the hydrosphere. Consequently, only planets maintaining hydrospheres are likely to be the sites of life. This immediately puts a severe limitation as to these sites. The properties of water imply that the mean radiation temperature of such a planet must lie roughly between 0° and 100°C and probably between 20° and 60°C, and the gravity must be such that water will not evaporate speedily and leave the planet. In other words, at the ambient temperature the mean velocity of a water molecule must be well below the velocity of escape. This, in fact, would seem to limit the life in this solar system to ourselves and to Mars. Venus is too hot and the Moon too small.

By an extended analogy, terrestrial life may be considered as one clone, all parts of it having a common descent, and limited to the planet Earth. Different planets would have, if they have any life at all, their own specific clones which will be in principle immiscible with the Earth's clone. All will have certain common features, what I would call the properties of life in general. This may indeed be so for a hypothetical common or invariant biology whose limits we still have to determine. There will be, however, as many local biologies as there are separated clones of life. This separation may not always be so absolute as our synthetic skill increases or may not be so at all in certain parts of the Universe where intercommunication between planetary systems has already been achieved. In that case there will be competition between clones and possibly a certain amount of mixing and mutual adaptation. We can imagine a kind of superlife made by blending the better parts of different life clones.

With these extreme speculations on space and time, I appropriately close my remarks. They are not, as can be seen, confined to any one or particular topics outlined for the molecular matrices. I had something to say at the outset on the micromolecules, especially in relation to their appearance on meteorites; on macromolecules I have had less to say, because this is more clearly a subject for synthetic chemistry. What I have said on molecules of precellular organization essentially based on cellular organization of today is an attempt to reconstruct the past by means of the present. To find the perspectives of life, I have attempted to outline the general possibilities for life in a functional and structural way. If I have not said much which is immediately verifiable, at the same time I hope I have not said anything that can be immediately disproved.

I said at the beginning that I am mostly concerned with questions but these are scattered in a large mass of explanatory material, and it might clarify things if I were to state them separately and put them in a list which could be joined to those questions posed by other participants in the conference.

The problem now is not just to carry out experiments or even work out chains of chemical reactions. It is to see how far those chemical reactions can be fitted into an ordered sequence and satisfy one of the basic and necessary characteristics of life—that it must be self-consistent at all stages. It is extremely difficult and becoming more so for any one person to do this. That is why I value the coming together of people from different disciplines in the hope that the problems may be laid out in such a way that each member of each discipline can contribute to their formation and solution. I should like to see, for instance, some publication for internal information purposes, in the form of a letter on biopoetic speculations, for instance, and a bibliography of supporting papers. Perhaps this might be a modest result of the present meeting.

The questions are listed in the order in which they occur in the paper. I have tried to make them fairly self-explanatory, but further explanation can be found by looking at the appropriate point in the text.

(1) Are the forms of life necessary or contingent?

(2) Is there any evidence that the cosmically abundant elements of hydrogen, carbon, nitrogen, and oxygen are not the major basis of alternative forms of life?

(3) How can we separate from the possible ways in which life might have originated the actual path which its evolution on Earth followed?

(4) Which of the various synthetic studies that have been made of the formation of elementary molecular compounds is relevant to the questions of the origin of life?

(5) Are the carbonaceous compounds of the meteorites similar to those which on Earth have been considered as possible precursors of life?

Alternatively:

(6) Were these compounds the product of pre-existing life on the parent bodies of the meteorites?

(7) Are there preformed molecular species such as purines in the carbonaceous meteorites?

(8) Were the carbonaceous materials in the meteorites formed of meteoric dust by the action of radiation and subsequently condensed by loss of gases and water?

(9) Was the primary material from which life originated on Earth formed from pre-existing carbonaceous compounds derived from the

meteoritic bodies from which the Earth was formed or was it produced on its surface or in its atmosphere subsequently by radiations (the Oparin-Haldane hypothesis)?

(10) Was stage 2 of biopoesis—the conversion of small molecular species such as purines and amino acids to the nucleic acid-protein mechanism—carried out in the first place in the hydrosphere?

(11) How did the basic elements of molecular reproduction themselves originate?

(12) Is there anything analogous to the nucleic acid-protein mechanism which can operate in conditions of much simpler molecular structures?

(13) Did life, in the sense of exchanging metabolites and using up of free energy, exist before there were definite organisms? In other words, were there indefinite and extensive prevital areas on which metabolic activities took place?

(14) Did the first stages of life occur in a free aqueous medium or were they absorbed in certain deposits, possibly of clay or iron oxides?

(15) At what stage did the colloid coacervates first appear?

(16) Were enzymatic actions first carried out by protoenzymes of essentially a transition-metal coordination type?

(17) What were the first protocoenzymes?

(18) Did the polymerizations of nucleotide protocoenzymes lead to the formation of nucleic acids?

(19) Was the nucleic acid-protein cycle necessary to produce elements of organellar and cellular structure?

(20) Are organelles formed by the association of specific proteins formed in the cell by a form of pseudocrystallization?

(21) How, from a set of fairly simple chemical substances, can the whole of the complex reproductory metabolic mechanism be evolved without the benefit of any preformed structures?

(22) Is the centrosome a modified form of ciliary base and is it reduplicated by a viruslike mechanism in the cell?

(23) Are the organelles found in cells made by an analogous mechanism; in other words, are they relics of earlier autonomous structures?

(24) Are the molecular structures on which muscle action is based derived from previous molecules of the myosin-actin type which originally had no contractile function?

(25) Are the complicated membrane foldings found in cells and mitochondria evidence that the size of the cell was once much smaller and that it contained only spherical particles like mucoplasmas?

(26) Do cells contain volumes of high and low concentration of proteins separated by partially permeable membranes?

(27) If biological structures and functions are determined by a prescription from a code carrier, how is the carrier affected by the results of the prescription?

(28) What are the general conditions necessary to produce any kind of life?

(29) Is the unity of life on Earth primitive or the result of blending of former partial lives?

(30) If life is the phenomenon of hydrospheres, are the life types in different hydrospheres of different planets radically different?

(31) Is life on Earth a fair sample of life types on any hydrosphere?

(32) Can the life forms in different hydrospheres mingle or be mingled to any extent?

Revised manuscript received December 20, 1963.

INTRODUCTION OF DR. OPARIN

J. B. S. HALDANE

Genetics and Biometry Laboratory, Bhubaneswar, India

Ladies and gentlemen, it is my very pleasant duty and my very easy duty to introduce Professor Oparin. I suppose that Oparin and I may be regarded as ancient monuments in this branch of science, but there is a very considerable difference, that whereas I know nothing serious about it, Dr. Oparin has devoted his life to this subject.

I am sure we are going to be very interested in what he has to tell us about the history of this subject. The only point I would like to make is that until not so long ago we thought that man had been specially created and that maggots arose from rotten cheese by spontaneous generation. It didn't much matter, but now we believe that human beings have been evolved and that spontaneous generation, wherever it occurs, is a rare event and it matters a very great deal. Thus, it is of the utmost importance that we should get to the truth of this matter.

Dr. Oparin.

HISTORY OF THE SUBJECT MATTER OF THE CONFERENCE*

A. I. OPARIN
A. N. Bakh Institute of Biochemistry, Academy of Sciences, Moscow, U.S.S.R.

I am sorry that I must proceed slowly because the translation takes some time. I will try to give you the history of the problem by means of a jet aircraft. In this case I must sound more dogmatic than I would like.

There are three great problems of natural science which always occupied human attention. These three problems can be solved only together, only jointly. First is the nature of life. Second, the origin of life. Third, the distribution of life in the cosmos, a problem which now becomes a practical possibility in connection with cosmic travel.

Heracleitus was the first, with Aristotle following him, who understood that to know the nature of things you have to know their origin. These profound words, of course, apply to the nature of life, which can also be understood only in the light of its origin. The most characteristic property of all that lives is the adaptiveness of living matter, the adaptation of the organism and the adaptedness of its parts to the functions which they fulfill in the life of the organism, on both the molecular and cellular levels.

This phenomenon of adaptiveness can be understood only through understanding the origin and development of life.

Similarly, an intimate connection exists between the problem of origin and development of life in the cosmos.

As a rule, the attempt to discover the possibility of life on Mars, Venus, and other places has been made by the following methods. Studies were made of the conditions prevailing on these planets, and the question was asked if under these conditions organisms resembling those on Earth could exist. This is a fallacious approach. Life is pro-

* Interpreted by T. Dobzhansky, Rockefeller Institute, New York City.

91

duced by a certain environment, and it changes and alters the environment to adapt itself to it and adapt the environment to itself.

I imagine that land life did not exist. It would be hard to imagine that such a thing could exist. From the standpoint of a jellyfish, life on dry land is sheer nonsense. Through a complex process of adaptation, of water exchange of circulation, such a form of life was able to arise.

Really, you have to ask the question whether life could have arisen on a given planet or celestial body of some kind. It is more and more recognized that our terrestrial life is not an accident, but has arisen necessarily. The origin of life is an integral part of the process of evolution of the Universe. The problem is to discover, by studying the data available on the nature of general regularity of this development. This point was reached by human thought, by a complex zig-zag way, by overcoming a series of preconceptions. The most unfortunate preconception was the assumption that the organisms have arisen and continue to arise now suddenly from inorganic matter in the form of complex units which we now observe exist.

This belief was not deduced from any particular theoretical basis, but was based on a naive interpretation of what we find around us in nature. This conviction was quite analagous to the convictions that the Sun gets from under the Earth in the East, and gets somewhere when it disappears in the West. Analogously, the conviction of spontaneous generation was accepted in olden times as an obvious empirical fact.

Different schools merely attempted to give to this assumed fact one or another theoretical basis. Later, at the dawn of European civilization, with the Greek philosophers, there were two clear tendencies in this problem. Those are the Platonic and the Democritian trends, either the view that dead matter was made alive by some spiritual principle or the assumption of a spontaneous generation from that matter, from dead or inert matter.

The Platonic view has predominated for centuries and, in fact, still continues to exist in the views of vitalists and neovitalists.

The Democritian line was pushed in the background and came into full force only in the seventeenth century in the work of Descartes. Both points of view really differed only in their interpretation of origin, but both of them equally assumed the possibility of spontaneous generation. But from the middle of the seventeenth century, a more precise study of nature caused people more and more to doubt this. The great achievements of Redi, Spallanzani, and Pasteur was a disproof of the age-old superstition.

This scientific heroism is comparable with the scientific heroism of Copernicus who was also able to achieve disproof of superstition.

Nevertheless, disproof of spontaneous generation, for a time, has undercut the basis of scientific study of the origin of life. It used to be considered a straightforward matter to observe in nature or to create in the laboratory conditions under which life could arise. But all these attempts proved to be wrong, due either to badly conducted experiments or to mistakes of one kind or another.

Only in the end of the last century and the beginning of our century was there a state of crisis on this problem of origin of life.

The problem of origin of life began to be considered something which serious scientists should not be concerned with. One could only dream and speculate about it without any solid basis for it.

Some people have even asserted that the problem of origin of life does not belong to science, but is in the province of faith. Others tried to escape the problem by supposing that life was introduced on Earth from other celestial bodies from outside. There were a lot of interesting and brilliant suggestions about that, but none of them approached really the fundamental problem: How did life arise, if not on Earth, in some other place?

The Darwinian evolutionists made the problem more acute, since it demanded an answer to the question: How arose the primordial organism from which everything else developed?

To be sure, the origin of life from inorganic nature in an evolutionary way was postulated by Tyndall, Schaeffer, and the Russian Timirayzev, all of whom have assumed that such origin must have taken place. But they encountered the generally accepted view that organic substances in nature can arise only biogenetically from a living organism. That created a vicious circle. The vicious circle was that in order to understand how the organisms appeared, you had to explain how the organic substances appeared. The organic substances were assumed to arise only in organisms.

Some authors tried to imagine the origin of life directly from inorganic nature, and that was extremely difficult to reconcile with the state of affairs known about inorganic matter. But the assumption that the organic substances can arise only from living organisms was based on the prejudice raised by familiarity with only existing conditions. If you take the problem more broadly and study other planets, other celestial bodies, as well, you will see that the problem is becoming more tractable once you detect life. And Earth is not an exception in this respect.

In the prebiological era, one could suppose the origin of organic substances abiogenetically in a way similar to what is observed on other celestial bodies. (In connection with this problem of abiogenetic origin of organic substances, I want to greet Professor Haldane, whose book was very important in the development of ideas about the subject.)

At present, there is an abundant factual material derived both from studies of different planets and from the study of geochemistry on the Earth. The Earth's crust has arisen by differentiation of the mantle of the Earth, as shown by the studies of Vinogradov, and in this process of differentiation hydrocarbons had to arise.

The formation of the Earth's crust is incomplete even now. It is conceivable that even now this process of formation of organic substances is going on. The geological work shows without doubt such an origin of gaseous hydrocarbons, liquid hydrocarbons, in the Earth's crust.

Most interesting are recent studies on Kola Peninsula, in the extreme north of Russia, in Apatites.

There it is possible to ascertain the origin of hydrocarbons in conditions which exclude the possibility of biogenetic origin. In addition to this formation of hydrocarbons on Earth, the Earth was, so to speak, fed continuously by accession from meteorites and comets. This latter possibility was particularly stressed by Professor Oró, here present.

It is interesting to point out that the meteorite which fell on Tunguska in Central Siberia in 1908, according to recent information, was nothing other than the nucleus of a comet.

These first stages of origin of organic matter, hydrocarbon and cyanide, can hardly be in any doubt at present, because they have been directly observed. It must be stressed that this stage is actually very widespread universally in the world around us. These carbon compounds can be detected on all celestial bodies which are accessible to study. So if you wish to discuss the question of the possibility of life on other celestial bodies, you may as well take into consideration that this simplest organic compound is present everywhere.

More difficult is the problem of transformations of these simplest compounds into more complex ones.

The conditions which we must postulate as having existed on lifeless Earth were doubtless different from the ones which exist at present. Before all else, one must mention the lack of free oxygen and the penetration of the ultraviolet and, most important of all, however paradoxical that may sound, the absence of living beings. In order to have evolution of organic substances, Earth must have been sterile.

Already Darwin in one of his letters has pointed out that, if at present some organic substances were to arise in some water basins, they would be immediately consumed by the inhabitants of the place.

No prolonged evolution of the substances is possible under present conditions. We are accordingly unable to approach this problem by direct observation in nature. For example, this problem of the origin of the primary primordial organic substances is inaccessible to direct observation. The only possible approach is to try to recreate in the laboratory the conditions which should have existed in lifeless, abiogenetic stages of the world, and see what sort of substance can arise under these conditions.

The work of geologists, particularly of the Dutch geologist Rutten, helped a great deal to picture these conditions, which may have existed in the prebiogenetic state of affairs.

Obviously, these studies raised many doubts and many difficulties, but this is, nonetheless, a real way to approach this problem experimentally.

Starting with the work of Miller on formation of organic substances by electric discharges, and the work of Pavlovskaya and Pasynskii, assistants of mine, who have extended these results, there is no need to continue this list of investigators, because many of those present have contributed important work on the origin of organic substances in the primordial Earth.

This applies to the origin of amino acids, purines, pyrimidines, and porphyrins. The same applies to the origin of polymers, the proteinlike polymers and the nucleic polymers.

(I like to reminisce about the tremendous impression made on me in 1955 by the investigation of Dr. Akabori on the origin of protein polymers, polypeptides.)

Recently a remarkable work by Dr. Schramm was published, which probably will be described by him here, also on the abiogenetic origin of organic substances.

To be sure, the problem of the origin of the nutrient soup and the primordial ocean requires considerable investigation. This problem was advanced by the Moscow Symposium in 1957. Our present meeting will probably also give advancement in this direction. But the problem at present is not so much how this primordial soup has arisen, but rather how from this originally sterile primordial soup arose the original living organisms.

There are two schools of thought regarding this matter. One school of thought is that this origin took the line of the evolution of the molecule, that in this original primordial soup there had arisen molecules with accidental arrangements, irregular arrangements of the monomers.

That in the subsequent evolution, this originally irregular sequence has gradually changed and approached the more perfect situation which we now observe in the RNA.

A second school of thought postulates that this change did not occur throughout this solution. It has taken place inside discrete systems, limited from the ambient medium, multimolecular systems. And those multimolecular systems have really evolved.

The essential part of this evolution was directed toward emergence of such structures which could survive. The origin of metabolism directed toward constant self-preservation and self-reproduction of the entire system interacts with the ambient medium, with the environment.

I hope that this meeting will produce much in the direction of settling this problem. The period of general discussion is over. The disagreements have now to be settled through experiments. The experiments must be arranged either as models or in some other form, which would be critical for decision for or against certain viewpoints.

Highly important in this respect is comparative biochemistry. By studying the phenomenon of metabolism in different stages of evolutionary development, we may hope to infer the initial stages of metabolism which lie at the basis of life. Basing this on the most primitive forms of metabolism, we may try to reproduce this self-producing and self-preserving system. This conference, hopefully, should lead, if not to the settlement of problems, at least to giving a right direction to the work on the problem of the origin of life.

Manuscript received October 27, 1963.

DISCUSSION

DR. GROSSENBACHER: I would like to ask a question.

Your jet speed through the history was so fast that I got lost a bit. From the standpoint of a former biology teacher, who was impressed by your book and your analysis of the fact that the absence of life was a necessary precondition for its origin, I would like to know where this idea came to you. I don't think it came from Darwin, because that letter wasn't published until the 1940s.

DR. OPARIN: I have, independently of Darwin, expressed this idea in my first book, but the priority is still that of Darwin.

DR. GROSSENBACHER: Very good. I want to mention that Chamberlain in 1916 published a book on the origin of the world, and in his last chapter also included this thought. But you probably never read it and neither had I and a lot of other people hadn't read it either, but that was published in 1916.

CHAIRMAN HALDANE: Who is this?

DR. GROSSENBACHER: Chamberlain, Department of Geology at the University of Chicago.

MR. PIRIE: Schäfer published this idea in his presidential address to the British Association in 1912 and he attributed it to Allen in a talk to the British Association in 1896. Only a summary of this talk was published by the B.A. and the comment does not appear in that, but it probably appeared in a fuller account elsewhere.

DR. BUCHANAN: At what point did Dr. Oparin decide that the synthesis of complex organic molecules would come from methane, ammonia, water, and hydrogen, and how did he choose these particular compounds?

DR. OPARIN: Almost 40 years ago, in 1924, in the book published at that time, I was led to this view by Mendeleyev, who has expressed the hypothesis of inorganic origin of oil, which was then subsequently rejected by geologists. Also, very stimulating to us was the discovery of methane in the atmosphere of the large planets. The presence of this methane could have hardly had any relationship to the terrestrial processes.

At any rate, according to Urey, the methane which was present in the gaseous cloud which gave rise to Earth, on account of the high temperature, escaped from there and froze on the larger planets farther away.

DR. SAGAN: If I may make a supplementary historical remark, as far as astronomy is concerned, the first realization that the universe was primarily of a reducing character came in 1929, when Henry Norris Russell published a classic paper on the chemical composition of the Sun, in which it was shown that hydrogen is the predominant constituent of the solar photosphere.

The recognition that the atmospheres of the Jovian planets contain methane and ammonia was first published in a series of papers by Rupert Wildt, beginning in 1931. So a firm astronomical foundation for the contention that the primitive Earth was reducing could not come until 1929 at the earliest.

Professor Haldane had an entirely independent argument, based on the anaerobic character of the early steps in the glycolytic metabolic pathways that are common to many organisms. The later steps—many of them aerobic—show a much greater diversity.

If I am not mistaken, Haldane's argument was published before the astronomical papers were.

CHAIRMAN HALDANE: I have very little doubt that Professor Oparin has the priority over me. I am ashamed that I haven't read his early work, so that I don't know. As far as I know, I didn't publish until 1927 and he did in 1924, and there was precious little in my small article which was not to be found in his books. I think if his first book was in 1924, the question of priority doesn't arise. The question of plagiarism might.

Part II

MICROMOLECULES

Chairman's Remarks

J. M. Buchanan

Division of Biochemistry, Department of Biology,
Massachusetts Institute of Technology, Cambridge, Massachusetts

The efforts of several groups over the last decade have shown that a large number of compounds of biological interest may be synthesized from the simple precursors, methane, ammonia, hydrogen, and water, under prebiological conditions. This list of compounds includes organic acids, purines, pyrimidines, and many of the amino acids. The synthesis of adenosine has been demonstrated and, under very specialized conditions with the reagent ethyl metaphosphate, adenylic acid has been formed.

We now have many if not all of the compounds of small molecular weight that are the components of macromolecules. It is indeed amazing, at least to a biochemist, that the synthesis of so many compounds could have been demonstrated under the atmospheric conditions of the primordial Earth. We must conclude then that these compounds were formed because they are plausible reaction products thermodynamically and kinetically.

Investigators have now reached a new plateau of attack on the problem of the origin of biological substances. They are now confronted with the difficult problem of demonstrating how functional macromolecules could have arisen. The aggregation of low molecular weight units into biologically inactive macromolecules has in fact been demonstrated, but the formation of biologically active units introduces a complexity of considerable magnitude. Yet short of supernatural intervention we know that this must have happened—not by the chance appearance of a highly specialized enzyme, but by the evolution of macromolecules with reactivities that are both chemically advantageous and biologically reinforcing.

There has been a discussion of whether a biologically active nucleic acid or protein was the first to arise. I should like to take the point of view expressed by Rich in an essay in "Horizons in Biochemistry," that the appearance of nucleic acids as carriers of genetic information or enzymes as biochemical catalysts would have been for naught without a system for translating the information of the former and the constant production of the latter. Rich believes that the evolution of the translation machinery, i.e., the development of an activating enzyme function and a transfer RNA function, must have been one of the earliest developments of chemical evolution.

Aside from the central role of transfer RNA in the translation machinery, there is much more to commend it as a key substance in the evolution of prebiological systems. A transfer RNA is composed of approximately 75 nucleotides, some of them containing unusual bases such as thymine, methylated derivatives of guanine and adenine, and a 5-substituted derivative of uracil (e.g., as in pseudouridine). By all criteria, this is a very small RNA, only 25,000 in molecular weight, and contrasts to some nucleic acid molecules that run as high as 100 million. Furthermore, a great deal of transfer RNA (approximately 80%) is in the form of a double helix. This leaves approximately 20% of the molecule consisting of nonpaired bases. Cantoni has pictured the transfer RNA as comprised of three parts, the amino acid acceptor end that has the sequence C–C–A, the staff or helical section, and finally the hairpin loop containing the unpaired bases. This is undoubtedly an oversimplified picture of the true structure since there is probably more than one area of unpaired, nonhelical bases. Cantoni postulates that this latter area, which he called the nodoc, contains the sequence of bases that pairs with the complementary triplet on the messenger RNA and thus codes for one amino acid.

The thesis that I would like to develop is that the structure of the nodoc area of a particular transfer RNA not only determines the interaction with a particular triplet of the messenger RNA but also provides the transfer RNA with a chemical bias to react more readily with a given amino acid at the acceptor site than with the other 19 possibilities. In the absence of the amino acid-activating enzyme, or in fact of any enzyme at all, this bias could indicate simply the progression of reactivity of a given species of transfer RNA with the 20 amino acids. Quite possibly the absolute specificity of one transfer RNA for a particular amino acid developed only after the appearance of the amino acid-activating enzymes.

Again we can only speculate about the nature of the activated amino acids with which the primitive transfer RNA's reacted; however, the best guess is that they were amino acid adenylates, which, in turn, could have been formed nonenzymatically from amino acids and ATP under the unique energy conditions of the prebiological Earth. Amino acid adenylates that have been prepared chemically are extremely reactive materials and have been shown by Meister and his colleagues to undergo spontaneous reaction to yield polypeptides. It is therefore conceivable that these compounds could undergo spontaneous reaction with transfer RNA and that the degree of reactivity could be regulated by the structure of the transfer RNA.

There are several advantages in addition to those already mentioned for assigning transfer RNA preeminent position in the evolution of prebiological systems. As has already been discussed, the transfer RNAs are of small molecular weight and there is therefore a greater probability that a macromolecule of this type containing the proper sequence of bases could have been formed by chance. Furthermore, this element of probability could be greatly increased if we assume that the important nucleotides are those of the nodoc area and that the sequence of nucleotides of the helical region did not play a particularly critical role in determining the chemical bias of a transfer RNA as an acceptor of amino acids. But if we must take into account the sequence of the nucleotides of the helical region, this number amounts to only 28 nucleotides rather than 56, since half of the nucleotides of the helical region is determined by the sequence of the other half. Quite possibly the nucleotides of the helical region are concerned with the interaction of the transfer RNA with the activating enzyme and hence are of more importance now than in prebiological systems.

A second consideration for the role of the transfer RNA is that in the evolution of the complex system for the transfer of genetic information and the synthesis of polypeptides each act took place as a succession of independent episodes. The formation of each transfer RNA responsible for the activation of a given amino acid took place independently of the formation of other transfer RNAs.

A final advantage is that the triplet coding system for the amino acids is not a rigid or perfect system. There are both degeneracies and ambiguities for some triplets; for instance, four nucleotide triplets exist for phenylalanine and one of the triplets, UUU, can code for either phenylalanine or leucine. If one agrees with the premise that the ability of a transfer RNA to accept a given amino acid is determined by the structure of the nodoc area, then one might anticipate that more than one sequence could accomplish the same end.

This speculation does not even take into account how the first meaningful messenger RNA came about nor does it suggest anything about the function of the first meaningful protein. Hopefully this first enzyme might have been an amino acid activating enzyme, an RNA polymerase or one of the enzymes that catalyze the polymerization of amino acids from amino acid RNAs. The appearance of any of these proteins would have greatly increased the efficiency of the complex system required for the synthesis of protein.

Finally, the basic premise of this speculation can be tested. Amino acid adenylates have been prepared chemically, and several of the transfer RNAs have been isolated in relatively pure form. It would be of interest to measure the nonenzymatic reactivity of amino acid adenylates with individual transfer RNAs and to determine whether there is any correlation with the known enzymatic reactivities of these systems.

In making these few far-fetched introductory remarks, I cannot miss the comparison of this effort with the experience of Lewis Carroll's Alice (of Wonderland) when she fell down the rabbit hole into a world of unreality. In contemplating problems as complex as those involved in the unraveling of the development of prebiological systems, the investigator is permitted a flight of the imagination not permitted in everyday scientific endeavor. With this apology then, I will conclude and yield the floor to Dr. J. R. Vallentyne who will speak on "Two Aspects of the Geochemistry of Amino Acids."

TWO ASPECTS OF THE GEOCHEMISTRY
OF AMINO ACIDS[1,2]

J. R. VALLENTYNE

Department of Zoology, Cornell University, Ithaca, New York

I. Amino Acids in Meteorites

A. Introduction

Kaplan *et al.* (1963) examined eight carbonaceous chondrites and five noncarbonaceous chondrites for several different types of organic compounds, including free and combined amino acids. Excluding the Lancé meteorite which was exceptionally high in combined amino acids, the seven other carbonaceous chondrites averaged 49 μg/gm total amino acids, as compared to 18 μg/gm for the noncarbonaceous chondrites. The most interesting feature of these results was not that amino acids were present in carbonaceous chondrites, but rather that they were present in stony chondrites. For a discussion of the nature of organic compounds in meteorites and the controversy over "organized elements" the volume edited by Nagy (1963) and the contributions of Fitch and Anders (1963), Mason (1962), and Wood (1963a,b) should be consulted.

B. Methods and Materials

All solvents used were reagent grade chemicals and were, with the single exception of ammonia, further purified by distillation before use. (Ammonia contained no detectable amino acids in 10 × the volume used in analysis.) The distilled water used was deionized by passage through columns of Amberlite IR120 (H form) and Amberlite IR400

---

[1] This paper was rewritten following the Conference and includes further information on the question raised by Oró of contamination from resins, and that raised by Haldane about similarities between amino acids of meteorites and those of living organisms.

[2] Note added in proof: Vanadyl porphyrins (Hodgson, G. W., and Baker, B. L. (1964) *Nature* **202**, 125) and optical activity (Nagy, B. *et al.* (1964) *Nature* **202**, 228) have been reported in extracts of the Orgueil meteorite.

(OH form), and then filtered through a prewashed Millipore HA filter of 0.45 μ pore size in order to remove all traces of the small particles that usually accompany samples of distilled water. Direct measurement showed that this water contained less than 0.5 μg of free amino acid in 10 liters.

In general, extreme care was taken to guard against contamination during the investigation. The ion-exchange column used for desalting the solutions was regenerated only with solutions made from ion-free, Millipore-filtered water. The samples and extracts of the meteorites only came into contact with thoroughly cleaned glass throughout the investigation, with the exception of resins and the filter paper used in filtering off HCl extracts of the meteorites (Nagy and Bitz, 1963). It is unlikely that this use of filter paper introduced any serious contamination. The air inlet to the vacuum distillation apparatus was provided with a glass wool filter 4 cm long to exclude dust. Also, the entire procedure of extraction, deionization, and concentration of the extracts was performed within 10 hours of the time that the hydrolysis tubes were opened. The samples were subsequently stored in a dry state at 4°C until further analyzed.

In spite of the extreme care taken to exclude contamination, it did occur in one instance. This was in the case of the Holbrook meteorite, where the large quantity of phenylalanine found undoubtedly entered via contamination from an improperly cleaned ion-exchange column that had just previously been used for the separation of phenylalanine. Exactly how the contamination occurred is not known, but that there was contamination from this source seems certain.

It is unfortunately quite impossible to know the extent of contamination of the meteorite samples with terrestrial matter between the time of fall and the time of analysis. The results reported here obviously refer only to the meteorite samples as received, and not necessarily to the meteorites when they were in space nor to the meteorites immediately after they had fallen to the ground. But it is also true to say that I would hardly have investigated the problem had I not been reasonably convinced that the degree of contamination was low, as has been reported on the basis of microscopic observations by Nagy et al. (1962).

The samples used were a 12.487 gm sample of the Holbrook meteorite and an 11.387 gm sample of the Orgueil meteorite. These have been amply described by Nagy and Bitz (1963) who had extracted the original meteorite samples for fatty acids prior to the time that I received them. [The meteorites were first ground to 40 mesh size and extracted in a Soxhlet apparatus using a glass thimble with 100 ml of a 6:4 mixture of benzene and methanol. The insoluble residue left after Soxhlet extraction was treated with 10% HCl to liberate any fatty acids that might occur as Ca salts. The HCl extract was filtered off through ether-washed filter paper, extracted with ether, and then recombined with the insoluble residue and sealed in a Pyrex glass tube. The paper by Nagy and Bitz (1963) can be consulted for exact details of treatment prior to the time that I received the samples.]

The meteorite samples were hydrolyzed in their sealed tubes by immersion in a boiling water bath for 24 hours. The tubes were then opened and the insoluble material removed by centrifugation, washing the sediment three times with 15 ml portions of water at 70°C. The HCl hydrolyzate and water washings were then combined and the bulk of HCl removed by vacuum distillation. After dilution to 400 ml with water, the samples were deionized by passage through a 22×2.2 cm column of Amberlite IR120 in the H form, using $1.5 N$ NH$_4$OH to elute the amino acids. The eluate was concentrated by boiling in an open flask to remove most of the ammonia, followed by evaporation to dryness *in vacuo*. Prior tests on recovery showed that arginine is not recovered, and that selective losses up to as much as 50% can occur for cystine, methionine, serine, and threonine, presumably by oxidative destruction during removal of the ammonia. The values for these amino acids should thus be regarded as minimal.

The determination of optical rotation was made with the entire amino acids extracts (concentrates of the ammonia eluates), each dissolved in 3 ml of water. A Rudolf Model 200 polarimeter was used at wavelengths of 436 and 546 mμ.

Three different types of control analyses were performed. In the first of these, three separate 10 gm samples of ignited quartz sand were subjected to acid hydrolysis. They were treated in every way identically to the meteorites with the one exception that the distilled water used was Millipore-filtered, but not deionized. The second control involved the same water, and consisted of a 10 gm sample of quartz sand which was first subjected to ignition over a Bunsen burner and then transferred between thumb and forefinger (hands unwashed for 12 hours prior to transfer) from the ignition crucible to the hydrolysis tube. This was to test the effect of contamination from handling. The third control was an "artificial meteorite" composed of 4 gm of ignited quartz sand, 5 gm of ignited MgSO$_4 \cdot$7H$_2$O, and 2 gm of anhydrous FeSO$_4$ that had been partly oxidized by ignition. The "artificial meteorite" was treated in exactly the same manner as the two meteorite samples without exception.

The dust samples were all collected from Stimson Hall, Cornell University. Dust No. 1 was taken from an automatic sprinkler pipe located near the ceiling at a point only a few feet from a basement exit. Dust

No. 2 was from a similar pipe located in my laboratory on the second floor, dust No. 3 from the shield on a fluorescent light fixture in my laboratory, and dust No. 4 from an automatic sprinkler pipe located in the attic. All samples were hydrolyzed directly with 6 N HCl in sealed tubes at 100°C for 24 hours. There was some initial frothing in all cases on the addition of acid. Following hydrolysis, the insoluble matter was removed by centrifugation, HCl was removed by distillation *in vacuo*, and the concentrates applied directly to an amino acid analyzer. Deionization was unnecessary.

Determinations of total-N were all made in duplicate by Carl Tiedke, microanalyst. The amino acid separations were all made on a Spinco amino acid analyzer of the type described by Spackman et al. (1958), except for some test tube determinations made by using the method of Moore and Stein (1954).

C. Results

The results of total-N determinations were as follows. The Orgueil sample contained 0.16% N when analyzed directly without drying, but only 0.12% N after drying to constant weight in a vacuum oven at 100°C. The insoluble residue left after hydrolysis of the Orgueil sample was jet black in color. It represented 29.0% of the initial dry weight of the sample, and contained 0.066% total-N. Thus, 88% of the total-N present in the Orgueil sample (based on 0.16% total-N content) occurred in an acid-soluble form after acid hydrolysis. The amino acids recovered after hydrolysis accounted for only 0.33% of the total-N present in the Orgueil. The nature of the other nitrogen compounds is not known. The sample of the Holbrook left an insoluble residue after hydrolysis that was light gray in color and represented 13.0% of the original sample weight.

The results of amino acid analysis of the meteorites are shown in Fig. 1, these being actual tracings of the original records. The Orgueil was analyzed only for acidic and neutral amino acids. Figure 2 shows comparable records for hydrolyzates of "hand-picked sand" and the "artificial meteorite." With regard to unknowns, No. 1 probably corresponds in all cases to cysteic acid, an oxidation product of cystine that was probably produced during analysis, No. 2 likely corresponds in all cases to urea; two of the three peaks # 3 to # 5 in Fig. 1D undoubtedly represent methionine sulfoxides probably produced during analysis from methionine; bl in the "artificial meteorite blank" of Fig. 2 is probably histidine. Nothing more than immature guesses can be presented for the other unknowns in the samples. With regard to certainty of identification it can only be said that the method of separation is good, but

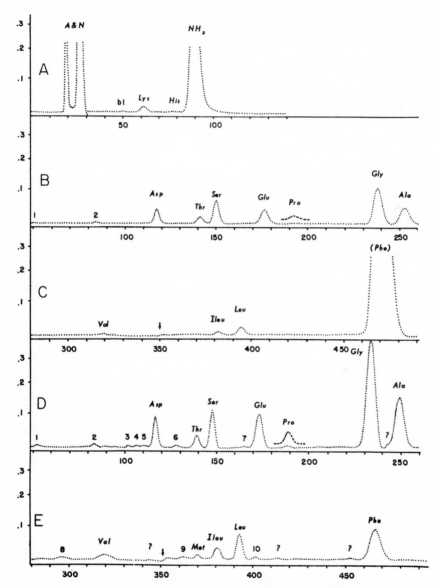

Fig. 1. Separation of amino acids in acid hydrolyzates of Holbrook (A–C) and Orgueil (D–E) meteorites according to the method of Spackman *et al.* (1958) for 50°C runs. The results shown for the Holbrook are based on 3.98 gm of air-dry meteorite, and those for the Orgueil on 7.30 gm of air-dry meteorite. Vertical axes are in units of absorbance and horizontal axes in units of milliliters of effluent from the column. Dotted lines represent absorbance at 570 mμ, and dashed lines absorbance at 440 mμ (the latter shown only in the region where peaks appeared). A&N refers to acidic and neutral amino acids. Arrows show when the effects of buffer changes became apparent on the records. See text for explanation of other terms.

not perfect. The most likely cases where confusion might have arisen are with lysine, where there could have been some overlap with ornithine, and with amines that would overlap ammonia. The amounts of ammonia in the samples are of no interest since large quantities of ammonia were added during the isolation procedure. The large amount

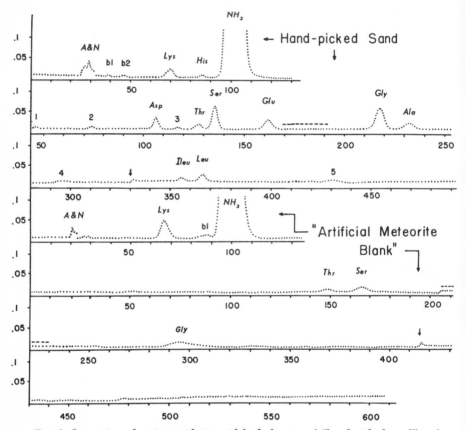

Fig. 2. Separation of amino acids in acid hydrolyzates of "hand-picked sand" and "artificial meteorite" according to Spackman *et al.* (1958) using a 50°C run in the former case and a 30–50°C run in the latter. The results for "hand-picked sand" are based on a 4.0 gm of sample, and those for the "artificial meteorite" on ⅖ of the total amount of sample used (see text). For explanation of other terms see Fig. 1.

of phenylalanine shown in Fig. 1C should not be considered as part of the meteorite since it undoubtedly arose through contamination (see Methods and Materials).

Quantitative data on the amino acid composition of the hydrolyzates of the meteorites and controls are given in Table I. Data for the sum

TABLE 1

AMINO ACIDS (FREE PLUS COMBINED) IN 10% HCl HYDROLYZATES OF METEORITES AND RELATED SAMPLES[a]

Amino Acid	Concentration (μg/gm)				
	H	O-V	O-K	HPS	AM
Aspartic acid	2.7	1.3	3.3	0.8	0.0
Glutamic acid	4.3	2.4	2.4	1.3	0.0
Glycine	7.0	6.3	13.1	1.5	0.6
Alanine	3.8	3.0	8.3	0.4	0.0
Valine	0.0	0.1	7.2	0.0	0.0
Leucine	2.0	1.3	{ 11.2	0.5	0.0
Isoleucine	0.7	tr		0.2	0.0
Serine	4.1	1.5	17.7	1.4	0.6
Threonine	1.4	0.5	5.0	0.3	0.3
Cystine/2	0.0	tr	—	0.0	0.0
Methionine	0.0	tr	0.3	0.0	0.0
Phenylalanine	—[b]	3.9	8.4	0.0	0.0
Tyrosine	0.0	tr?	5.8	0.0	0.0
Proline	0.1	tr	—	0.0	0.0
Histidine	0.0	n.d.	3.8	0.2	0.0
Lysine	1.5	n.d.	5.1	0.7	0.0
Arginine	n.d.	n.d.	7.7	n.d.	n.d.
Urea	3.7	3.0	n.d.	4.0	—[c]
Cysteic acid	tr	tr	—	tr	0.0
Sum (μg/gm)	31.3	23.4	115.5	11.2	2.5(ca.)
Sum less urea (μg/gm)	27.6	20.4	115.5[e]	7.2	1.5(ca.)
Sum (μmoles/gm)	0.27	0.38[d]	0.96[e]	0.07	0.015

[a] H. Holbrook meteorite; O-V, Orgueil meteorite sample analyzed in this study; O-K, Sum of free and combined amino acids in Orgueil meteorite sample analyzed by Kaplan et al. (1963); HPS, hand-picked sand; AM, artificial meteorite. See text for explanation.

[b] This sample was contaminated with phenylalanine from previous use of the demineralizing column.

[c] There was a slight indication of a rise in the baseline of the recording at a position corresponding to that of urea. This would imply about 0.5–1.0 μg/gm of urea in the sample. Urea is only $\frac{1}{25}$ as sensitive to ninhydrin as most amino acids.

[d] This value is based on a test tube determination of total amino acids by the method of Moore and Stein (1954) after distilling off ammonia.

[e] These values include data for ornithine and β-alanine that are not shown in the table.

of free and combined amino acids in the Orgueil sample analyzed by Kaplan *et al.* (1963) have been included for comparison. The value for total amino acids in the Orgueil is based on a determination with ninhydrin (Moore and Stein, 1954) after removal of ammonia.

The three 10 gm samples of ignited quartz sand were analyzed for total amino acids only (Moore and Stein, 1954). The results were 0.04, 0.00, and 0.07 μmoles of total amino acid per gram of initial sample used (average 0.04 μmoles/gm).

The amino acid composition of four samples of dust is given in Table II. Note that the concentrations of amino acids are given as mg/gm of sample in Table II rather than as μg/gm as in Table I. The levels of amino acids in dust are thus about 1000 times higher than in the meteorites. The identity of urea(?) in the dust samples is somewhat uncertain, and may require revision on the basis of subsequent tests now in progress. At present we shall only refer to it as urea(?). In the separations that were conducted on the two meteorites and the sample of "handpicked sand" the analyses were unfortunately stopped before the position at which β-alanine appears (after phenylalanine). In the case of the dust samples and the "artificial meteorite" this was not the case. Had β-alanine been present in dust we would have detected it, but we did not.

The determination of optical rotation on the amino acid extracts of the meteorites yielded only negative results. The reason was evident after the amino acid analyses had been completed; the amounts were too small to have been detected with the instrument used.

D. Discussion

In discussing the origin of a particular class of compounds in meteorites, it is important at the outset to recognize that not all compounds need have been formed at the same time, nor need all have been formed by the same general mechanism. What pertains to hydrocarbons need not pertain to amino acids, and what pertains to amino acids need not pertain to carbohydrates.

With regard to the origin of amino acids in meteorites, Kaplan *et al.* (1963) considered four possibilities:

(a) origin by catalysis during the laboratory treatment of samples;
(b) contamination with terrestrial matter between the time of fall and the beginning of analysis;
(c) biogenesis (terrestrial or extraterrestrial).
(d) abiogenesis (terrestrial or extraterrestrial).

TABLE II

AMINO ACID COMPOSITION OF SAMPLES OF DUST[a]

Amino Acid	Concentration (mg/gm air dry weight)			
	No. 1	No. 2	No. 3	No. 4
Aspartic	2.41	—[b]	5.48	5.65
Glutamic	3.97	10.06	10.19	9.55
Glycine	2.37	6.23	8.42	6.98
Alanine	0.47	4.84	3.36	3.15
Valine	tr	2.18	2.21	2.15
Leucine	1.63	4.74	5.21	4.40
Isoleucine	0.76	2.13	2.35	1.95
Serine	2.36	6.56	7.09	5.88
Threonine	1.13	6.92[b]	4.16	3.20
Cystine/2	0.00	0.00	0.00	0.00
Methionine	0.03	0.03	tr	0.27
Phenylalanine	tr	3.01	3.32	2.53
Tyrosine	tr	0.07	1.14	1.00
Proline	0.00	2.11	2.57	2.43
Histidine	n.d.	?	—	0.73
Lysine	n.d.	1.52	3.14	1.98
Arginine	n.d.	n.d.	n.d.	n.d.
Cysteic acid	tr	1.80	1.43	0.45
Unknowns[c]	n.d.	3.02	1.15	tr
Ammonia	n.d.	5.31	5.37	1.58
Urea(?)	6.49	11.20	9.10	10.40
Sum of above (mg/gm)	21.62	71.73	75.69	64.28
Total amino acids (mg/gm)	15.13	52.20	60.07	52.30
Ash in dust (%)	65.1	45.1	49.6	44.6

[a] Samples taken from ceiling fixtures in Stimson Hall, Cornell University. See text for explanation.

[b] Aspartic acid was not detected at its usual position in this sample. There was, however, some suggestion that the aspartic acid and threonine peaks may have run together.

[c] The only unknowns that appeared in more than trace amounts were found on short columns used for the separation of basic amino acids. It is noteworthy that they occurred only in dust collected from my laboratory, and not elsewhere in the building. The unknowns were excluded from the values for total amino acids.

Kaplan *et al.* (1963) excluded (a) on the ground that second treatments of their samples yielded concentrations an order of magnitude lower. Although the logic is not unreasonable, the test is really not critical since the initially reactive materials could have been extracted or transformed during the first treatment.

In regard to (b), no one today is particularly happy with the fact that most of the meteorites of interest have had long and uncertain histories following initial collection. About all that can be said is that the problem of contamination is probably most serious for carbonaceous chondrites, but in no case is it so serious as to negate *all possibilities* of obtaining informative results from existing samples.

Kaplan *et al.* (1963) excluded (c) largely on the basis of negative evidence—the apparent lack of optical activity and lack of such compounds as chlorins, porphyrins, purines, pyrimidines, fatty acids, etc., that would be expected to accompany any terrestrial contamination of a biological sort. While these points are well taken, it must be stressed that they are based on negative evidence. Also, fatty acids have since been detected in the Orgueil (Nagy and Bitz, 1963). In the case of optical activity there was no proper control to see if an optically active mixture of amino acids added to a meteorite would have retained its full activity after being subjected to the complete analytical procedure. We have, however, since hydrolyzed L-alanine in the presence of the acid-insoluble residue of the Orgueil meteorite and found no evidence of appreciable racemization. I have, also taken the trouble to calculate what the observed rotation would have been for the concentrations reported by Kaplan *et al.* (1963) and found their conclusion to be quite correct. If all the amino acids in the final extracts had been all L or all D, a rotation of polarized light would have been observed, providing of course that there were no other substances present that would have neutralized this effect.

The fourth explanation (d) was the one accepted as most likely by Kaplan *et al.* (1963) with the information then on hand. Although (d) was largely accepted by default, certain data did fit that explanation, notably the presence of β-alanine in some carbonaceous chondrites, and the relative abundance of certain amino acids in meteorites (glycine, serine, aspartic acid) which are also known to predominate in the products of many "primitive soup" experiments (Oró, 1963).

In relation to the new data presented in this paper, the first point to be made is that our results definitely confirm those of Kaplan *et al.* (1963) in showing that amino acids do occur in samples of both carbonaceous and noncarbonaceous chondrites. There is no way in which our results can be accounted for on the basis of contamination during analysis. There are some minor differences, however, from the results reported by Kaplan et al. (1963). It can be seen from Table I, for example, that our analysis of the Orgueil meteorite revealed markedly lower values (less than ⅓) for serine, threonine, valine, leucines, and tyrosine than those reported by Kaplan et al. (1963). The quantities of valine and tyrosine in the Holbrook and Orgueil samples that we analyzed were indeed so low as to make them typical of no known unmodified protein or protein mixture (see Block and Weiss, 1956). Also, the total quantity of amino acids that we found (free and combined) for the Orgueil was less than half that reported by Kaplan et al. (1963). Whether these differences are due to the fact that different samples were used, or due to the different methods of analysis applied, remains to be seen.

One of the more interesting results of the present study was the general similarity in the pattern of amino acids found in the two meteorite samples as compared with that of "hand-picked sand." All three contained about the same relative amounts of urea, cysteic acid, and different amino acids. Part of the amino acid content of the sample of "hand-picked sand" must be attributed, however, to the general background level of contamination in addition to that arising from dirty hands. But in any case, the results do show that at least part of the meteoritic amino acids could easily have arisen from handling and other types of terrestrial contamination. Further tests will be required to show if this is a realistic possibility. The demonstration that chondrules contain mostly glycine after ultrasonic cleaning (Kaplan et al., 1963), for example, argues against this idea for all the amino acids in meteorites.

The amino acid analyses of dust show that it has about 1000 times the amino acid content of meteorites. To put it another way, it would take about 1 mg of dust per gram of meteorite to account for the entire amount of amino acids in most meteorites (Lancé excluded). (Of course, one does not know how representative the dust of Stimson Hall may be of dust in general, but we shall take it as representative for present purposes.) As will be noted from a comparison of Tables I and II, there are some differences between the relative amino acid compositions of dust and meteorites. Dust, for example, is relatively higher in proline and cysteic acid (probably occurring as cystine or cysteine in the dust itself), and somewhat higher in glutamic acid than are meteorites [present analyses plus those of Kaplan et al. (1963)]. It is also of interest that β-alanine was not detected in any of the dust samples analyzed, though it had been reported in traces by Kaplan *et al.* (1963) in four of seven carbonaceous chondrites analyzed (but not in any noncarbonaceous chondrites). This would argue against any idea that dust was the actual source of the meteoritic amino acids.

The same meteorite samples analyzed in this study for amino acids were analyzed separately for long-chain fatty acids by Nagy and Bitz (1963). Fatty acids ranging from C_{14} to C_{30} showing an even-number chain length preference were found in extracts of samples of the Orgueil meteorite. No such acids were detected in extracts of the Holbrook meteorite, nor in extracts of granite (Nagy and Bitz, 1963).

Kaplan *et al.* (1963) considered chemical synthesis as the most likely explanation for the origin of the hydrocarbons, amino acids, and diazonium-sensitive compounds that they found in the meteorites studied. To what extent noncarbonaceous chondrites contained diazonium-sensitive compounds is not entirely clear, but their data for amino acids clearly show a distribution that is largely independent of the amount of organic carbon present in the meteorite, and independent of the presence of volatile constituents in general.

Present data on meteoritic amino acids do not allow final distinctions to be made between terrestrial-extraterrestrial, biogenic-abiogenic, or ancient-recent. Had some unusual amino acids been encountered in the meteorites, there might have been just suspicion for regarding the sources as extraterrestrial; but this was not the case. The close resemblance between the amino acid spectra of meteorites and those recent biogenic materials (organisms, soils, surface sediments) can be interpreted in several ways. The simplest, of course, is on the basis of terrestrial contamination; however, this seems rather unlikely *in toto,* particularly for the noncarbonaceous chondrites because of their compact nature and general availability in pieces of considerable size. Some contamination is inevitable, but not to the extent implied.

If the meteoritic amino acids are considered to be extraterrestrial in origin, then this implies a remarkable similarity either between the amino acids of primitive soups and terrestrial organisms on the one hand, or between terrestrial and extraterrestrial organisms on the other. Such patterns of common, perhaps chemically predetermined, building blocks would not be unexpected on evolutionary grounds; but the degree of resemblance, should it actually prove to be the case, would be much higher than has hitherto ever been suspected.

One final point deserves mention. Although one does not know what the initial amino acid composition of meteoritic material may have been at the time of formation, one would expect to find some evidence of a fractional destruction of certain amino acids if ionizing radiations, heat, oxidation, and other factors had been acting on the meteoritic amino acids for geologically long periods of time. In the case of thermal action, the results of Abelson (1957) and Vallentyne (1964) lead one to suspect that serine and threonine would be more readily destroyed than other amino acids, as is discussed in more detail below. However, such effects may be negated at the low temperatures of space. The effects of radiation on various amino acids and proteins are more difficult to predict since they depend on dosage rate, concentration, water content, etc. However, the last thing that could be expected would be equal rates of destruction for all amino acids due to ionizing radiations (Barron *et al.*, 1955; Alexander and Hamilton, 1960; Alexander and Rosen, 1961; Ambe *et al.*, 1961). If such radiation effects have occurred, then one should expect serious departures from the original amino acid composition of the meteorites or their parent body. To put it another way, similarities between meteoritic amino acids on the one hand and those of either primitive "soups" or living organisms on the other, would not be expected if either heat or radiation had exerted major effects on the meteorite samples analyzed.

II. Synthesis and Decomposition in Primitive Soups

My only purpose in this section is to draw attention to one fact that seems to have been neglected in most of the work that has proceeded during the decade since Miller (1953) originally initiated the experimental study of primitive "soups." This is the fact that the concentrations of various molecules in a "soup" reflect a balance between synthesis and decomposition. The results obtained from experiments run over a few hours or a few days could be quite different from those that operate over thousands or millions of years particularly if there is something in the reaction that tends to shut off further synthesis with the passage of time (e.g., exhaustion of starting materials). What is true of molecules is just as true of organisms, and must have been true of eobionts as well. Time, in other words, could be a critical factor in many of the processes that we have been discussing at this conference.

My remarks will be limited to some absurdly naive studies that we have made (Abelson, 1963; Vallentyne, 1964) on the decomposition rates of several amino acids in 0.01 M solution in sealed tubes in the absence of oxygen—naive in the sense that the results have been used to interpret nature. The results of these experiments are shown in Fig. 3 in the form of an Arrhenius plot (0.37-life vs $1/T$, rather than k vs $1/T$). To make the interpretation simpler, I have translated the reciprocals of absolute temperatures on the horizontal axis into degrees Centigrade, as shown in parentheses. It can be seen that serine and threonine as a group are much less stable than phenylalanine; phenylalanine in turn is much less stable than either alanine or pyroglutamic acid. In one experiment 98% of the initial threonine present was decomposed during

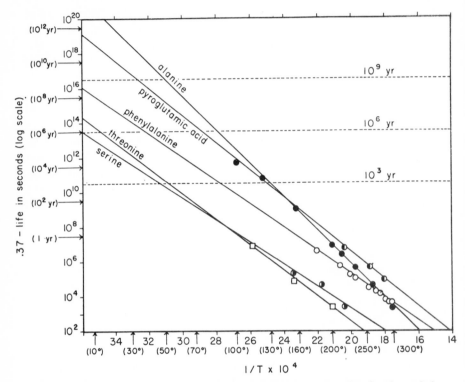

FIG. 3. Linear regression lines based on Arrhenius equations for the thermal decomposition of five amino acids in 0.01 M aqueous solution. Vertical axis: 0.37-life in seconds (years in parentheses) plotted on a logarithmic scale. Horizontal axis: the reciprocal of the absolute temperature multiplied by 10^4 (values in parentheses give the corresponding temperatures in °C). Open squares: threonine; half-solid circles, dark on right: serine; open circles: phenylalanine; solid circles: alanine; half-solid circles, dark on left: pyroglutamic acid. Data for alanine from Abelson (1957), otherwise from Vallentyne (1964).

the period of 1 year at 113°C. (It is of some interest that 90% of the decomposed threonine was transformed directly into glycine.) To cite another example, glutamic acid either alone or in the presence of water at near neutral pH values readily cyclizes to form pyrrolidonecarboxylic acid (Wilson and Cannon, 1937). In the course of a few hundred years at temperatures of 50–80°C, glutamic acid would not be available as such unless it was repeatedly formed anew.

E. Summary

(1) Amino acids and a substance tentatively identified as urea were detected in hydrolyzates of samples of the Orgueil and Holbrook meteorites. The quantities could not be accounted for by contamination during analysis, but there was a resemblance between the results of meteorite analyses and the amino acids found in a hydrolyzate of "hand-picked sand."

(2) Quantitative data on amino acids are given for four samples of dust, the total concentrations being about 1000 times higher than in meteorites. Dust hydrolyzates contained much higher relative amounts of proline and cysteic acid, and somewhat higher relative amounts of glutamic acid than did those of the meteorites analyzed.

(3) A reminder was made that some attention might profitably be given to rates of decomposition in "soup" experiments. Labile compounds necessary for biopoiesis could exert a controlling influence on the rate of evolution of eobionts in a primitive sea.

ACKNOWLEDGMENTS

This investigation was undertaken at the suggestion of Bartholomew Nagy, who also provided the samples of meteorites for analysis. I am likewise indebted to Egon T. Degens for making the results of his meteorite analyses available to me long before they were published (Kaplan *et al.*, 1963). I am indebted to Patricia Mahool for operation of the amino acid analyzer. The present study was undertaken with support from the National Science Foundation (G-12452).

Revised manuscript received December 27, 1963.

REFERENCES

Abelson, P. H. (1957). *In* "Treatise on Marine Ecology and Paleoecology," *Geol. Soc. Amer. Mem. Vol. II*, 67, 87.

Abelson, P. H. (1963). *In* "Organic Geochemistry" (Irving Breger, ed.), pp. 431–455. Pergamon Press, New York.

Alexander, P., and Hamilton, L. G. D. (1960). *Radiation Res.* 13, 214.

Alexander, P., and Rosen, D. (1961). *Radiation Res.* 15, 475.

Ambe, K. S., Kumta, U. S., and Tappel, A. L. (1961). *Radiation Res.* 15, 709.

Barron, E. S. G., Ambrose, J., and Johnson, P. (1955). *Radiation Res.* 2, 145.

Block, R. J., and Weiss, K. W. (1956). "Amino Acid Handbook." Charles C Thomas, Springfield, Illinois.

Fitch, F. W., and Anders, E. (1963). *Science* 140, 1097.

Kaplan, I. R., Degens, E. T., and Reuter, J. H. (1963). *Geochim. Cosmochim. Acta* 27, 805.

Mason, B. (1962). "Meteorites," pp. 1–274. Wiley, New York.

Miller, S. L. (1953). *Science* 117, 528.

Moore, S., and Stein, W. H. (1954). *J. Biol. Chem.* 211, 907.

Nagy, B., ed. (1963). Life-like forms in meteorites. *Ann. N.Y. Acad. Sci.* 108, 339.

Nagy, B., and Bitz, M. C. (1963). *Arch Biochem. Biophys.* **101**, 240.
Nagy, B., Claus, G., and Hennessy, D. J. (1962). *Nature* **193**, 1129.
Oró, J. (1963). *Ann. N.Y. Acad. Sci.* **108**, 464.
Spackman, D. H., Stein, W. H., and Moore, S. (1958). *Anal. Chem.* **30**, 1190.
Vallentyne, J. R. (1964). *Geochim. Cosmochim. Acta* **28**, 157.
Wilson, H., and Cannon, R. K. (1937). *J. Biol. Chem.* **119**, 309.
Wood, J. A. (1963a). *In* "The Solar System" (Middlehurst and Kuiper, eds.), Vol. IV, pp. 337–401. Univ. of Chicago Press, Chicago, Illinois.
Wood, J. A. (1963b). *Icarus* **2**, 152.

DISCUSSION

DR. FOX: The subject of meteorites has been brought into purview. Adequate coverage of this aspect requires an entire conference such as was held at the New York Academy of Sciences in 1962. The volume has been recently published (*Ann. N. Y. Acad. Sci.* **108** (Art. 2), 1963). Dr. Vallentyne's work emphasizes the major problem of terrestrial contamination.

There are also problems with respect to contamination of meteorites in their passage through the Earth's atmosphere.

DR. QUIMBY: Atmospheric contamination is *not serious* and indeed minimal compared to other sources of contamination. First of all, meteorites are glazed by the searing heat of the fire ball entry in the upper atmosphere. Although there are some cracks, the outer shell is not as porous as the main body of the meteorite. There is also a ram-jet air flow which sweeps material off the surface except that which impacts on the leading or front area. Naturally some air will enter as the pressure increases in the lower atmosphere. Except over cities, the atmosphere contains few bacteria, about one or two per liter. There are many molds, spores, and pollen grains seasonally in the lower atmosphere and for some peculiar reason two fungi, *Cladosporium* and *Alternaria*, everywhere at all altitudes up to the stratosphere. But unlike bacteria, these contaminants are too large to penetrate the meteoritic matrix. Someone has suggested that there are volatile organic materials in the atmosphere in general, presumably from plants.

The carbonaceous chondrites are fragile, often crumbling to pieces over a period of time. They are not "finds." I believe the 20 or so known meteorites of this type are all "falls"—that is, picked up shortly after landing. This lack of durability, as compared with other types of meteorites, in part accounts for the fact that there are so few of them. The harder stones and the irons are not all finds, but many of them are.

With respect to Orgueil, there is a fragment in Montaban Museum in southern France which, according to Anders, is contained in a sealed jar and has been opened only two or three times since the fall in 1864. If this is true, unless the preseal history is poor, this material should be better than any of the other known samples.

Finally, if we could see the fire ball on photographic plate, calculate the trajectory and area of impact, then immediately send out a recovery team to pick it up and wrap it in a plastic barrier before rain or sedimentation take place, we would then have something useful for Dr. Vallentyne and others to work with. We are preparing to do this now with 16 camera triangulation stations covering about a million square kilometers in the Midwest. But our expectations are now less than one meteorite a year and we shall have to be lucky for any one of the falls to be a carbonaceous chondrite. But supposing one falls tomorrow and we minimize initial contamination by the procedure I have outlined. This is exactly the time to estimate if not immediately measure any level of contamination there may be on the surface of the body, and to then invoke the most rigorous methods possible to prevent any further contamination.

DR. ORÓ: I would like to make a brief comment in the spirit of Dr. Fox's remarks. Dust has been suggested by Dr. Vallentyne as a possible source of contamination because it only takes about 1 mg of dust per gram of meteorite to give an amino acid analysis which is comparable with that obtained from the meteorite. I would like to suggest another source of possible contamination, namely, the ion-exchange resin which was used for desalting in these experiments. There are two reports in the literature which show clearly that a large number of amino acids are present in ion exchange resins [Lindlar, F., *Naturwissenschaften* 47, 14 (1960); Steven, F. S., and Tristram, G. R. *Biochem. J.* 83, 245 (1962)]. Depending on the nature of the resin used for desalting and on how extensively it has been regenerated prior to its use, one may find significant amounts of amino acids in the blanks.

CHAIRMAN BUCHANAN: Do I understand that in your analysis of the meteorite particles the amino acids that might have been contributed from the sweat of your hands during handling has been accounted for in your control in which sand particles were handled in a similar manner?

DR. VALLENTYNE: Yes, that is right.

CHAIRMAN BUCHANAN: Of course, the easiest way to avoid such contamination would have been to use plastic gloves although I can appreciate the difficulty of separating meteorite dust particles with plastic gloves.

DR. VALLENTYNE: It doesn't really matter what gloves you use, you don't know what someone else used. My point about this was that I don't think any amount of handling that we gave the glassware that we used in this case contributed anything in the way of a major amount of contamination.

CHAIRMAN BUCHANAN: Because the amounts that were there were far greater than anything that came from your hands?

DR. VALLENTYNE: Right. Our blanks, without touching the samples, were low. The hand blank was appreciable but still essentially low. But of course we don't know what happened in prior times.

DR. HALDANE: Assuming that there is no quarrel with Dr. Vallentyne's analytical methods, I take it that all these results with amino acids are based on chromatography in a wide sense. It would be a very amazing thing if under abiological conditions, just these 18 or 20 biological amino acids were formed and no others. One would say that this tells us something very surprising about the nature of the new materials in living substances.

I should like to ask how far you are reasonably sure to say that what you call leucine or isoleucine are those and not fairly closely related homologs.

DR. VALLENTYNE: Yes, I am glad you raised that point. This is quite correct, that the quantitative suite of amino acids in the meteorites is unquestionably biological in the sense of Earth biological. I don't think intuitively one would expect something of this sort from an abiogenetic synthesis.

The only other thing I should say is that in Kaplan's work, which is not true in ours, he analyzed for β-alanine and found a fairly high concentration there. Whether this is indicative of an abiogenesis I don't know.

Unfortunately, we had become so used to running a more routine type of mixture that we forgot about β-alanine, and stopped the analysis before the time of appearance of β-alanine in the eluate. Thus, it was not analyzed for in these determinations.

The procedure for analysis is essentially as described. We take a sample, hydrolyze it in acid that has been distilled, and then put that hydrolyzate on an ion exchange resin, which in this case was Amberlite IR-120, from which we don't get a recovery of arginine. That is what is missing. We elute amino acids with ammonia, remove the ammonia and then put the sample on an amino acid analyzer column and the results that you see here are from the column.

DR. GROSSENBACHER: Do the blanks receive the same analyzer treatment, so the determination of the resin itself would show up in the blanks?

DR. VALLENTYNE: The blanks are exactly the same in every respect as the sample, with one exception. In the case of the meteorite samples, the distilled water we used had been deionized and membrane-filtered. In the case of the three sand blanks and "hand-picked sand" the distilled water was membrane-filtered only, not deionized.

I don't know what your suggestion would be about this, whether the use of resins treated in this way might be more effective in adding amino acids or in removing them.

DR. ORÓ: One of the most difficult problems concerning the analysis of amino acids in meteorites using desalting by ion exchange is running a proper blank. This is because a proper blank would have to contain all the salts and other ionic species (organic as well as inorganic, known and unknown), and in identical concentration as they are present in the meteorite. The presence of magnesium, calcium, iron, and other ions in the meteorite will enhance processes of ion exchange and force out residual amino acids which may exist entrapped in the resin matrix. Other chemical effects (chelation, catalytic decomposition, etc.) can also be expected from certain organic and inorganic ions. Therefore, from this point of view a quartz blank or a sand blank cannot be considered a proper blank. Perhaps this problem could be obviated by eliminating any treatment which involves the use of ion-exchange resins and organic materials during the process of analysis. The desalting should be performed by the electrolytic, rather than by the ion-exchange method.

DR. VALLENTYNE: Before doing these analyses, we made a run which contained two amino acids—glutamic acid and phenylalanine—in the presence of ferric chloride and magnesium sulfate in about the concentration they would have occurred in the meteorite.

We didn't come up with extra material. We didn't come up with all we put in.

DR. ORÓ: You probably lost it. We have observed that ferric ion causes the decomposition of amino acids.

DR. VALLENTYNE: Yes. I wondered if it wasn't the iron on the resin perhaps absorbing something that it wouldn't have done otherwise.

DR. SAGAN: Primarily through the work of Anders and his coworkers, (see, e.g., Anders, E. (1963). *Ann. N.Y. Acad. Sci.* **108**, 514), we have some information on the thermal history of the carbonaceous chondrites, and some idea of the amount of time spent in each thermal regime. It is then possible to make the following thought experiment: Start with a mixture of amino acids, in which the relative abundances follow the abundances obtained in primitive Earth simulation experiments. If this mixture is then subjected to the thermal regimes which the carbonaceous chondrites have passed through, it would then be possible to make preliminary estimates of which amino acids survive the chondrite thermal history, and which do not. Such an analysis would be useful in assessing the probability of terrestrial contamination of the carbonaceous chondrites. The presence of large amounts of a temperature-labile amino acid would be *prima facie* evidence for contamination.

In a more general sense, such an analysis might provide some information on when the amino acids got into the meteorite. What was the sequence of origins in the meteorite parent body? Were the amino acids formed after any mineral inclusions which have high-temperature origins, or before? Here's a way of finding out.

Dr. BLOIS: In line with the question that Dr. Sagan just raised, I noted in Fig. 3 that at moderate temperatures alanine was the most stable and serine perhaps the least; if you look at the slopes of these curves, phenylalanine when extended will win.

I believe it would surpass alanine, and if you consider the higher temperatures, which may or may not be geochemically relevant, it looks like phenylalanine would win.

One should therefore keep in mind the thermal history of the particles, as Dr. Sagan mentioned.

Dr. VALLENTYNE: I might add some comments to that and to Dr. Sagan's remarks.

I have some data in which I can make predictions under an assumption of maximum rates of change that could be expected for a given temperature history, but they are all based on a medium rich in liquid water.

Dr. SAGAN: There is evidence for a long, aqueous period during the history of the interior of the parent bodies of the carbonaceous chondrites (Anders, E. (1963). *Ann. N.Y. Acad Sci.* 108, 514).

Dr. VALLENTYNE: Then we can get together on that. If you have time-temperature combinations, I can make predictions on the basis of them very easily. The only other thing to note is that there is a reversal of some of these relations in water-deficient media. When we take, for example, mollusc-shell protein as ground-up shell, and heat it in the absence of water, phenylalanine turns out to be the most stable amino acid. This is reversed by adding excess water.

So the environment must exercise a serious control.

Dr. OPARIN: I want to ask whether these amino acids are optically active or racemic.

Dr. VALLENTYNE: I don't think the present evidence indicates one way or the other. Kaplan has taken the extracts and put them through a polarimeter that will detect 5×10^{-4} degrees, and found no optical activity in the extract.

We have done the same thing in a less sensitive polarimeter, but in our case if you make the calculation, it turns out that we wouldn't have been able to detect rotation had optically active amino acids been there. The concentrations were too low.

We have a much better system envisaged for this than using a polarimeter: that is to split our samples in the future in half (and we intend to do this with fossils material as well as in this case), one half for regular analysis and the other half for analysis after treatment with an enzyme like D-amino acid oxidase.

This should be far more sensitive, I think, than any other method. We haven't done it as yet.

DR. GAFFRON: I wonder whether this Orgueil meteorite could not be removed from the literature by taking a piece and heating it up to, let's say, 150° for a year and looking for what's left. At least one could extrapolate back to the age of the bulk of the material, and guess how much organic matter it might have contained originally.

DR. SZUTKA: I have a remark with respect to the racemization. When you treat an optically active compound with acid and heat, you will racemize the compound. This is true, for example, with lysine. One of the methods of racemization of lysine in d-form is to treat the compound with HCl and heat. Therefore, I would be careful with the interpretation of your results.

DR. FOX: Apropos of the last remark by Dr. Haldane, a review of the many reported laboratory syntheses of amino acids under simulated prebiological conditions indicates that the amino acids so formed are predominantly of the natural structures. Thermodynamic and evolutionary theory can be invoked to explain that this kind of result should not be surprising; a different kind of result might rather be unexpected. When Dr. Harada reports on the thermal synthesis of amino acids, you will note a roster of amino acids which is remarkably natural in their identity. Also, the high proportion of glycine is provocatively similar to the analysis from meteorites. Apropos of such experiments, we should not lose sight of relative stabilities and the fundamental position of the second law of thermodynamics, even as it may be clothed by such qualities as "urge" referred to by Dr. Mora.

ASYMMETRIC HYDROGENATION OF CARBONYL COMPOUNDS

SHIRO AKABORI

Institute for Protein Research, Osaka University, Osaka, Japan

Asymmetric formation of organic substances is one of the characteristics of chemical reactions taking place in the living world. Various
types of reactions are involved in the biosynthesis of physiological substances and almost all of them are brought about in the presence of
enzymes which could be considered asymmetric catalysts.

The asymmetry of enzymatic reactions must be attributed mainly
to the stereospecific adsorption of substrates to the active site of enzyme
molecules. The stereospecific adsorption is undoubtedly a manifestation
of the asymmetric comformation of the active site of enzymes, and
this must be closely related to the asymmetric structure of amino acids
composing enzymatic protein.

The problem of the prebiological formation of optically active biological substances has been repeatedly discussed by many distinguished
scientists. I remember the problem was also actively discussed on the
occasion of the Symposium on the "Origin of Life on the Earth" held in
Moscow in 1957 (Terent'ev and Klabunovskii, 1959; Klabunovskii, 1959;
Pasynskii *et al.*, 1959). It seems to me that the problem is still unsolved
but I do not wish to go any further into this fundamental but difficult
problem.

I would like to present at this conference some results of our
investigation on an asymmetric modification of catalytic activity of
Raney nickel carried out in my laboratory at the Institute for Protein
Research, Osaka University, by Dr. Izumi and his associates.

Newly prepared Raney nickel is usually active for the hydrogenation
of both C=C and C=O bonds, the activity being affected by the
presence of small amounts of various substances. In our previous experiments (Fukawa *et al.*, 1962), it was observed that, on treating the
catalyst with various amino acid and peptide solutions, the activity

toward the C=O bond was remarkably decreased, whereas that for the C=C bond remained almost unaffected. This fact suggests that adsorption of an optically active amino acid upon Raney nickel might so modify the active center of the catalyst that it asymmetrically hydrogenates carbonyl compounds of the R—CO—R′ type to optically active secondary alcohols as follows.

$$CH_3—CO—CH_2—COOCH_3 \xrightarrow{+H_2} CH_3—\overset{※}{\underset{OH}{CH}}—CH_2—COOCH_3$$

(I) and (II) could be distinguished in the absorbed but not in the free state, and if (I) produces the D form, (II) must produce the L form by hydrogenation.

Actually, in our recent investigation, (Izumi et al., 1963), nickel treated with optically active α-amino acids or α-hydroxy acids showed distinct stereospecific hydrogenation of carbonyl compounds.

The greatest effect was observed in the hydrogenation of methyl acetoacetate; methyl β-hydroxybutyrate of high optical activity was obtained. Therefore, in our present work we used mostly methyl acetoacetate as the substrate for catalytic hydrogenation.

Ni Catalyst and its Modification. One and a half grams of powdered Ni–Al alloy (Ni:Al = 40:60) was added in small portions to 20 ml of 20% sodium hydroxide solution while stirring and was allowed to stand for 45 minutes at 80°C. The Ni powder which remained was washed several times with distilled water. Most of the experiments in the present work were carried out with this quantity (1.5 units) of Raney nickel for 17 gm of methyl acetoacetate. For the asymmetric modification, newly prepared nickel catalyst was immersed in 225 ml of 2% L-glutamate solution (the pH of which had been adjusted to a specified value) with occasional shaking. After the solution was removed by decantation, the nickel catalyst was washed once with water and twice with methanol, and then was separated by centrifugation. The modification by other reagents was performed in similar ways.

Catalytic Hydrogenation. Purified methyl acetoacetate mixed with the modified nickel catalyst was placed in a small autoclave and shaken under an initial hydrogen pressure of 90 kg/cm.[2] Hydrogen uptake was usually complete within 10 hours. The reduction product was filtered from the nickel catalyst and distilled under reduced pressure; the fraction boiling at 61–62°C/12 mm Hg was identified as methyl β-hydroxybutyrate by elemental analysis and gas chromatography.

Asymmetric Yield. The optical rotation of the purified reduction product was measured in a conventional polarimeter at 20°C without dilution in a 1 dm tube and the observed value of rotation was taken as the specific rotation, because the specific density of methyl β-hydroxybutyrate is nearly 1.0. According to Levene and Haller (1925), the specific rotation of pure methyl L-β-hydroxybutyrate is $[\alpha]_D^{20}-20.9°$ and therefore the per cent asymmetric yield, P, was calculated by:

$$P = \frac{[\alpha]_D^{20} \times 100}{20.9}$$

Effect of pH of Modifying Solution. Asymmetric yields of catalytic hydrogenation by means of Raney nickel treated with 2% L-glutamate solution at various pH values at 0°C were measured. It was observed that the pH of the modifying solution greatly influenced the asymmetric yield in catalytic hydrogenation of methyl acetoacetate as shown in Fig. 1.

It is highly interesting that a pH optimum was clearly observed around pH 5.1. The amount of glutamic acid adsorbed on Raney nickel also varied markedly with the pH of the glutamate solution, but there was no direct relationship between asymmetric yield and the adsorbed amount of glutamic acid.

Effect of Modifying the Temperature. The relationship between the asymmetric capacity of the modified catalyst and the temperature of the modifying solution was studied by use of Raney nickel immersed in 2% glutamate solution at pH 5.1. Methyl β-hydroxybutyrate obtained by using Raney nickel modified at 0°C showed the highest levorotatory power; this was decreased with the elevation of the modifying temperature, the temperature of hydrogenation being fixed at 60°C. It is remarkable that the product obtained using the catalyst modified above 80°C was dextrorotatory (Fig. 2).

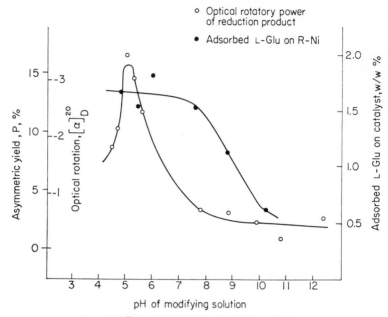

Fig. 1. Effect of pH of the modifying solution.

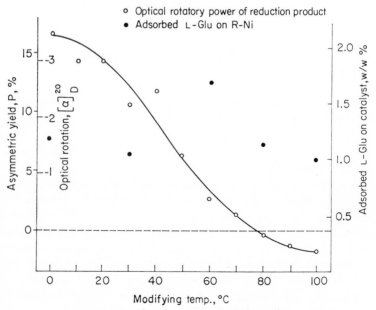

Fig. 2. Effect of modifying the temperature.

The effect of the pH of the modifying solution on the asymmetric capacity was somewhat different if Raney nickel was treated at 100°C (Fig. 3).

Effect of Immersion Time in the Modification of Catalyst. The effect of immersion time in the modification was measured by varying the time from 2 minutes to 47 hours. It was found that the catalyst was saturated

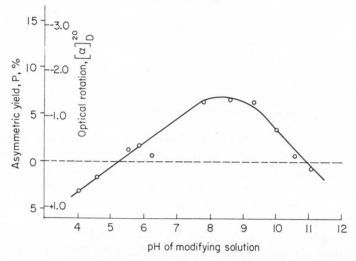

Fig. 3. Effect of modifying the solution with L-glutamate at 100°C.

in 10 minutes with glutamic acid. A longer immersion showed no appreciable effect for several hours, and then a slow decrease of the asymmetric capacity was observed (Table I).

TABLE I

Effect of Immersion Time on Asymmetric Yield

Immersion time	$[\alpha]_D^{20}$ of product	P
minutes		
2	−2.56°	12.2
10	−3.51°	16.8
hours		
1.5	−3.46°	16.5
19	−3.30°	15.8
47	−2.98°	14.3

Effect of Mixing of D-*and* L-*Glutamate.* The effect of mixing D- and L-glutamate in different ratios upon the asymmetric yield has been measured and a nearly linear relationship was observed between the optical activity of the reaction product and the mixing ratio (Table II).

TABLE II

EFFECT OF RATIO OF L-GLUTAMIC ACID TO D-GLUTAMIC ACID ON ASYMMETRIC YIELD

L-Glu:D-glu		$[\alpha]_D^{20}$ of product	P
10	0	−2.86°	13.7
9	1	−1.90°	9.1
6	4	−0.45°	2.2
0	10	+2.95°	14.1

Effect of Successive Modification. When the catalyst was treated with D-glutamate, washed, and then treated with L-glutamate, or treated in the reverse order, the asymmetric capacity was always determined by the second agent rather than by the first one. This means that the adsorption of glutamate upon the nickel catalyst is very loose and can be easily replaced.

Effect of Various Amino Acids. Various natural α-amino acids have been tested for their modifying effect. Most of the L-α-amino acids showed an asymmetric effect upon Raney nickel, but to a much lesser extent than glutamic acid, and the effect varied with modifying conditions. In the case of L-valine and L-isoleucine, contrary to that of other amino acids, modifying temperature had little influence on the asymmetric yield, and the rotatory power of methyl β-hydroxybutyrate was in both cases nearly $[\alpha]_D^{20} - 2.0$.

Hydrogenation of Acetophenone. Acetophenone (16 gm) was hydrogenated with modified Raney nickel in the same way as above. The phenylmethylcarbinol obtained showed $[\alpha]_D^{20} + 0.90°$.

Effect of L-*Malic Acid and* D-*Tartaric Acid.* Raney nickel treated with L-malate gave dextrorotatory methyl β-hydroxybutyrate, while L-aspartate gave the levorotatory product, in the hydrogenation of methyl acetoacetate.

D-Tartaric acid showed the highest asymmetric effect upon Raney nickel among the various reagents tested. The asymmetric yields in this case differed markedly according to the difference in pH of the modifying solutions (Fig. 4).

A pH optimum was observed around pH 5.0 similar to that found with the glutamate modification. However, in the case of tartrate modification, the effect of temperature of the modifying solution was entirely different from that of glutamate. A marked increase in the asymmetric

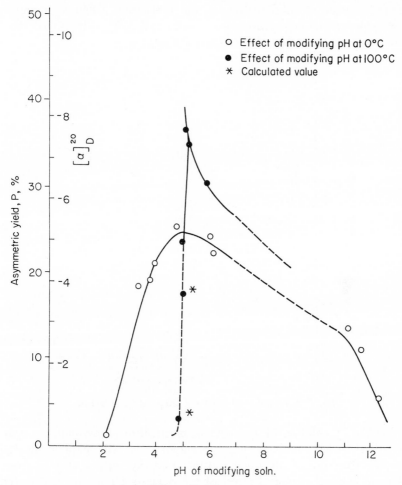

FIG. 4. Effect of modifying the pH.

capacity was observed with the elevation of temperature of the modifying solution (Fig. 5).

Our present work does not offer any information concerning the problem of abiogenic asymmetric formation of organic substances. It is impossible to propose any model mechanism for asymmetric hydrogenation because we have, at present, no conception of the chelated states of modifying agents nor the adsorbed state of the substrate on the surface of a catalyst. Nevertheless, this work might suggest a possibility of asymmetric formation of organic substances in the adsorbed state on the surface of solid matter. In the best result obtained in our experiments methyl-L-β-hydroxybutyrate showed $[\alpha]_D^{20} - 10°$. That means the product is composed of 75% L- and 25% D-form.

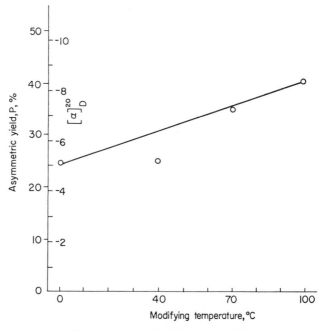

FIG. 5. Effect of modifying the temperature at pH 5.1.

For the elucidation of the precise mechanism of asymmetric hydrogenation, we have to devise a new technique that will enable us to study the fine structure of absorbed substance on the surface of a catalyst. I hope an eminent chemical physicist can devise such an excellent method in the near future.

Revised manuscript received February 28, 1964.

REFERENCES

Fukawa, H., Izumi, Y., Komatsu, S., and Akabori, S. (1962). *Bull. Chem. Soc. Japan* **35**, 1703.

Izumi, Y., Imaida, M., Fukawa, H., and Akabori, S. (1963). *Bull. Chem Soc. Japan* **36**, 21 and 155.

Klabunovskii, E. I. (1959). *Origin Life Earth Rept. Intern. Symp. Moscow 1957* p. 158.

Levene, P. A., and Haller, H. L. (1925). *J. Biol. Chem.* **65**, 51.

Pasynskii, A. G., Vol'kenstein, M., and Akabori, S., (1959). *Origin Life Earth Rept. Intern. Symp. Moscow 1957* pp. 174–175 (discussion).

Terent'ev, A. P., and Klabunovskii, E. I. (1959). *Origin Life Earth Rept. Intern. Symp. Moscow 1957* p. 95.

DISCUSSION

DR. BERNAL: Professor Akabori's contribution on asymmetric synthesis takes us a step further in dealing with one of the most obstinate problems of the origin of life, but it is clearly not the final solution because his symmetrically enzymatic Raney nickel requires pretreatment from an asymmetric molecule.

[1] *In absentia*

STAGES AND MECHANISMS OF PREBIOLOGICAL ORGANIC SYNTHESIS

J. Oró

*Department of Chemistry, University of Houston,
Houston, Texas*

I. Introduction

It would be difficult to do justice to this topic in about 30 minutes. Therefore this presentation will be limited in more than one way. I will first consider briefly the probable stages of synthesis of organic compounds prior to and during the formation of the Earth. Then I will briefly discuss some of the possible mechanisms involved in the abiotic synthesis of amino acids, purines, pyrimidines, and monosaccharides, limiting myself to work carried out mainly in our laboratory, and leaving out of consideration more complex biological molecules—which will be taken up in another session of this meeting. Additional information may be found elsewhere (Oró, 1961a, 1963d,e, 1964a,b).

As will become immediately obvious, there are more questions to be asked than answers to be given on the subject of stages and mechanisms of prebiological organic synthesis. Although we do not seem to have in the audience meteorite chemists or geochemists who could give us a hand on cosmochemical matters, we are, on the other hand, fortunate enough to have an illustrious group of biochemists who, no doubt, will help us in the elucidation of some of the synthetic mechanisms. Before I begin I would like to take this opportunity to congratulate Dr. Buchanan for his very stimulating presentation this morning on a very reasonable approach to the problem of the emergence of the first superordinated organic system.

II. Different Forms of Energy

The formation of organic compounds in the universe appears to take place by the action of at least three main forms of energy: thermal,

137

ionizing radiation, and ultraviolet light (Table I). Stars are the primary sources of these three forms of energy which ultimately are generated by thermonuclear processes.

Thermal energy starts to play a chemical role in the atmospheres of relatively cool carbon stars (spectral classes R and N) where temperatures of about 3000°K prevail (Struve and Zebergs, 1962). Temperatures of this order of magnitude and higher may also result from collisions of cosmic bodies and from impact and explosion phenomena in general (Oró, 1961a; Hochstim, 1963). Lower temperatures must also

TABLE I

EFFECTS OF DIFFERENT FORMS OF ENERGY

Form	Energy	Effect
Thermal	10^3–10^4 °K (star atmospheres, impact phenomena, etc.)	Formation of ions and radicals which may recombine upon cooling
	425–1000°K (localized processes)	Formation of anhydrides and pyrolysis products
Ionizing radiation	Protons, electrons, and α-particles from the Sun or the protosun Radioactivity *in situ*	Formation of ions and radicals followed by recombination
Ultraviolet light	From the Sun or the protosun	Ionization (short-wave UV) and/ or excitation followed by chemical reaction

have been generated by other general and localized phenomena such as gravitational contraction, radioactive decay, and the process or processes responsible for the formation of chondrular bodies in chondritic meteorites. At temperatures between 10^3 and 10^4 °K, only very simple molecules, radicals, and ions will exist. From 425 to 1000°K the formation of anhydrides and pyrolytic products of organic compounds can be expected to occur.

Ionizing radiation, whether in the form of protons, electrons, α-particles, or X-rays coming from the protosun, or the Sun, or due to radioactivity *in situ* in the solar nebula, would cause the formation of radicals and ions which upon recombination would be ultimately transformed into more stable products (Swallow, 1960).

Ultraviolet (UV) light causes ionization and excitation phenomena which are followed by chemical reactions. The effects of ultraviolet light are, however, more selective than those caused by the other two forms of energy because the absorption of this electromagnetic radiation is very dependent on the nature of the compound being irradiated. Electrical discharges can be considered, in a broad sense, as a combination of the above three forms of energy.

Now, I would like to emphasize that it does not matter much which form of energy is involved, so long as the species produced are highly reactive. So, leaving aside small differences in selectivity, the end result of the application of the above three forms of energy is that of forming highly reactive intermediates, which upon recombination—assuming the existence of quenching zones of relatively low temperatures—are transformed into more complex molecules.

III. Stages of Prebiological Organic Compound Synthesis

Table II outlines the four main stages of prebiological synthesis as they probably occurred during the formation of the solar system. Syn-

TABLE II

STAGES OF PREBIOLOGICAL ORGANIC SYNTHESIS

Stage	Average prevailing temperatures (°K)	Predominant energy
Star atmosphere	3,000–6,000	Thermal (from nuclear processes)
Solar nebula	Matrix < 425 Chondrule $> 1,000$	Radioactivity Thermal
Preplanetary stage (planetesimals, cometesimals)	General < 425 Localized $> 1,000$	Corpuscular and electromagnetic radiation Thermal (from inpact phenomena, shock waves, etc.)
Early planetary stage (primitive Earth, comets, Jupiter, etc.)	General < 425 Localized $> 1,000$	Corpuscular and electromagnetic radiation Thermal (from impact phenomena, electrical discharges, etc.)

thesis of simple organic compounds probably occurred first in the "star atmosphere stage," i.e., in the atmospheres of stars which provided the matter for the formation of the solar nebula. Such synthetic processes occur today in the atmospheres of carbon stars. The synthesis presumably begins as soon as H, C, O, N (also S and P) leave the star's interior and become part of its atmosphere. Spectroscopic analysis of the atmospheres of carbon stars reveal molecular spectra which are dominated by the bands of carbon compounds. These compounds are simple diatomic combinations of carbon with hydrogen, carbon with oxygen, carbon with nitrogen, and carbon with carbon. Thermodynamic calculations of dissociative equilibria between 2500 and 6000°K (Aller, 1961) show that these simple carbon molecules, and also H_2, OH, and NH, are some of the most thermally stable diatomic combinations observed in the universe.

It is conceivable that some of the matter formed in carbon stars a very long time ago was ejected into interstellar space, was condensed into more complex forms, and eventually became a part of the solar nebula. In fact it has been suggested recently by Hoyle and Wickramasinghe (1962) that a pulsating carbon star of type N produces carbon compounds in the form of particles which are ejected by radiation pressure into interstellar space at the rate of 5×10^{25} gm per year. This is several orders of magnitude higher than the total carbon present in living organisms on the Earth today.

The second stage is the "solar nebula stage." If a low-temperature model for the formation of the solar system is used (Urey, 1952, 1957; Hoyle, 1960), the prevailing temperatures in the solar nebula are supposed to have been quite low. Therefore, chemical activity must have been relatively low during this stage except for the effects of short-lived radioisotopes and decay of potassium-40. The situation would be different if a high-temperature model (Cameron, 1962) is used.

In the following "preplanetary stage," high activity probably occurred, particularly as soon as the protosun was formed. Then an intense radiation flux prevailed (Fowler, 1962) which would have led to the formation of organic compounds on the planetesimals. It is also possible that, in the more central regions of the solar system, very short periods of heating, perhaps of the order of 2000°K, may have occurred owing to sporadic shock waves coming from the protosun.

In the "early planetary stage," we had a situation very similar to that of the preplanetary stage, except that the bodies of metric dimensions (planetesimals) had been aggregated into much larger bodies which eventually became the planets and other bodies of the solar system. From a chemical point of view, and leaving aside orbital and other considerations, comets and the Jovian planets can be considered in a sense as "fossil" examples of this stage.

Now, the main point that I wish to make after this description is that the formation of organic compounds took place long before the

Earth was formed, a conclusion which has been made elsewhere (Lederberg and Cowie, 1958; Oró, 1961a; Fowler, 1962) and in this meeting by Professor Bernal.

IV. Conditions and Models of the Early Planetary Stage

Table III summarizes the probable conditions prevailing during the early planetary stage. These conditions are essentially those prevailing in carbonaceous chondrites (DuFresne and Anders, 1962; Mason, 1962). The system was aqueous, it had basic properties, and it was reducing. These three properties are a logical consequence of the fact that hydrogen, water, and ammonia are three of the most abundant molecules in the universe. The temperatures were in general relatively low, perhaps

TABLE III

PROBABLE GENERAL CONDITIONS PREVAILING DURING THE LAST TWO STAGES OF PREBIOLOGICAL ORGANIC SYNTHESIS

Aqueous system (solid, liquid, or vapor)
Basic properties (ammonium hydroxide)
Reducing (lack of free oxygen)
Relatively *low temperature* ($<425°K$)
Appreciable concentration of carbon compounds

not higher than 425°K (Urey, 1952), although higher temperatures may have occasionally occurred in localized environments.

The fifth condition calls for appreciable initial concentrations of carbon compounds, a conclusion which appears to be at variance with considerations made elsewhere (Horowitz and Miller, 1962). It may be pointed out that in our case we do not have to depend on the terrestrial sea waters containing a very small concentration of organic compounds. If we go on the basis of atrophysical, cometary, and meteoritic evidence we must reach the conclusion that the relative concentration of carbon compounds was, indeed, very high. For instance carbonaceous chondrites contain up to 5% carbon, which must represent an even higher concentration of carbon compounds. Similar high concentrations of organic compounds are probably present in comets (Whipple, 1950, 1963). Comets are cosmic bodies which exist today in the solar system and can be studied spectroscopically in some detail (Swings and Haser, 1956). Because of this we have chosen them as realistic models for the experimental study of abiotic organic synthesis. A summary of their chemical composition together with some other pertinent information is given in Table IV. The presence of diatomic and triatomic carbon in comets is very well established and both of these reactive chemical species can be produced easily in the laboratory. The direct conversion of solid carbon into C_3 has been recently demonstrated (Skell and Wescott, 1963). Hydrogen cyanide, cyanogen, methane, ammonia, and water are considered among the most prevalent

TABLE IV

CHEMICAL SPECIES DETECTED IN COMETS AND OTHER COMETARY DATA

Composition[a]	CN, CH, CH_2, C_2, C_3, NH, NH_2, OH, CH^+, CO^+, CO_2^+, N_2^+, OH^+, and Na
Parent compounds[b]	HCN, NH_3, H_2O, CO, C_2N_2, CH_4, C_2H_2, and other hydrocarbons
Average mass[b,c]	$10^{18\pm3}$ gm (10^{18} gm minimum mass for Halley's comet)
Probability of collision with the earth[b]	100 collisions in 5×10^9 years
Cometary matter trapped by the Earth[b]	$10^{20\pm3}$ gm in 5×10^9 years

[a] From spectrochemical evidence.
[b] Calculated or estimated.
[c] See Richter (1963), pp. xxvii and 37–39.

molecules in the cometary nucleus. Additional data on comets may be found elsewhere (Richter, 1963; Oró, 1961a).

V. Synthesis of Amino Acids

A. Experimental

Now we come to the second part of this presentation which has to do with the question of how biochemical compounds are formed; particularly, how amino acids, purines, pyrimidines, and monosaccharides can be synthesized under conditions similar to those previously described. I think it would be reasonable to use mixtures of the compounds presumed to exist in comets in order to carry out these experiments of synthesis. One can use any of the suggested forms of energy—thermal, ionizing radiation, or ultraviolet light. One can also use an electrical discharge which in a sense is a combination of the above three forms of energy in different proportions depending on the nature of the spark. If, however, one starts with quite reactive species, for instance HCN, CH_2O, NH_2OH, NH_2NH_2, one does not need to use any of these highly activating forms of energy.

Figure 1 shows the reaction vessel used in an experiment with ionizing radiation made in an attempt to simulate the irradiation of a cometary nucleus. Methane-C^{14}, ammonia, and water were introduced into the chamber and these compounds were condensed to the solid state by the addition of liquid nitrogen to the Dewar flask on the left of the chamber. The solid disc of methane, ammonia, and water was then irradiated with 5 Mev electrons (Oró, 1963b). Other irradiations were carried out at room temperature with the components in the gas and

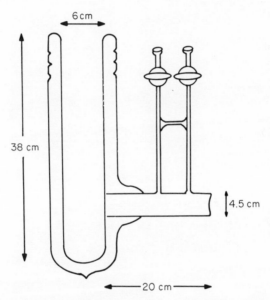

FIG. 1. Vessel used in the irradiation of solid methane-C^{14}, ammonia, and water with 5 Mev electrons (after Oró, 1963b).

liquid states as it had been done previously by Calvin (1961) and by Palm and Calvin (1962). Synthesis was observed in all these cases, as shown by autoradiography of paper chromatograms (Fig. 2), and a number of amino acids including glycine, glycinamide, alanine, and aspartic acid were identified (Palm and Calvin, 1962; Oró, 1963b). These results are similar to those obtained with electrical discharges (Miller, 1955; Oró, 1963a), an example of which is shown in Fig. 3. Amino acid analysis by ion exchange of the product from electrical discharges is also shown in Fig. 4 (Oró, 1963a).

More recently, in collaboration with Mr. H. S. Skewes, we have been concerned with the formation of amino acids and other organic com-

pounds at high temperatures in an attempt to simulate processes occurring in the quenching zones of stellar atmospheres and cometary
collisions (Oró, 1961a). By passing mixtures of methane, ammonia, and
water through a hot tube at approximately 1300°K, a number of amino

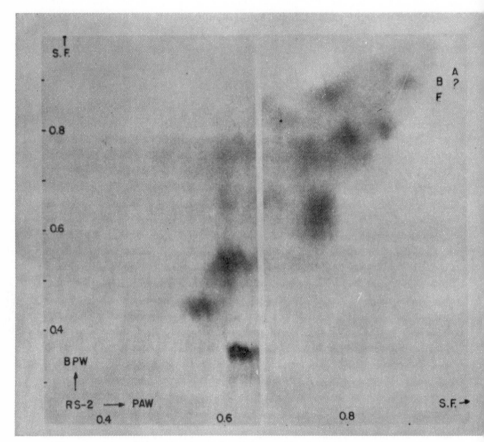

Fig. 2. Autoradiograph of a two-dimensional chromatogram of the products
formed by irradiation of a methane-C^{11}–ammonia–water mixture (after Oró, 1963b).

acids have been obtained (Table V), as shown by ion exchange on
a Beckmann-Spinco amino acid analyzer. So far, only glycine, alanine,
aspartic acid, and β-alanine have positively been identified by other
methods. The identification of the amino acids remains at present an
open question. Additional ninhydrin-positive compounds were observed,
and spectrophotometry showed also the formation of ultraviolet-absorbing

compounds in the region of 260 and 280 mμ. We have not yet completely identified these compounds. The thermal treatment of other simple mixtures has produced other compounds of biochemical significance. For instance, in addition to most of the above α-amino acids, β-alanine and its

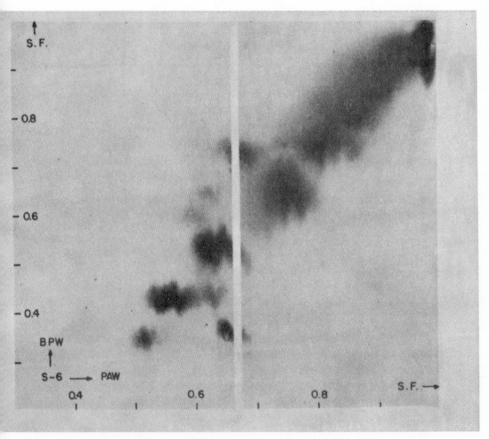

Fig. 3. Autoradiograph of a two-dimensional chromatogram of the products formed by the action of electrical discharges on a methane-C[11]–ethane–ammonia–water mixture (after Oró, 1963a).

intermediate β-aminopropionitrile have been obtained by thermal decomposition of acetamide which in turn is known to be produced by the proton irradiation of methane ammonia, and water (Berger, 1961). Amino acids can also be synthesized with ultraviolet light, and this work has been reviewed elsewhere (Oró, 1963d).

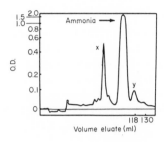

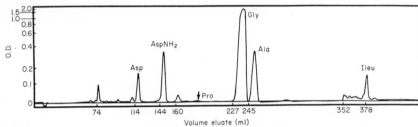

Fig. 4. Ion-exchange amino acid analysis of the products formed by the action of electrical discharges on a methane–ethane–ammonia–water mixture (after Oró, 1963a).

TABLE V

AMINO ACID ANALYSIS OF THE REACTION PRODUCT FROM METHANE, AMMONIA, AND WATER AT ABOUT 1300°K

Ninhydrin-positive compound	Amount $(\mu M \times 10^3/\text{mole of } CH_4)$
U_1	2
U_2	40
Aspartic acid	10
U_3	4
Threonine	100
Serine	40
Glutamic acid	40
U_4	10
Glycine	9300
Alanine	5600
Alloisoleucine	10
Isoleucine	10
Leucine	20
Tyrosine	2
Phenylalanine	2
β-Alanine	100

It is clear that amino acids can be obtained with any of the three forms of energy (thermal, ionizing radiation, or ultraviolet light). Furthermore, as I have suggested earlier, one should also be able to synthesize these biochemical compounds without the use of any of these activating forms of energy so long as highly reactive precursors are used. In fact, amino acids have been synthesized from mixtures of formaldehyde,

TABLE VI

AMINO ACIDS SYNTHESIZED IN AQUEOUS SOLUTIONS FROM MIXTURES OF REACTIVE COMPOUNDS

Amino acid or amino amide	Approximate relative amount
A.[a] Glycinamide	+ + +
Glycine	+ + +
Alanine	+ +
Aspartic acid	+ +
Serine	+ +
Glutamic acid	+
Threonine	+
Leucine	+
Isoleucine	+
Arginine	+
α-Amino-n-butyric acid	+
β-Alanine	+ +
α,β-Diaminopropionic acid	+ +
B.[b] Glycine	+ +
Valine	+ +
Lysine	+ +

[a] A: from $HCN + NH_3 + H_2O$; or $CH_2O + NH_2OH + H_2O$.
[b] B: from $CH_2O + N_2H_4 + H_2O$.

hydroxylamine, and water (Oró et al., 1959), formaldehyde, hydrazine, and water (Master, 1957), and hydrogen cyanide, ammonia, and water (Oró and Kamat, 1961; Lowe et al., 1963). They are listed in Table VI.

B. Mechanisms

Now, we come to the question: How are amino acids synthesized in some of the above experiments? If for simplification we limit ourselves to the experiments with methane, ammonia, and water, and accept that one of the final steps involves a Strecker condensation (Miller, 1957; Oró et al., 1959), the question can be divided in two parts. How is the aliphatic or aromatic aldehyde first formed? And, how does the final condensation or condensations take place?

With regard to the formation of the low molecular weight aliphatic hydrocarbons which eventually are transformed into aliphatic aldehydes, two alternative mechanisms are possible, as shown in Fig. 5. If a mechanism of radical recombination in a homogeneous system were operative, one would end up with a predominance of isomeric or branched hydrocarbons. If, on the other hand, the mechanism involved

Fɪɢ. 5. Possible mechanisms of formation of low molecular weight hydrocarbons. (1) Radicals of secondary carbons have a higher stability; thus, formation of branched hydrocarbons predominates. (2) Addition occurs at one end of a growing chain; thus, straight-chain hydrocarbons are preferentially formed.

were surface-dependent with steric restrictions, i.e., something like a Fischer-Tropsch catalysis (Friedel and Sharkey, 1963), then one could expect to get a predominance of normal or straight-chain hydrocarbons.

Let me say that we do not have a complete answer to this question. Previous experimental results (Franck, 1960; Oró, 1963d) and some of the present ones, indicate that a radical mechanism predominates. It would be interesting in this respect to analyze the low molecular weight hydrocarbons of carbonaceous chondrites to find out the relative distribution of branched and normal hydrocarbons. This would give us information on which of these two mechanisms did prevail in the cosmos before the Earth was formed. A radical mechanism, involving the intermediate formation of acetylene, was proposed earlier (Oró, 1963e) for the formation of the aromatic hydrocarbon styrene, which eventually could have been transformed into phenylalanine and tyrosine.

Once the hydrocarbons have been formed, they must be transformed into aldehydes. This may occur (Fig. 6) by a process which is essentially a dehydrogenation by the action of hydroxyl radicals. Hydroxyl radicals are produced from water by thermal decomposition, by ionizing radiation, by short-wave ultraviolet light, and also by electrical discharges. The process starts with an OH radical removing one hydrogen from the

				ALDEHYDE	AMINO ACID
RCH_3 $\xrightarrow[-H_2O]{2\ (\cdot OH)}$ RCH_2OH		$\xrightarrow[-H_2O]{2\ (\cdot OH)}$ $RCHO$			
METHANE	$CH_4 \longrightarrow CH_2O$			FORMALDEHYDE	GLYCINE
ETHANE	$CH_3CH_3 \longrightarrow CH_3CHO$			ACETALDEHYDE	ALANINE
ISOBUTANE	$CH_3-\overset{CH_3}{\underset{|}{CH}}-CH_3 \longrightarrow CH_3-\overset{CH_3}{\underset{|}{CH}}-CHO$			ISOBUTYRALDEHYDE	VALINE
2-MeBUTANE	$CH_3-\overset{CH_3}{\underset{|}{CH}}-CH_2-CH_3$	$CH_3-CH_2-\overset{CH_3}{\underset{|}{CH}}-CHO$		2-MeBUTYRALDEHYDE	ISOLEUCINE
		$CH_3-\overset{CH_3}{\underset{|}{CH}}-CH_2-CHO$		3-MeBUTYRALDEHYDE	LEUCINE

FIG. 6. Formation of aliphatic aldehydes as precursors of aliphatic amino acids. Secondary alcohols tend to form olefins by dehydration. Primary alcohols give aldehydes rather than glycols.

hydrocarbon and forming an alkyl radical which on combination with another OH radical yields an alcohol. The alcohol is then transformed into aldehyde by a similar process. One may ask why don't we get a glycol, instead of an aldehyde, once the primary alcohol has been formed. It is an observation of radiation chemistry that primary alcohols give aldehydes rather than glycols. Apparently the electronegativity of the oxygen makes the hydrogens on the hydroxyalkyl carbon more susceptible to removal by OH radicals and once the hydroxyalkyl radical is formed it becomes stabilized by resonance, allowing the addition of a second OH radical. Therefore, the end result is the predominant formation of aldehydes.

From the aldehydes, in the presence of ammonia and hydrogen cyanide, the α-amino acids are formed with the intermediate formation of α-aminonitriles (Miller, 1957) and amides (Oró *et al.*, 1959). Additional reactions are required for the formation of serine, threonine, aspartic acid, and other amino acids (Miller, 1955, 1957; Oró, 1936d).

The mechanisms operative in the formation of amino acids from hydrogen cyanide, ammonia, and water and from other mixtures of reactive compounds have been discussed briefly elsewhere (Oró, 1963d) and will not be taken up here.

VI. Synthesis of Purines

A. Experimental

Some time ago we became interested in the synthesis of polymeric hydrogen cyanide (from HCN, NH_3, and H_2O) since it had been suggested (Abelson, 1959) that certain amino acids could be obtained by hydrolysis of this polymer. When a compound with the chromatographic behavior of adenine unexpectedly appeared in the reaction product from the above mixture, the finding was not immediately accepted. Six months passed before the skepticism was laid aside and the experiment repeated to obtain more substantial evidence.

Figure 7 shows the first convincing chromatographic evidence obtained on the formation of adenine from hydrogen cyanide (Oró, 1960). After this work, the synthesis of adenine was studied in detail and the compound was identified in a number of different ways (Oró and Kimball, 1961).

The reaction of hydrogen cyanide, ammonia, and water was carried out usually at 70°C although lower and higher temperatures were used. Figure 8 shows the rate of adenine synthesis and disappearance of hydrogen cyanide at about 90°C. At 70°C and lower temperatures, the synthesis is linear with time for a number of days. As much as 685 mg of adenine per liter was synthesized in one experiment, and the yields were of the order of 0.1% or less, which compares favorably with the concentration of this compound in biological materials. As you know, the synthesis of this purine has been confirmed by Lowe *et al.* (1963) and in an indirect way by Calvin (1961), Palm and Calvin (1961), and Ponnamperuma *et al.* (1963) using radioactive tracer methods.

B. Mechanism

Now, the question that we must ask is: How is adenine formed? In order to answer this question we have to try to find possible inter-

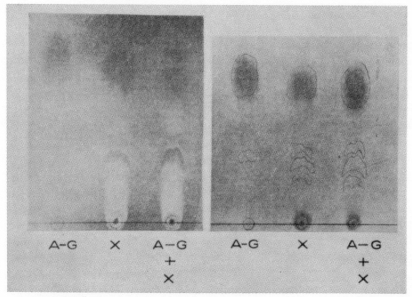

FIG. 7. Identification of adenine in the reaction product of a mixture of hydrogen cyanide, ammonia and water. Chromatogram photographed with ultraviolet light (2537 Å) and treated by the method of Gerlach and Döring (after Oró, 1960). A: adenine standard; G: guanine standard; ✕: reaction product from HCN, NH₃, and H₂O.

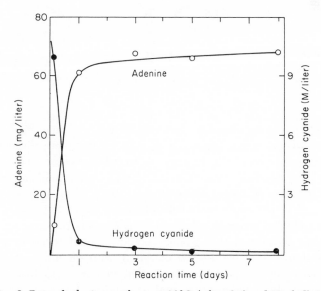

FIG. 8. Rate of adenine synthesis at 90°C (after Oró and Kimball, 1961).

mediates in the reaction mixture where adenine was being synthesized. This was done, and 4,5-disubstituted imidazoles—including 4-amino-imidazole-5-carboxamidine (AICAI) and 4-aminoimidazole-5-carbox-amide (AICA)—and monocarbon reactants—including formamidine, formamide, and formic acid—were identified (Oró and Kimball, 1962). In another investigation it was also found that AICAI condensed with formamidine to form adenine (Oró, 1961b). On the basis of this and other information available on the condensation of hydrogen cyanide

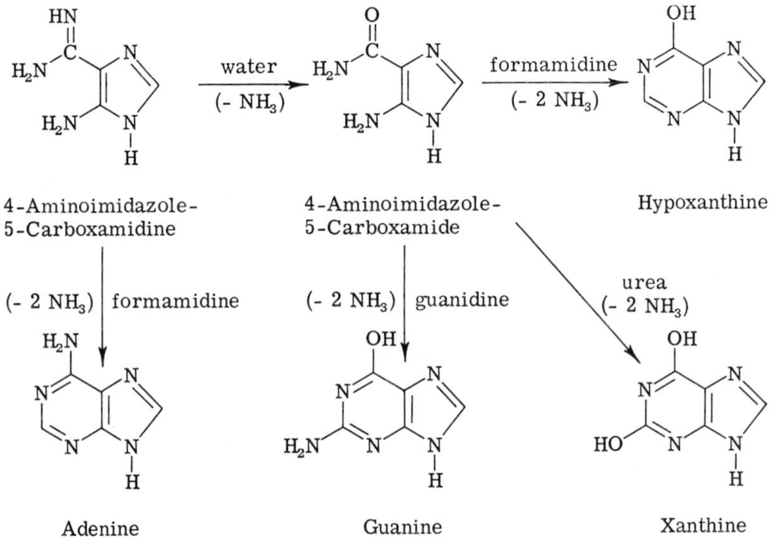

FIG. 9. Mechanism of formation of adenine from hydrogen cyanide (after Oró, 1961b).

(Völker, 1957), the mechanism shown in Fig. 9 was suggested for the synthesis of adenine from hydrogen cyanide. A complete discussion of this and alternative mechanisms may be found elsewhere (Oró, 1961b, 1963d; Oró and Kimball, 1962; Kimball, 1962). A mechanism involving exclusively nitriles (Calvin, 1961; Ruske, 1962; Kliss and Matthews, 1962) is possible, although less likely (Ruske, 1962).

The next question we may ask is: How is guanine formed? As shown in Fig. 10, we postulated that guanine could be synthesized in aqueous ammonia systems by condensation of AICA with guanidine (Oró and Kimball, 1962), and in fact we found that guanine was formed from AICA not only by condensation with guanidine but also with urea

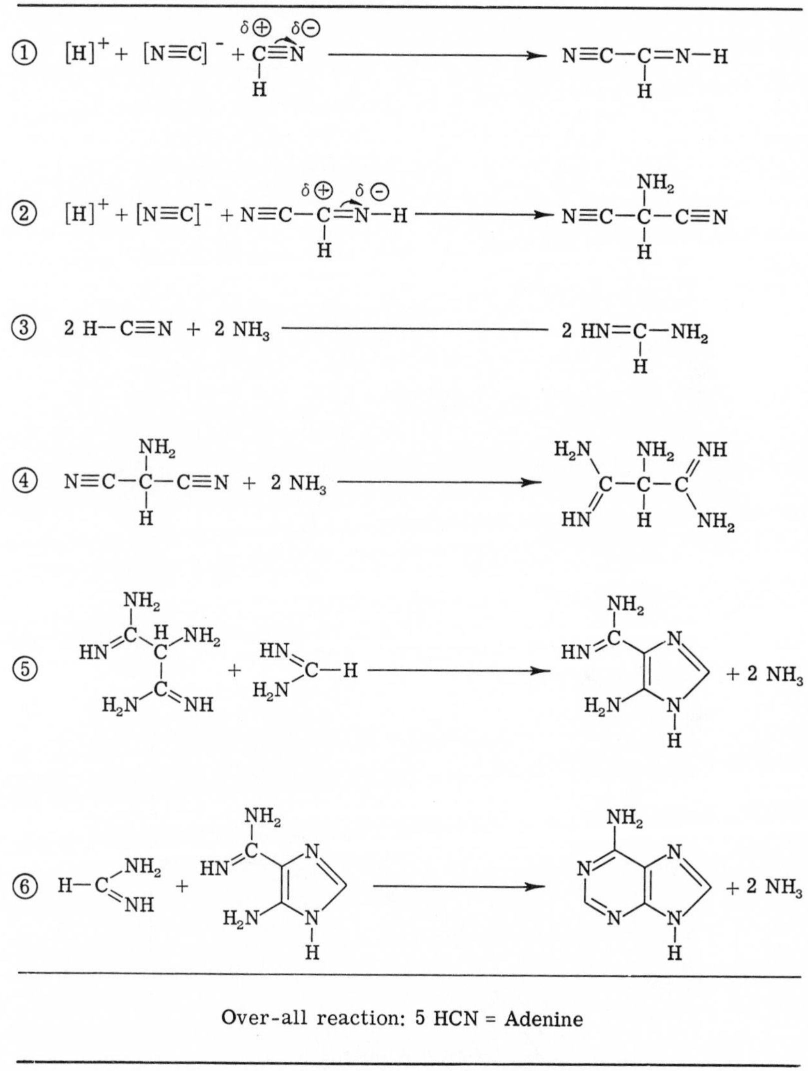

Fig. 10. Proposed mechanism for the synthesis of purines on the primitive Earth (after Oró and Kimball, 1962).

(Oró, 1963c) as shown in Figs. 11 and 12. These condensations take place at about 125°C. When urea is used, not only guanine but also xanthine is formed. It may be pointed out here that hypoxanthine has also been detected among the products formed from hydrogen cyanide, ammonia, and water (Lowe et al., 1963).

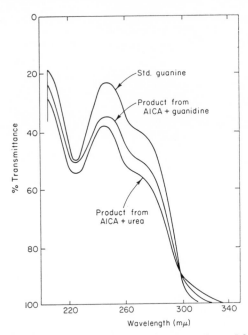

Fig. 11. Spectrophotometric identification of guanine formed by condensing AICA with either guanidine or urea.

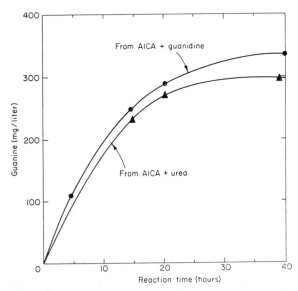

Fig. 12. Rate of guanine synthesis from AICA and guanidine and from AICA and urea.

VII. Synthesis of Pyrimidines

A. Experimental

Having shown that the four purines can be synthesized from simple precursors, we can now turn our attention toward the formation of pyrimidines. One may recall that β-alanine and β-aminopropionitrile have been synthesized in a number of experiments (Oró, 1963d) and that acrylonitrile (AN), β-aminopropionitrile (APN), and β-aminopropionamide (APA) are the logical intermediates in the formation of this

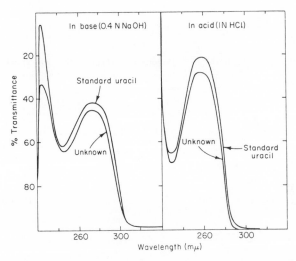

FIG. 13. Spectrophotometric identification of uracil formed by heating a solution of acrylonitrile (AN), urea, and ammonium chloride.

compound. It appears that these intermediates can also act as precursors of pyrimidines, for we have found that urea in aqueous systems condenses at 135°C with each of these intermediates (AN, APN, and APA) to form small amounts of uracil (Oró, 1963c) as shown in Figs. 13 and 14. The process must involve a dehydrogenation either prior to or after condensation of the tricarbon compound with urea.

B. Mechanism

This synthesis is in line with a suggestion made earlier (Oró, 1961a) that the diatomic and triatomic carbon species detected in comets could

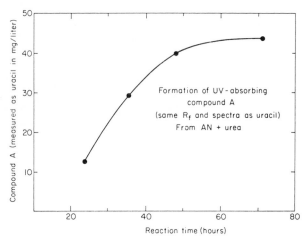

FIG. 14. Rate of synthesis of compound A (same R_f and spectra as uracil) formed by heating a solution of acrylonitrile, urea, and ammonium chloride.

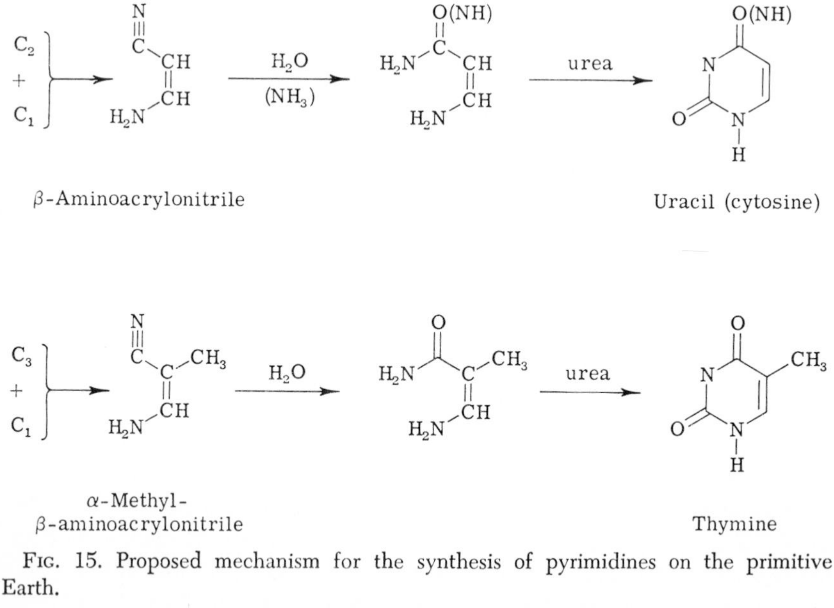

β-Aminoacrylonitrile   Uracil (cytosine)

α-Methyl-
β-aminoacrylonitrile   Thymine

FIG. 15. Proposed mechanism for the synthesis of pyrimidines on the primitive Earth.

be precursors of pyrimidines. This suggestion is further elaborated in Fig. 15, where possible mechanisms for the formation of uracil, cytosine, and thymine are outlined. In order to substantiate this mechanism, experiments will have to be carried out with these highly reactive C-2 and C-3 homonuclear compounds.

VIII. Formation of Monosaccharides and Mechanism of Ribose and Deoxyribose Synthesis

So far, we have seen—with the detail allowed by the time available—how amino acids, purines, and pyrimidines might have been formed abiotically. In order to complete the picture we should now ask the question: How could monosaccharides, particularly ribose and deoxyribose, have been formed? Well, since the early work of Butlerow

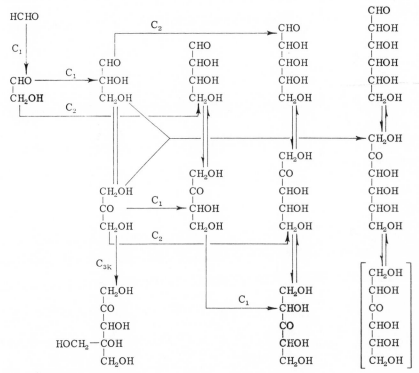

FIG. 16. Formation of monosaccharides from formaldehyde by base catalysis (after Pfeil and Ruckert, 1961).

(1861) and Loew (1886), we know that formaldehyde in aqueous solution condenses into sugars by the action of basic catalysts. A more recent study by Mariani and Torraca (1953) shows that at least some 30 monosaccharides are formed from formaldehyde by base catalysis. Essentially all the common hexoses, pentoses (including ribose), tetroses, and trioses (including glyceraldehyde) have been identified by paper chromatography (Mariani and Torraca, 1953; Mayer and Jäschke, 1960; Pfeil and Ruckert, 1961). As shown in Fig. 16, which is a diagram taken from Pfeil and Ruckert (1961), the synthesis starts with the formation of glycolaldehyde. This is supposed to be a rate-limiting reaction, which is responsible for the induction period observed in the condensation of formaldehyde into sugars. The mechanism of glycolaldehyde synthesis remains obscure (Breslow, 1959), but once sufficient amounts of glycolaldehyde have been formed, an autocatalytic process ensues which

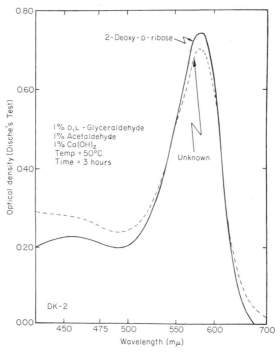

Fig. 17. Spectrum of the Dische's derivative obtained from the reaction product of glyceraldehyde and acetaldehyde.

uses up in a short time all the available formaldehyde and transforms it into glyceraldehyde, tetroses, pentoses, and hexoses. The operative mechanism in this case is that of a base-catalyzed aldol condensation.

The synthesis of ribose from formaldehyde was confirmed in our laboratory and the following question was then asked: How is 2-deoxyribose synthesized? It appeared obvious that the aldol condensation of glyceraldehyde with acetaldehyde should lead to the formation of 2-deoxyribose and its isomer 2-deoxyxylose, and in fact this was found to be the case (Oró and Cox, 1962). These 2-deoxypentoses have also been obtained from formaldehyde and acetaldehyde, and in this case it is reasonable to assume that formaldehyde was first converted into glyceraldehyde which then condensed with acetaldehyde. Figure 17 shows the identification of 2-deoxyribose in the reaction product of glyceraldehyde and acetaldehyde by spectrophotometry of its derivative with diphenylamine (Dische's test). The total yield observed in some cases was as high as 15%.

The reaction of 2-deoxyribose synthesis was found to be catalyzed by a number of oxides and hydroxides some of which are listed in Table VII. Divalent metallic oxides were found to be excessively efficient catalysts. With calcium oxide as catalyst the reaction could only be followed if

TABLE VII

BASES WHICH CATALYZE THE SYNTHESIS OF 2-DEOXYRIBOSE

High activity	Moderate activity	
MgO	NH_4OH	LiOH
$Ca(OH)_2$	$N(Me)_4OH$	NaOH
$Ba(OH)_2$	$N(Et)_4OH$	KOH

Reaction conditions:
0.1% Glyceraldehyde + 0.1% acetaldehyde
0.1 M base; temp., 50°C; time, 1 hour

it was carried out at 0°C. At higher temperatures the reaction reached completion in a few minutes and then 2-deoxyribose was transformed into other products. On the other hand, ammonium hydroxide and the other nitrogen bases were found to be slower and more suitable catalysts. The reaction went nicely at room temperature and one could follow it for a long time (Fig. 18) without observing any breakdown or transformation into other products. It is of interest in this respect to recall that ammonium hydroxide is the most abundant base in the universe, and that the basicity of some carbonaceous chondrites is in part due to this compound (DuFresne and Anders, 1962). Therefore, it is possible that this simple base has played an important role in the abiotic synthesis not only of amino acids and purines but also of monosaccharides, particularly of 2-deoxypentoses.

IX. Summary and Conclusions

1. Observations on the composition of carbon star atmospheres, interstellar matter, the Jovian planets, comets, and meteorites indicate that

the synthesis of organic compounds in the universe is a more general process than has been thought heretofore.

2. Prior to and during the formation of the solar system, but before the Earth was completely formed, organic syntheses probably occurred in the following four stages (or sites): carbon star atmospheres, solar nebula, planetesimals, and protoplanets.

3. The energy for these syntheses was provided initially by the high temperature of star atmospheres and then mainly by the ionizing radia-

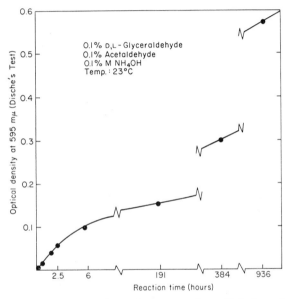

Fig. 18. Rate of synthesis of 2-deoxyribose from glyceraldehyde and acetaldehyde using ammonium hydroxide as catalyst.

tion and ultraviolet light coming from the Sun. Catalytic processes and other localized sources of energy were probably also involved in the formation of organic compounds.

4. Astronomic and meteoritic observations indicate that the conditions prevailing in the majority of cosmic bodies during the latter stages of evolution of the solar system were as follows: reducing or oxygen-free atmosphere, aqueous environment, basic or neutral pH, moderate temperature, and presence of a relatively high concentration of organic compounds.

5. A number of general mechanisms can be postulated to have been involved in the abiotic formation of simple biochemical compounds:

(a) a radical mechanism in the synthesis of the aliphatic and aromatic aldehydes which are the precursors of α-amino acids, (b) a base-catalyzed aldol condensation of simple aldehydes in the formation of pentoses, 2-deoxypentoses, and other monosaccharides, and (c) a base-catalyzed condensation of hydrogen cyanide and other nitriles, followed by other condensations reactions, in the synthesis of purines, pyrimidines, and other heterocyclic compounds.

ACKNOWLEDGMENTS

This study was supported in part by research grant NsG-257-62 from the National Aeronautics and Space Administration.

Revised manuscript received January 15, 1964.

REFERENCES

Abelson, P. (1959). Private communication.
Aller, L. H. (1961). "The Abundance of the Elements." Wiley (Interscience), New York.
Berger, R. (1961). *Proc. Natl. Acad. Sci. U.S.* **47**, 1434.
Breslow, R. (1959). *Tetrahedron Letters No. 21*, 22.
Butlerow, A. (1861). *Compt. Rend.* **53**, 145.
Calvin, M. (1961). "Chemical Evolution." Univ. of Oregon Press, Eugene, Oregon.
Cameron, A. G. W. (1962). *Icarus* **1**, 13.
Cox, A. C. (1962). M.S. Thesis, University of Houston, Houston, Texas.
DuFresne, E. R., and Anders, E. (1962). *Geochim. Cosmochim. Acta* **26**, 1085.
Fowler, W. A. (1962). *Science* **135**, 1037.
Franck, B. (1960). *Chem. Ber.* **93**, 446.
Friedel, R. A., and Sharkey, A. G., Jr. (1963). *Science* **139**, 1203.
Hochstim, A. (1963). *Proc. Natl. Acad. Sci. U.S.* **50**, 200.
Horowitz, N. H., and Miller, S. L. (1962). *Fortschr. Chem. Org: Naturstoffe* **20**, 423.
Hoyle, F. (1960). *Quart. J. Roy. Astron. Soc.* **1**, 28.
Hoyle, F., and Wickramasinghe, N. C. (1962). *Monthly Notices Roy. Astron. Soc.* **124**, 417.
Kimball, A. P. (1962). Ph.D. Thesis, University of Houston, Houston, Texas.
Kliss, R. M., and Matthews, C. N. (1962). *Proc. Natl. Acad. Sci. U.S.* **48**, 1300.
Lederberg, J., and Cowie, D. B. (1958). *Science* **127**, 1473.
Loew, O. (1886). *J. Prakt. Chem.* **33**, 321.
Lowe, C. U., Rees, M. W., and Markham, R. (1963). *Nature* **199**, 222.
Mariani, E. and Torraca, G. (1953). *Intern. Sugar J.* **55**, 309.
Mason, B. (1962). "Meteorites." Wiley, New York.
Master, F. (1957). M.S. Thesis, University of Houston, Houston, Texas.
Mayer, R., and Jäschke, L. (1960). *Annalen* **635**, 145.
Miller, S. L. (1955). *J. Am. Chem. Soc.* **77**, 2351.
Miller, S. L. (1957). *Biochim. Biophys. Acta* **23**, 480.
Oró, J. (1960). *Biochem. Biophys. Res. Communs.* **2**, 407.

Oró, J. (1961a). *Nature* **190**, 389.
Oró, J. (1961b). *Nature* **191**, 1193.
Oró, J. (1963a). *Nature* **197**, 862.
Oró, J. (1963b). *Nature* **197**, 971.
Oró, J. (1963c). *Federation Proc.* **22**, No. 2, 681.
Oró, J. (1963d). *Ann. N.Y. Acad. Sci.* **108**, 464.
Oró, J. (1963e). *Proc. Lun. Plan. Expl. Colloq.* **3**, No. 2, 9.
Oró, J. (1964a). In "Problems of Evolutionary and Industrial Biochemistry," p. 63. Volume in honor of A. I. Oparin, Academy of Sciences, U.S.S.R.
Oró, J. (1964b). In "Current Aspects of Exobiology." Pergamon Press, New York, In press.
Oró, J., and Cox, A. C. (1962). *Federation Proc.* **25**, No. 2, 80.
Oró, J., and Kamat, S. S. (1961). *Nature* **190**, 442.
Oró, J., and Kimball, A. P. (1961). *Arch. Biochem. Biophys.* **94**, 217.
Oró, J., and Kimball, A. P. (1962). *Arch. Biochem. Biophys.* **96**, 293.
Oró, J., Kimball, A. P., Fritz, R., and Master, F. (1959). *Arch. Biochem. Biophys.* **85**, 115.
Palm, C., and Calvin, M. (1961). *Univ. Calif. Lawrence Radiation Laboratory, Bioorganic Chemistry Quarterly Report* **9900**, 51.
Palm, C., and Calvin, M. (1962). *J. Am. Chem. Soc.* **84**, 2115.
Pfeil, E., and Ruckert, H. (1961). *Annalen* **641**, 121.
Ponnamperuma, C., Lemmon, R., Mariner, R., and Calvin, M. (1963). *Proc. Natl. Acad. Sci. U.S.* **49**, 737.
Richter, N. B. (1963). "The Nature of Comets." Methuen, London.
Ruske, W. (1962). Private communication.
Skell, P. S., and Wescott, L. D. (1963). *J. Am. Chem. Soc.* **85**, 1023.
Struve, O. and Zebergs, V. (1962). "Astronomy of the 20th Century." Macmillan, New York.
Swallow, A. J. (1960). "Radiation Chemistry of Organic Compounds," p. 244. Pergamon Press, New York.
Swings, P., and Haser, L. (1956). "Atlas of Representative Cometary Spectra." University of Liege Astrophysical Institute, Louvain.
Urey, H. C. (1952). "The Planets. Their Origin and Development." Yale Univ. Press, New Haven, Connecticut.
Urey, H. C. (1953). *Proc. Roy. Soc.* (London) **219A**, 281.
Urey, H. C. (1957). *Progr. Phys. Chem. Earth* **2**, 46.
Völker, T. (1957). *Angew. Chem.* **69**, 728.
Whipple, F. L. (1950). *Astrophys. J.* **111**, 375.
Whipple, F. L. (1963). In "The Moon, Meteorites, and Comets," "The Solar System," Vol. IV (B. M. Middlehurst and G. P. Kuiper, eds.), p. 639. Univ. of Chicago Press, Chicago, Illinois.

DISCUSSION

Dr. Bernal[1]: Dr. Oró's systematic work on the synthesis of the small molecules out of which the key biochemical macromolecules were formed, has marked a notable advance. Previous work had shown that it was sufficient, starting with almost any gaseous sources of hydrogen,

[1] *In absentia*

carbon, nitrogen, and oxygen to form bases and amino acids. What Dr. Oró has done is to show the actual chemical steps by which this synthesis takes place, beginning with the very small molecules detected spectroscopically in carbon stars and cometary tails. His greatest contribution here seems to have been somewhat on the side, the discovery that it was possible from hydrogen cyanide to synthesize the bases, particularly adenine. Especially important, it seems to me, was the discussion as to whether the hydrocarbon compounds, from which life was formed, were secondary distillates, primitive hydrocarbons which originally were located on meteorites or planetismals and were then, so to speak, squeezed out in the geothermal process of the interior of the Earth. It would appear, however, that irrespective of the particular earth-forming method, there would be available for the formation small molecular compounds and a great variety of conditions of temperature and hydration. As Dr. Fox pointed out, primitive soup would not lack ingredients or cooking utensils.

DR. VALLENTYNE: In this last business, do you get formation of brown polymer with the ammonia?

DR. ORÓ: Oh, yes. As a matter of fact, most of the product is polymeric.

DR. VALLENTYNE: I am talking about the formaldehyde and ammonia at the moment.

DR. ORÓ: Under the conditions used in these experiments we have not observed the formation of any brown polymers from formaldehyde and ammonia. However, it is not inconceivable that they would be formed, since under slightly different conditions polymeric products have been obtained from formaldehyde. For instance, by irradiation of an aqueous solution of formaldehyde with ultraviolet light [Baly, E. C. C. *Ind. Eng. Chem.* **16,** 1016 (1924)], a polymeric substance was obtained which J. C. Irvine and G. V. Francis [*Ind. Eng. Chem.* **16,** 1019 (1924)] suggested to be a polyhydroxy phenol. The formation of polymers from formaldehyde solutions irradiated with ultraviolet light has also been observed in my laboratory by Mr. R. Fritz.

DR. VALLENTYNE: What I was thinking of was the "browning" or melanoidin reaction.

DR. ORÓ: The products obtained from formaldehyde by successive aldol condensations are mainly monosaccharides of five and six carbon atoms (pentoses and hexoses). The reaction does not appear to continue indefinitely to give polyhydroxy compounds with many carbon atoms, probably because of the stability of the five- and six-membered cyclic structures of pentoses and hexoses. Another reaction pertinent to this discussion is the "browning" reaction which involves the condensation of the carbonyl group of a monosaccharide with the amino group of an amino acid, and leads to the formation of brown polymers. If this reaction went to completion, it would be impossible to detect the net synthesis of monosaccharides in an environment containing an excess of amino acids, and vice versa [Abelson, P., personal communication (1959)]. It appears, however, that monosaccharides and amino acids can be synthesized concomitantly from a simple mixture of methane, water, and ammonia by the action of ionizing radiation [Palm, C., and Calvin, M., *J. Am. Chem. Soc.* 84, 2115 (1962)]. Perhaps the ammonium hydroxide present in the mixture shifts the equilibrium of the browning reaction in such a manner that the condensation of the carbonyl groups of monosaccharides with the amino group of amino acids is minimized. I understand that Dr. Ponnamperuma will also speak on the formation of sugars in the presence of ammonia.

DR. AKABORI: I would like to ask Dr. Oró if he has found pyrimidines in that reaction.

DR. ORÓ: Yes, uracil has been found as a product of the condensation of urea with either β-aminopropionamide or β-aminopropionitrile, and also with acrylonitrile plus ammonium chloride.

DR. PONNAMPERUMA: I want to make a statement about the point Dr. Oró made at the beginning about the possibility of the chemical synthesis having taken place even before the planet Earth was formed. This was stated by Professor Bernal in his paper yesterday. Dr. Oró states it now. I would, however, like to point out that Dr. Young and I have written a brochure for high school students in biology where this simple idea was expressed by us. We are not staking a claim for the idea, but I would like Dr. Oró to know that we did not steal the idea from him.

DR. SAGAN: Perhaps there is no need to quarrel about the priority of this idea, since (1) it has already been proposed at least as early as 1955 (Hoyle, F., "Frontiers of Astronomy", p. 102, Harper, New York), and (2) it is very likely wrong. There is some reason to believe that the Earth went through a high-temperature phase during the early stages of its formation. There are two sources for the thermal energy. One is the gravitational potential energy of accretion. The second is the presence of radioactive isotopes—particularly the short-lived variety no longer present on the Earth—which were concentrated to the surface, and contributed to local surface melting. If the Earth did go through a high-temperature stage, any organic matter produced in an earlier epoch would be fried, denatured, or otherwise have its utility in the origin of life diminished.

I am also a little apprehensive about making too strong an analogy between cometary and planetary atmospheres. Cometary spectra certainly show the presence of radicals which, if put together, would make many of the same kinds of molecules we expect in planetary atmospheres. But the cometary atmospheres are comparatively cold and diffuse, while planetary atmospheres are comparatively hot and dense. Especially for such questions as the stability of free radicals and of long-lived excited states, the two situations are very different. Free radicals and excited states which will never be found in planetary atmospheres will survive in the comets.

The cometary spectra certainly do support the view that organic molecules and their precursors are extremely prevalent in the universe.

DR. ORÓ: I would say that instead of providing answers you are adding more questions, and that is fine. With regard to the first question I would like to say that the idea that the Earth was formed in a molten state has been abandoned. A cold origin for the Earth appears more probable [Urey, H. C., Geochim. Cosmochim. Acta 26, 1 (1962)] and, although it is very difficult to give an exact figure for the surface temperature of the primitive Earth, the concentration of certain volatile elements, namely mercury and arsenic, on the Earth's surface [Urey, H. C., Proc. Roy. Soc. London 219A, 281 (1953)] indicates that the average temperature was not higher than 150°C, which is the temperature used in my presentation (<425°K). Similar conclusions can be arrived at from thermodynamic data on the formation of solid carbon and organic compounds in primitive planetary atmospheres [Suess, H. E., J. Geophys. Res. 67, 2029 (1963)]. Furthermore, the prevalence of low temperatures in primitive planetary surfaces is indicated by data obtained from carbonaceous chondrites, meteorites, which are presumed to have been derived from a primitive planetary body. The water, hydrates, and organic compounds present in these meteorites show that the prevailing temperature during all their existence after their formation was below 100°C and probably close to room temperature, as concluded by DuFresne and Anders.

With regard to the second question, I am quite aware of the differences between planetary and cometary atmospheres. It is the cometary nucleus which I consider similar to a protoearth which had not yet undergone gravitational differentiation. It is on the basis of this analogy that I say that the protoearth had large amounts of organic matter.

DR. SAGAN: I entirely agree that the primitive Earth had a large amount of organic matter on it. The question is whether these molecules survive thermal decomposition and whether any postulated synthetic pathways occur well after the maximum surface temperatures are achieved. I was referring to a high-temperature origin of the Earth in the context of molecular dissociation, not surface melting. There are still many geologists and astronomers who maintain that the Earth has passed through a molten phase. But even if no molten phase occurred, the expected temperatures cause molecular decomposition. Harold Urey, one of the principal advocates of "low" temperature origins of the Earth, writes ". . . the body of the Moon accumulated at low temperatures, i.e. 300–400°K, but . . . * * * . . . the surface regions of the solid lunar objects were heated to high temperatures by the adiabatic compression of gases towards the end of the accumulation process." (H. C. Urey, In "The Moon," I. A. U. Symposium 14, Academic Press, New York, 1960). Because of the much greater gravitational potential energy per unit mass during the aggregation of the Earth, we expect terrestrial surface temperatures to exceed lunar surface temperatures during accumulation. Temperatures of, say, 600°K will not melt ordinary rocks, but will provide a source of embarrassment for organic molecules. Incidentally, I might mention that the bulk of the evidence (e.g., E. Anders, G. Goles, and R. Fish, (1960) *Astrophys. J.* **132**, 243), does not support the contention that the meteorites originated in objects of planetary mass.

DR. ORÓ: Although the evidence pointed out is in favor of a low temperature for the surface of the primitive Earth, I agree that we do not know with certainty the exact prevailing temperature. If for the sake of discussion we assume that the surface of the Earth was very hot, then most of the organic matter would have been transformed into hydrocarbon radicals and pyrolysis products (hydrogen cyanide, nitriles, olefins, aldehydes) which by their very nature are very reactive. Assuming that they were not completely lost into space, they would have eventually recombined into biochemical compounds. Therefore all the reactions that I have described would occur again, and essentially the same mechanisms would apply. Perhaps the only advantage that such a fifth stage in the synthesis of biochemical compounds may have had, if it occurred, is that of allowing a more uniform and complete mixing of all the organic compounds on the Earth's surface.

DR. SAGAN: Yes. Actually, the thermal degradation and dissociation of the primary organic matter formed very early in the history of the Earth does bear on the origin of life. The decomposition products were not all lost to space at the time that the primary terrestrial atmosphere was lost. It takes time for the products to diffuse out from the interior of the Earth. At a later time, when the Earth had settled down to approximately its present mass, radius, and exosphere temperature, the outgassing of these degradation products from the interior must have been a major source of the Earth's secondary atmosphere. Since the outgassed material must have been reducing, the early secondary atmosphere must have been reducing. It is *this* atmosphere which we are simulating, in laboratory reactions relevant to the origin of life.

Dr. Fox: The worry about an exact temperature seems to me to be a phantom worry, because at the present time we have a range of temperatures in the crust of the Earth from below 0°C, up to above 1000°C, and there is every reason to believe, according to the geological reasoning I have consulted, that this is the way it has been for a long time. And really, all that is needed is a range of plausible temperatures, comparable to the temperatures which are employed in the experiments performed in the laboratory.

Dr. Oró: Right. It was clear in my presentation (Table II) that the general temperature was 425°K and that localized temperatures higher than 1000°K were possible.

Dr. Mora: It would not have taken me 6 months to believe that I could form adenine from hydrogen cyanide. I think you have just the right ratio of carbon, hydrogen, and nitrogen, and if you activate it just right, then the atoms would rearrange into new interatomic linkages, and the probability to add five hydrogen cyanide molecules together is not so unexpected. I would have believed it much faster.

If you cook ammonium cyanide, then you again have a nice ratio of these atoms. I wouldn't be surprised if you get all kinds of purines and pyrimidines. The same thing is true if you cook formaldehyde. You have the right ratio of carbon and oxygen (about equal) and twice as much hydrogen, and you multiply this, and you get the ratio of atomic components in the sugars.

So I don't think this is so exciting.

Dr. Sagan: Compared with your optimism, our optimism seems pessimistic.

Dr. Oró: I am gladly surprised to see the increased optimism of Dr. Mora.

Dr. Buchanan: Is it possible that the reactions for purine synthesis in prebiological systems copied those now known for the enzymatic synthesis, e.g., the successive reaction of the simple precursors, formate, CO_2, glycine, aspartate, glutamine, and ribose 5-phosphate with the elimination of water at each step? All of these precursors may be formed under prebiological conditions and would have been available for synthetic purposes. Would Dr. Oró comment on the relative plausibility of such a reaction sequence as compared with the one that he has studied in which purines are formed from condensation products of hydrogen cyanide?

DR. PONNAMPERUMA: I don't want to anticipate what I shall say later, but this kind of reaction can be carried out.

DR. FOX: Can I answer Dr. Buchanan's question for pyrimidines? Uracil has been synthesized thermally from urea and malic acid, itself of course derivable from aspartic acid [*Science* 133, 3468 (1961)]. In such cases [and there are other such parallelisms, e.g., ureidosuccinic acid from aspartic acid reported in *Science* 124, 923 (1956)], we might have finally to conclude that the biochemical reaction copied the abiochemical rather than the reverse.

DR. PONNAMPERUMA: I would like to point out to Dr. Mora that when Wöhler in 1828 synthesized urea from ammonium cyanate, everybody was surprised. We are not any more, for after all he started organic chemistry.

DR. ORÓ: It took Berzelius about 2 years to accept Wöhler's discovery.

DR. SCHRAMM: As an organic chemist, I am very pleased that Dr. Oró tried to isolate the intermediates and I hope the same will continue. It is much more believable if you see the intermediate steps.

Another question is: Is there any evidence that in the sugars certain chain lengths are preferred in this mixture you spoke about?

DR. ORÓ: There seems to be a preference for the formation of the bonds corresponding to ordinary pentoses and hexoses. The essence of the explanation is that as soon as the condensation has proceeded to the pentose and hexose level, cyclization and formation of five- and six-membered rings occurs. This gives stability to the molecule and in addition causes the virtual disappearance of the carbonyl group from the monosaccharide so that it does not condense any further. Therefore, contrary to what one would predict on a pure probabilistic basis without any knowledge of the operating reaction mechanism, the synthesis of monosaccharides from formaldehyde appears to virtually stop at the level of pentoses and hexoses. The obvious corollary is that, in talking about the abiotic synthesis of organic compounds, the formulation of a probability is meaningless without an adequate knowledge of the reaction mechanisms involved.

DR. LIPMANN: I found it very interesting to learn from these experiments that from the small fragments that—with ATP as the condensing agent in known enzyme systems—yield biochemical building blocks, similar molecules may be formed when other energies are offered. That one finds, when one looks rather sharply, that such compounds are formed doesn't tell us that this is a process really related to the origin of life. It means only that what the living organism does effectively in an organized way, can ineffectively be done in an unorganized way outside the living organism. Comparatively speaking, I can see a parallel between this situation and the one that developed when Wöhler synthesized urea from ammonium cyanate.

DR. ORÓ: I agree one hundred per cent, yet I feel that a logical and sound approach to a difficult problem requires a stepwise attack from the very bottom. If we had the experimental answer to how the first living organism was formed, we would not be meeting here today talking about prebiological systems.

DR. GAFFRON: Summarizing, what Dr. Oparin and Dr. Haldane really put the finger on was that if we have proved that these special organic substances were formed spontaneously, we can go ahead with our speculations. If anyone would have shown that these organic compounds could never have been formed in the early stages, then we would face a blank wall. The encouragement consists in having recognized that we can approach logically the impossible problem and try to find out more.

DR. CHARGAFF: I was very much impressed by Dr. Oró's talk in many ways. I was wondering about many of these reactions—what, for instance, in the adenine synthesis is the percentage distribution of so-called gunk? I don't know what the hierarchical ladder is. There seems to be a subtle difference between gunk and goo.

Are there many other compounds—polymers, in the sugar synthesis—formed in which the predominant products should be an obstacle to those compounds getting together that Dr. Oró is specifically looking for? Then if we take life on its present basis, can we find a trace of deoxyribose in a mixture of compounds that would produce the deoxyribose in minor form?

DR. ORÓ: If someone would make the claim to have succeeded in obtaining abiotically a metabolizing self-replicating organic system from a simple mixture of the elements H, C, O, N, S, and P, I am sure no one of us would accept the claim unless the investigator in question would give experimental evidence, with some detail in each step, of the sequence of events leading from element to living organism. The first step he would have to demonstrate would be the transformation of that simple mixture of elements into the essential biochemical compounds out of which the self-replicating system was formed. What I attempted to do in my presentation concerns this first step.

Putting it in more general terms, I feel that the fact that we know practically nothing about the origin of life is precisely the main reason that forces us to follow a slow, stepwise, and systematic approach in the solution of this problem.

With regard to the former question I would like to say that we know something about the nature of the polymers and other compounds formed, which we were not specifically looking for. One of the polymers formed in very large amounts, from hydrogen cyanide–water–ammonia mixtures is polymeric hydrogen cyanide, a polymer which has been studied in detail by Völker and others. This polymeric compound does not appear to interfere with the formation of adenine and amino acids. Following the suggestion of Dr. Blois, perhaps it may even act as a surface catalyst for other important synthetic reactions.

Some of the other polymers formed contain amino acids. These polymers, rather than being opposed to the formation of amino acids, take the amino acids a step further in the synthetic ladder. They are converted into peptides. Polymers containing glycine, alanine, aspartic acid, and other amino acids have been isolated from these mixtures by Lowe et al. In particular a polymer of glycine has also been found in the reaction product. Since we have done previous studies on the formation of polyglycines from glycine and glycinamide in aqueous ammonia systems, we think that we know something about the mechanism of formation of these polymers.

There are other compounds formed which also have biological significance. A number of pteridines have been identified among the reaction products of hydrogen cyanide in aqueous systems. The formation of pteridines may be considered as a step toward the formation of the first coenzymes. I may add that, interestingly enough, if the condensation of hydrogen cyanide is carried out under what could be considered unnatural conditions, that is, by means of acid, then triazines and other compounds which are completely foreign if not opposed to life are formed.

DR. BLOIS: From my remarks yesterday, it would be reasonable that I should defend the viewpoint of the "gunks" and "goos." Dr. Pirie commented after my paper that he finally understood what the freshman chemistry student was throwing down the drain.

In one respect, if a beginning chemistry student has difficulty in avoiding formation of random polymers, their production must be a very probable event, and it seems to me that in an origin-of-life context they cannot be simply dismissed.

My point is this: The libraries are full of organic chemistry books which have been carefully compiled to describe improbable mechanisms for producing high-yield results, and perhaps we should look on organic chemistry as the chemistry of improbable events. If we are talking about the spontaneous formation of organic compounds under heterogeneous conditions and using chaotic mechanisms, I suggest we should begin to look at the chemistry of highly probable events.

In this sense, I think the "gunks" and the "goos" should not be skirted around but faced, and we should try to understand how such mechanisms as Dr. Oró has explained, could possibly arise in the presence of these materials.

Dr. Schramm: To understand the formation of biologically interesting substances, we have to consider first the reaction of the starting material. In the polymerization of different sugars with metaphosphate ribose behaves quite differently from glucose. If we can apply more organic chemistry to these mixtures we can make some more reliable predictions.

I think it is difficult to exclude reactions. But probably we can say that under certain conditions, some will be preferred.

Dr. Mora: I would like to speak mainly to Dr. Oró, but in the vein that Dr. Schramm just started. I repeat again what I said at the very beginning. Chemical kinetics and polymerizations follow the rule of probability. What I discussed was the current practice of invoking probability in speculations on the origin of life. Then I went on talking about certain much more complex questions than polymerization.

Since Dr. Schramm mentioned the polymerization of sugars, when the macromolecular syntheses will be discussed, I will attempt to present what I hope to be a sophisticated use of probability to predict the condensation of sugars fairly well. This was my major work in the fifties.

Dr. Schramm: So long as we have to do with random polymerization, we are in the order of reasonable probabilities. But the improbability of living organisms is of a much higher level. As long as we have an improbability of 1×10^{23}, we are near Avogadro's number. That means that we have one mole of substance. If we come to living organisms, we come to much higher orders of improbability and we need higher amounts of material.

I don't know whether you are discussing the formation of polymers or the formation of highly organized organisms.

AMINO ACIDS, PEPTIDES, AND SPHERULES OBTAINED FROM "PRIMITIVE EARTH" GASES IN A SPARKING SYSTEM

KARL A. GROSSENBACHER AND C. A. KNIGHT

Department of Soils and Plant Nutrition, and Virus Laboratory,
University of California, Berkeley, California

Only a little more than a hundred years ago, Darwin and Wallace opened a new era in biology with their proposal that living things had developed by an evolutionary process. This idea, although strongly opposed in religious circles, was widely accepted among scientists.

A logical extension of the idea of biological evolution is the concept of abiogenesis, that is, the evolution of life from nonliving matter. Darwin was apparently aware of this potential extension of his theory as judged from the contents of a somewhat obscure passage written in 1871,[1] but the extended theory of evolution was not accepted even among scientists for many years. The disrepute of abiogenesis was due in large part to the brilliant work of Pasteur who proved conclusively that the living things with which he dealt were not originated *de novo* but rather that such living things came only from other living things.

Today, owing to the stimulating work of Oparin and others, the theory that life did evolve from inanimate matter is accepted by many. In spite of the insight shown by Darwin as early as 1871, it was Oparin (1938) who must be given credit for pointing out to modern biologists: (1) that inanimate biochemical compounds could be formed, accumulate, and evolve into very complex states before life existed but that this could not happen in today's world, and (2) that the primitive atmos-

---

[1] Although written in 1871, this passage occurs as a footnote in a section dealing with letters written by Darwin in 1863–1864, in the book by F. Darwin, "The Life and Letters of Charles Darwin," Volume 2, p. 202, 1898, Appleton, New York. Other printings of the book appeared in 1888, 1896, and 1959. The passage in question appears to be first discussed in current literature by G. Hardin, *Scientific Monthly* **70**, 178–179 (1950).

173

phere was a reducing one, as postulated by Arrhenius (1923). Urey brought new evidence to support this theory, and his student, Miller, about 10 years ago (1953) reported the production of amino acids and other organic materials in a glass apparatus containing a spark source and a mixture of methane, ammonia, hydrogen, and water. Hydrogen cyanide and aldehydes were shown to be precursors of amino acids in this system (Miller, 1959).

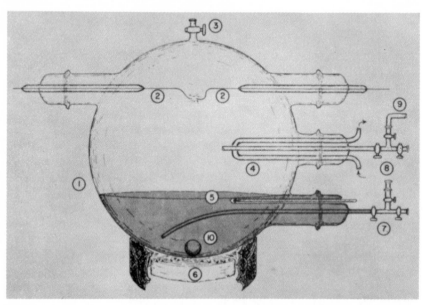

Fig. 1. Sketch of sparking apparatus constructed from a 12-liter flask (1). Various parts include electrodes (2), evacuation port (3), condenser tube (4), thermometer well (5), electric heater (6), gas inlet and liquid sampling port (7), gas sampling port (8), connection to manometer (9), and stirring marble (10).

We have repeated the Miller-Urey experiments with modified apparatus operating at lower temperatures and have obtained some of the same amino acids reported by Miller and some additional ones. We have also demonstrated cases of autocatalytic reaction as evidenced by the rate of accumulation of organic nitrogen and cyanide ion.

The apparatus employed (Fig. 1) consisted of a spherical 12-liter Pyrex flask, equipped with two adjustable platinum electrodes, connected to a Tesla coil and ground, a 10 mm evacuation tube, a cooling coil, thermometer well, heating coil, lower sampling port, upper sampling port, and a connection to a mercury manometer (0–90 cm Hg). The two sampling ports were each equipped with three stopcocks so that contamination of the flask could be avoided by evacuating the midspace. The whole apparatus was mounted in a frame which permitted the flask to be rocked by a motor-driven arrangement, and the addition of glass marbles to the liquid provided a mechanism for stirring during the rocking. In a typical run, the thoroughly cleaned flask was evacuated and tested for leaks. When a reasonably leak-proof state had been demonstrated, the flask was charged through the upper port with just less than one atmosphere of NH_3 gas followed by 1 liter of evacuated double-distilled water. As the water entered, it dissolved the NH_3 and lowered the pressure to a few centimeters Hg. Approximately one half atmosphere each of methane and of hydrogen was added, bringing the internal pressure up to 80–90 cm Hg. Often a period of 12–48 hours was taken to adjust the temperature and check for leaks before starting the spark.

Samples taken at 24 hours after starting the spark usually had little color, but by 48 hours the liquid acquired a straw color which gradually deepened to amber during the runs, which were often continued for 10–30 days. It is presumed that this colored material consists largely of polymeric cyanides, since cyanide is known to be a product of the sparking reaction and is further known to polymerize readily to form amber products.

I. Demonstration of the Presence of Amino Acids

Paper Chromatography

Samples were tested for the presence of compounds reactive with ninhydrin in the following manner. At desired time intervals, an approximately 25 ml sample was withdrawn from the sparking apparatus into an evacuated sample bottle. A 10 ml aliquot (or 20 ml in the case of samples withdrawn in the first 100 hours) of this was evaporated to dryness in a flash evaporator *in vacuo* and the residue was dissolved in 1 ml of distilled water. A 0.1 ml portion was applied to Whatman 3 MM filter paper for chromatography in butanol:acetic acid:water (60:15:25). A spot of a standard amino acid mixture was placed alongside as a marker. After about 24 hours the chromatogram was removed, dried, and sprayed with a ninhydrin mixture consisting of 250 mg ninhydrin, 160 ml ethanol, 75 ml acetic acid, and 10 ml of 2,4,6-collidine.

As a general rule, no ninhydrin-reactive spots were observed in chromatography of the liquid removed before sparking was begun. Between 24 and 48 hours after the spark was applied, one or two definite ninhydrin-reactive spots were observed in the glycine–serine–aspartic acid area of the chromatogram and two or three other faint spots.

By 100 hours the number of definite ninhydrin-reactive spots had increased to about four and by 200 hours, eight to twelve; the colors observed include purple, turquoise, gray, peach, yellow, and various shades of brown. The location of the spots covered most of the areas in which standard amino acids are found, after chromatography in butanol–acetic acid–water, with some spots occurring in areas in which the 20 common amino acids are not usually found, such as beyond proline and tyrosine or beyond leucine. Thus, some ninhydrin-reactive compounds are found that apparently are not among the 20 common amino acids, and they have not been identified.

Amino Acid Analyses Made in a Spinco Analyzer

Several samples were analyzed for amino acid content in a Spinco amino acid analyzer, usually at the termination of a sparking run. After it was found that the product could be decolorized with acid-washed Norite A without apparent change in the intensity of the major ninhydrin-reactive spots revealed by paper chromatography, the material was routinely decolorized before concentration and application to the ion exchange column of the Spinco Analyzer.

A variety of amino acids was found, and the proportions of these differed from run to run, although in most cases alanine, glycine, and serine were major components. In one of the several analyses, the following amino acids were found in roughly the indicated molar proportions: 2 aspartic acid, 4 threonine, 14 serine, 1 glutamic acid, 16 glycine, 14 alanine, 2 isoleucine, 2 leucine, and 4 lysine.

II. Evidence for Peptide-Like Material

Subsequent to spraying chromatograms with ninhydrin, some of them were also subjected to the chlorination, starch-iodine reaction for peptide bonds. Some of the spots which had reacted with ninhydrin also gave color with the starch-iodine test. Two of these ran beyond the most rapidly migrating standard amino acid (leucine). Preliminary attempts were made to separate amino acids and more complex substances on an ion exchange column (Dowex 1×2, 1×150 cm column). Around 16 fractions could be obtained by this method, but when samples of the peak tubes (the fractions giving maximum ninhydrin or Folin-Lowry color tests) were tested by paper chromatography, evidence was obtained that these fractions were all mixtures. In general, there was not enough material in the fractions to permit successful refractionation. Therefore, attention was turned to other approaches.

Next, attempts were made to separate dinitrophenyl (DNP) derivatives rather than the unsubstituted compounds. Toward this end, 400–500 ml of liquid from the sparking apparatus were decolorized by treatment with Norite A (using 25 mg of charcoal per milliliter of liquid) and, after filtering to remove the charcoal, the resulting filtrate was concentrated to dryness *in vacuo* in a flash evaporator. The residue was taken up in 60% ethanol adjusted to pH 8.5 with NaOH and treated with fluorodinitrobenzene (FDNB). The pH was again adjusted to 8.5 and the reaction mixture was allowed to stand for 2 or 3 hours in the dark with occasional adjustment of the pH. After the reaction, the products were separated by extraction into ether, ethyl acetate, and aqueous fractions. In one run, the ether extract was found, by paper chromatographic comparison with standard DNP-amino acids to contain DNP-aspartic acid, DNP-serine, DNP-glycine, DNP-threonine, and DNP-alanine. These represent free amino acids present in the original mixture, and the nature of the results generally confirms the analyses made directly in a Spinco Amino Acid Analyzer. The ethyl acetate fraction, which might contain small peptides, contained several yellow products, separable on paper, but which were not identified with known compounds, owing to a lack of sufficient material. The aqueous fraction, which would be expected to contain larger DNP-peptides and material which did not react with FDNB, was found on chromatography with amyl alcohol-ammonia to yield one narrow yellow band and a wide band of material which reacted with ninhydrin and starch-iodine. The yellow band was eluted and chromatographed on paper again but in butanol–acetic acid–water. Two yellow bands were obtained and the stronger of these was eluted, and the material hydrolyzed in 6 N HCl for 24 hours. The DNP-amino acid (i.e., the end group) failed to extract with ether from the hydrolyzate and thus appeared to be a basic amino acid such as arginine. It was separated from the free amino acids by passage through a column of Amberlite IRC-50 and its chromatographic behavior was then compared with standard DNP-amino acids. This comparison showed that it was not arginine, and it appears to be an uncommon amino acid. It could not be identified at this point. The free amino acids from the hydrolyzate were subjected to analysis on a Spinco Analyzer and found to consist of glycine and isoleucine in the proportions of 2 to 1. Therefore, it appears that a peptide containing three different amino acids was isolated. This peptide has an uncommon N-terminal amino acid and as yet unknown numbers of glycine and isoleucine residues.

In another experiment, an amino acid-containing polymer was obtained by similar methods which on analysis was found to contain glycine and alanine in the proportions of 5 to 1, and a trace of isoleucine.

III. Rate of Formation of Organic Nitrogen Compounds and of Cyanide Ion

It was assumed that inorganic nitrogen would be present largely in the form of ammonium salts in view of the strongly ammoniacal character of the liquid in the sparking apparatus. Therefore, it seemed that the difference between ammonia nitrogen detected in evaporated samples before and after digestion with sulfuric acid would be a measure of organically bound nitrogen. Nitrogen analyses were made by nesslerization and colorimetry. Samples from the sparking apparatus appeared to contain very little inorganic nitrogen after flash evaporation to dryness *in vacuo*, whereas they yielded considerable nitrogen, increasing in content with time of sparking, after digestion by the micro-Kjeldahl method. The striking feature about the increase in organic nitrogen was that in several runs, but not all, the organic nitrogen appeared to increase exponentially, as shown in Fig. 2.

In the figure, we have shown on the same curve, and plotted against time, the milligrams per milliliter of organic nitrogen and micrograms of cyanide per milliliter.

In two different runs, organic nitrogen was observed to follow an exponential curve quite closely. The cyanide in the first of those runs also increased exponentially with time. However, in one run cyanide increased linearly with time and in still another case it was observed to decrease. In the latter instance it would appear that the balance of cyanide formation and cyanide utilization or destruction was shifted by the formation of other materials.

IV. The Development of Solid Phase Products

Typically, during the course of a run, water and a film of yellow-brown material appeared on inner surfaces of the apparatus. Also, solid material built up around the electrodes. A technique was developed to clear these deposits enough to keep the spark functioning. Often, significant amounts of these materials fell into the liquid phase.

In one case, the solid film on the inner surfaces of the flask was allowed to remain at the start of the next run. The presence of this film did not have a marked effect on the reaction rate. In other words, this surface appears not to be catalytic. The long time build-up of the film did provide a sample for analysis and it was found to contain 70.7% carbon, 7.5% hydrogen, and 3% nitrogen. These results are inconsistent with the notion of polycyanide, and obviously more analyses must be made in order to determine the precise chemical nature of the film material.

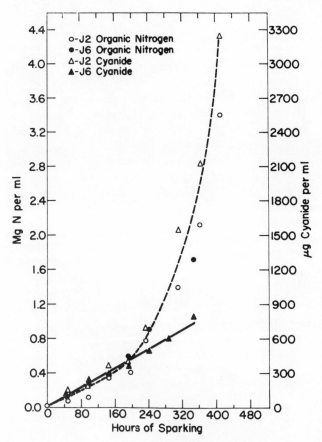

Fig. 2. Relation of cyanide and organic nitrogen content of the aqueous phase to time of sparking. Two selected runs, J2 and J6, are represented.

Turning from the films to the body of the liquid, it was observed in several runs that the liquid phase became cloudy. It was assumed that this was due to amorphous insoluble material, but it seemed advisable to exclude the possibility of bacteria. No clear-cut decision could be made from microscopic examination, but some stained material looked

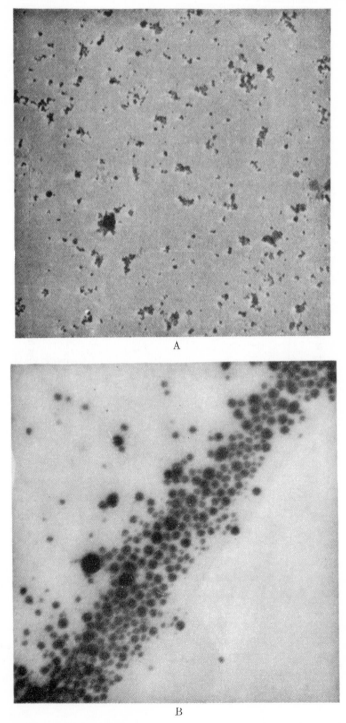

A

B

FIG. 3. A: Electron micrograph of spherules in sample taken 48 hours after sparking was begun. Shadowed with uranium. B: Electron micrograph of a sample taken at 504 hours showing spherules gathered at the edge of a droplet. Unshadowed.

180

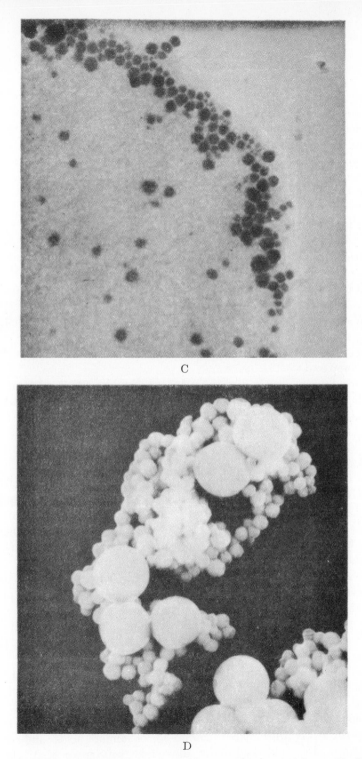

C

D

FIG. 3. C: Same as B except that sample was taken at 624 hours. D: Electron micrograph of washed spherules coated with palladium. The largest objects shown are polystyrene latex particles which were added as a size standard and which are about 0.26 μ in diameter.

vaguely suggestive of bacteria. However, subsequent culture trials all gave negative results, and, in fact, the material killed lactic acid bacteria. Examination with the electron microscope failed to reveal any bacteria, but did show the existence of small solid bodies which ranged in size from about 800 Å down to 50 Å or less. It has been found that these particles appear as early as 48 hours after beginning the sparking. Some of the results obtained with the electron microscope are illustrated in Fig. 3.

In Fig. 3A can be seen many small spherules along with amorphous materials which may or may not have been solids before the sample was dried. In all samples observed directly, amorphous masses appeared, but in some cases the spherules were the predominant form.

In Fig. 3B is shown the edge of a droplet of a sample taken at 504 hours. Note the wide range in size of particles and the absence of amorphous material. About 120 hours later in the same run, the material looked much the same, as shown in Fig. 3C. Evidence of increase in size has been obtained only when materials obtained at 48 and 500 hours were compared.

In one case a sample was subjected to a mild centrifugal treatment. The deposit, which consisted primarily of the large particles, was resuspended, washed once, and examined in the electron microscope. Fig. 3D shows a preparation of this material. The magnification here is the same as in Figs. 3A–C. The large spheres are polystyrene, deliberately introduced as magnification standards, and are 0.26 μ in diameter.

The nature of the spherules and the possible role they may play in our experiments is yet unexplored. They are in the same size range as virus but are much more electron dense. Analysis indicates that they contain large amounts of mineral. The average of two determinations shows C, 10.3%; H, 1.9%; N, 1.0%; and from density gradient centrifugation, the density of the material appears to be more than 1.8.

It seems doubtful that our spherules are in any way related to the coacervates that Oparin and others have suggested may have played such an important role in abiogenesis. Their organic content, however, leaves open the possibility that the spherules might have played some role in the formation of the organic material associated with them, although nonspecific adsorption is not precluded.

Inasmuch as the carbon content of the spherules was observed to be low, and the density high, it is possible that the spherules are silicates derived from the borosilicate glass of the sparking apparatus upon continuous exposure to ammonia. The organic matter associated with the spherules is presumably composed of amino acids and similar compounds, for acid hydrolysis did yield substances that chromatographed like amino acids and gave positive ninhydrin reactions. These speculations provide a basis for further investigations.

V. Gas Analyses

In addition to the analyses of dissolved and insoluble products found in the sparking apparatus, some preliminary analyses of gas samples have also been made. (These analyses were made in a mass spectrograph through the courtesy of Mr. Fred Walls.) It was found that after 26 days ammonia and hydrogen were still in abundant supply, but that methane had been reduced to the point where it constituted only 0.1% of the gaseous mixture.

In summary, the data from our experiments with a modified Miller-Urey system indicate that: (1) under some conditions the formation of compounds appeared to be autocatalytic; (2) ten different amino acids were produced; (3) peptides were formed as indicated by two lines of evidence; and (4) spherules ranging from 50–800 Å in diameter were produced and that these consist in small part of organic material.

REFERENCES

Oparin, A. I. (1938). "The Origin of Life" (a translation with annotations by S. Morgulis). Macmillan, New York.
Arrhenius, S. (1923). "Life Course of a Planet." Gozidat, Russia.
Miller, S. L. (1953). *Science* **117**, 528.
Miller, S. L. (1959). *In* "The Origin of Life on Earth" (A. I. Oparin, A. G. Pasynskii, A. E. Braunshtein, T. E. Pavlovskaya, F. Clark, and R. L. M. Synge, eds.). Pergamon Press, New York.

Revised manuscript received January 13, 1964.

DISCUSSION

DR. SZUTKA: I would like to ask what was the source of electrical current?

DR. GROSSENBACHER: It was a Tesla coil, the same model number that Miller used. We had to have two or three extra ones, and put them, in as replacements as they ceased functioning.

DR. SZUTKA: Your voltage was approximately 25,000 to 30,000 volts. I therefore suspect that the temperature of the gas phase was much higher than 25–45°C. I would rather suspect that the gaseous layer was of the order of 60–80°C or higher.

I would suggest measuring the temperature of the gas phase between the two electrodes where the synthesis takes place.

DR. GROSSENBACHER: In one model of our apparatus we had two thermometer wells, one in the gas near the upper part of the equipment and another in the liquid near the bottom. The thermometers in these two locations gave very close to the same readings.

When we heated the vessel so that the upper thermometer read about 40°C, we would get water condensed on the surface of the glass, which was at room temperature. So the bulk of the gas in this volume did not get appreciably above the 40°C and was probably much of the time below, because of the cooling action of the surface of the vessel.

The temperature in the arc or immediately above it would be higher. So there would be quite a temperature variation in that region.

DR. SZUTKA: Did you look for other products, for example, pyrroles, and porphins?

DR. GROSSENBACHER: There is a lot of stuff produced in our reaction mixtures. We have not attempted to make exhaustive analyses of our products. Our attention has been centered on amino acids, peptides, and nucleic acid derivatives.

We also looked for asymmetry. In fact, that is what brought me into the picture, with some ideas I had about asymmetric synthesis. So far our search for optical asymmetry has given only negative results.

DR. QUIMBY: Was your experiment similar to Miller's except for the sparking temperature?

DR. GROSSENBACHER: There were also differences in percentages of gases present and the pressure is a little higher.

DR. QUIMBY: In other words, there were several differences?

DR. GROSSENBACHER: Yes.

We initially started at low pressures but later we shifted to a pressure of a little more than an atmosphere to prevent contamination in case leaks occurred.

One other point we might mention: Typically, when the experiment was started, the pressure increased for a few hours or the first few days, and then leveled off or decreased. If the initial internal pressure is below atmospheric, any subsequent increase in pressure in this kind of apparatus is suspect because one can't tell conveniently whether the increased pressure is due to a leak or to the formation of more gas molecules.

DR. QUIMBY: I would like to ask the speaker if he knows what the temperatures were in the Miller experiment.

DR. GROSSENBACHER: 70–80°C and possibly even higher. He had boiling water and a condenser in a closed system at less than atmospheric pressure.

DR. SZUTKA: 70–80°C in the gap, because he was heating the water and circulated the water vapor.

DR. QUIMBY: What I have been really trying to get at is what the temperature was in the spark itself.

DR. GROSSENBACHER: A blue spark might have a very high temperature. I don't know what it would be, over 1000°C, maybe. However, I don't really know what the concept "temperature" means in such a situation.

DR. PONNAMPERUMA: The voltage is pretty high. I think the amount of carbon is small, in the order of a few milligrams. We are doing an experiment of the same type. In the gap itself the temperature itself may be high, in the immediate vicinity it is about the same as in the whole apparatus. I would like to ask Dr. Grossenbacher a question. You mentioned 0.1% of your methane left at the end of 26 days. Is there a possibility that the methane may have been used up much earlier?

DR. GROSSENBACHER: Yes, and we intend to check on this now that we have started making gas analyses.

DR. PONNAMPERUMA: In our experimental work, we find that at the end of half an hour, 1% of the methane is converted into organic material and at the end of 18 hours, 15%, but we haven't carried on any experiments beyond that. I was just wondering whether you had any comments.

DR. GROSSENBACHER: We have little to offer on that point except the one methane determination at 26 days and the indirect and partial measure of methane consumption based on our cyanide production curves.

DR. BLOIS: In some earlier experiments along very similar lines, we also had this black deposit at the electrode that had to be cleared to prevent a short circuit. This material was insoluble. The small amounts that were available seemed to us to be either inorganic carbon, perhaps graphite, or polymeric material. We examined this with electron spin resonance, and an absorption spectrum was obtained. The absorption line was that typical for the high polymers that are formed by free radical polymerization, and our assumption was that this material was probably polymeric.

DR. LIPMANN: I wonder if you would expand on the autocatalytic nature of the reaction that you briefly mentioned. I may not have followed you, but did you think of the possibility that an intermediate is formed which is then more rapidly converted into the amino acids?

DR. GROSSENBACHER: Yes, this would be quite possible. All we can say is that the rate of formation of cyanide or organic nitrogen increased exponentially with time in the case to which you refer. The fundamental characteristic of an autocatalytic process is that its rate should increase with time. In our closed system energy was continuously supplied, raw materials were depleted, and end products accumulated, and yet the rate of reaction increased with time. It was somewhat shocking to find an autocatalytic process in such a primitive system.

DR. VALLENTYNE: Could I ask what sort of pH you get in this system?

DR. GROSSENBACHER: It was high. It's dominated by ammonium hydroxide.

DR. VALLENTYNE: After the ammonia gets used up?

DR. GROSSENBACHER: We haven't run that far. We've run it with too much ammonia for the ammonia to be used up. The ammonia is high. The ammonia is still there at the end of the run. It's a dominant characteristic of the system. The pH is in the neighborhood of 9–11.

THE THERMAL SYNTHESIS OF AMINO ACIDS FROM A HYPOTHETICALLY PRIMITIVE TERRESTRIAL ATMOSPHERE

KAORU HARADA AND SIDNEY W. FOX

Institute for Space Biosciences, The Florida State University,
Tallahassee, Florida

The primitive atmosphere of the Earth has been regarded as a reducing atmosphere comprising such gases as methane, ammonia, hydrogen, and water vapor (Oparin, 1938; Urey, 1952). With the escape of hydrogen molecules from the Earth, the reducing atmosphere has been changed to a more oxidizing atmosphere (Bernal, 1951). At the same time, the primitive atmosphere has been altered chemically by many kinds of energy such as solar radiation (ultraviolet), electric discharge, α-, β-, and γ-rays, heat, etc.

Some natural and some unnatural amino acids have been synthesized in the laboratory from simple compounds by the use of each of many kinds of energy. Miller (1953, 1955) produced glycine, alanine, aspartic acid, glutamic acid, and several unnatural amino acids as well as many organic acids and urea by electrical discharge. Groth and von Weysenhoff (1957) and Deschreider (1958) synthesized amino acids by UV irradiation. Hasselstrom *et al.* have synthesized amino acids by the use of α- (Hasselstrom and Henry, 1956) and β- rays (Hasselstrom *et al.*, 1957). Vermeil and Lefort (1957) and Dose and Rajewsky (1957) have reported formation of amino acids by the irradiation with γ-rays and X-rays, respectively.

Elevated temperatures have not been reported as having been employed for the synthesis of simple organic compounds of biological significance from a postulated primitive atmosphere. The explanation for this state of affairs is probably that thermal energy has been considered to be inadequate for primordial synthesis (Miller and Urey, 1959).

Under appropriate conditions thermal energy has, however, been successfully employed for the polycondensation of free amino acids. The

187

resulting products can contain the 18 amino acids common to protein (Fox and Harada, 1960). The protein-like material (proteinoid) resembles natural proteins in many properties.

Also, thermal energy has been shown to produce hydrogen cyanide in high yield from methane and ammonia (Kotake et al., 1956) by the use of alumina or silica.

$$CH_4 + NH_3 \xrightarrow{Al_2O_3SiO_2} HCN + 3H_2 - 60 \ Cal$$

the methane and ammonia being regarded as components of the primitive atmosphere of the earth (Oparin, 1938; Urey, 1952). Hydrogen cyanide has been proposed as one of the key components in prebiological synthesis (Miller, 1957).

A primitive atmosphere composed of methane, ammonia, hydrogen, and water vapor might come into contact with a site of high temperature on the Earth, and hydrogen cyanide would thus be produced by the gas reaction (Harada, 1961). Thermal energy thus could plausibly contribute to the formation of HCN from the reducing atmosphere of the primitive Earth. The hydrogen cyanide produced could be used for the formation of many kinds of organic acids, purines, and pyrimidines (Oró and Kimball, 1961). One interesting fact of the above-mentioned reaction is that sulfur compounds enhance the yield of hydrogen cyanide (Kotake et al., 1956). The primitive reducing atmosphere is believed to have contained a small amount of hydrogen sulfide.

The thermal reaction of methane, ammonia, and water in the vapor phase may well produce organic compounds of biological significance other than hydrogen cyanide. The organic compounds produced by thermal synthesis in this study included, in particular, many natural amino acids. The mixed gas (CH_4, NH_3, H_2O) was passed through silica sand, silica gel, volcanic lava, and alumina, respectively, while these were heated to the temperatures indicated in Table I. These solid materials have been, as is well known, common in the crust of the Earth.

A typical experimental procedure is as follows. Methane gas is passed through concentrated aqueous ammonia and this mixed vapor is introduced into a hot Vycor glass reaction tube (900–$1100°C$) containing one of the above-mentioned solid materials. The reacted gas is absorbed in 3 N aqueous ammonia in the cold. The ammoniacal solution is then heated in a sealed bottle at $75°C$ for varying lengths of times. The ammonia and water are evaporated under reduced pressure and the residue is refluxed with 4 N hydrochloric acid for 5 hours. The hydrolysate is then evaporated to dryness *in vacuo*. The residue is dissolved in citrate buffer (pH 2.2) and the solution is then applied to a Phoenix K-5000 automatic amino acid analyzer. Acid hydrolysis was employed in the laboratory for prompt study. A slower hydrolysis in a primitive ammoniacal or acidic sea is, however, visualized for the reaction in nature.

Typical reaction apparatuses are shown in Figs. 1 and 2. Figure 1 shows the apparatus used for a single pass reaction. Figure 2 shows the closed apparatus in which the reaction gases are cycled during the reaction. These apparatuses were made of Pyrex glass and the reaction tubes were of Vycor glass (96% silica). The thermocouple inserted in

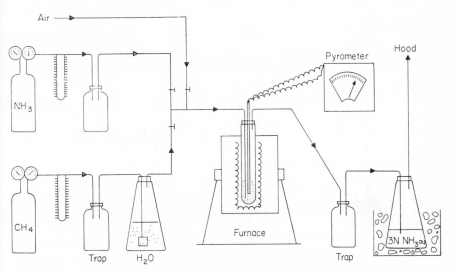

FIG. 1. Apparatus used for single pass reaction.

the various solid materials was Chromel-Alumel and the temperatures were measured by a calibrated potentiometer.

In the preliminary experiments, natural gas and oxygen were used with a burner. In later studies, a Hoskins-type combustion furnace heated by Chromel A wire was employed.

In each run, nearly all of the natural amino acids were produced, except for cystine and methionine. Sulfur-containing amino acids cannot be expected inasmuch as no compound of sulfur was present in the reaction. Basic amino acids are not listed in Table I, because the formation of these amino acids has not yet been fully studied. In some amino acid analyses, however, peaks corresponding to lysine (or ornithine) and arginine are present. Histidine, if present, is obscured by the large amount of ammonia. Tryptophan requires a special search, which has not been made.

The compositions of the amino acids prepared at 950°C by the use of silica beach sand or by silica gel were almost the same. At the higher temperature of 1050°C, the glycine content was lower and the other amino acid contents higher. The composition of amino acids prepared by the use of alumina (Kotake *et al.*, 1956) was quite different. Hydrogen

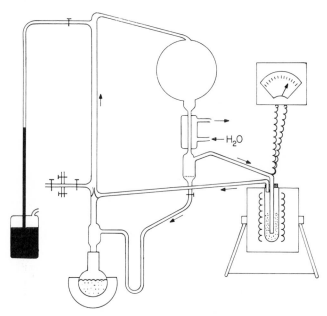

FIG. 2. Closed apparatus for cycling of reaction gases.

cyanide was produced in considerable amount in this reaction; the amino acids found were glycine, alanine, aspartic acid, and sarćosine (or serine). Other amino acids were absent or present in trace amounts. The hydrogen cyanide absorbed in cold 3 N ammoniacal solution was titrated with silver nitrate. The reaction on alumina produced about 100–300 times more hydrogen cyanide than that produced in the reaction on silica. This difference is consistent with the fact that the alumina was especially prepared for hydrogen cyanide synthesis (Kotake *et al.*, 1956). The reactions of the hydrogen cyanide produced by the use of alumina should yield essentially the same reactions as those studied by Oró and

Kimbal (1961) in the synthesis of adenine and amino acids in aqueous ammoniacal solutions of hydrogen cyanide. This suggests the possibility that the thermal synthesis from methane, ammonia, and water may yield nucleic acid bases in addition to many natural amino acids. Paper

TABLE I

COMPOSITIONS[a] OF AMINO ACIDS PRODUCED THERMALLY IN THE PRESENCE OF SILICA AND BY ELECTRIC DISCHARGE

Amino Acid	Thermal synthesis			Electric discharge synthesis	
	Quartz sand (950°C) (%)	Silica gel (950°C) (%)	Silica gel (1050°C) (%)	Spark discharge[b] (%)	Silent discharge[b] (%)
Aspartic acid	3.4	2.5	15.2	0.3	0.1
Threonine	0.9	0.6	3.0	—	—
Serine	2.0	1.9	10.0	—	—
Glutamic acid	4.8	3.1	10.2	0.5	0.3
Proline	2.3	1.5	2.3	—	—
Glycine	60.3	68.8	24.4	50.8	41.4
Alanine	18.0	16.9	20.2	27.4	4.7
Valine	2.3	1.2	2.1	—	—
Alloisoleucine	0.3	0.3	1.4	—	—
Isoleucine	1.1	0.7	2.5	—	—
Leucine	2.4	1.5	4.6	—	—
Tyrosine	0.8	0.4	2.0	—	—
Phenylalanine	0.8	0.6	2.2	—	—
α-NH$_2$ Butyric acid	0.6	—	—	4.0	0.6
β-Alanine	?[c]	?[c]	?[c]	12.1	2.3
Sarcosine	—	—	—	4.0	44.6
N-Methylalanine	—	—	—	0.8	6.5

[a] Basic amino acids are not listed in the table, because these amino acids have not been fully studied. Some analyses of the thermal products showed peaks corresponding to lysine (ornithine) and arginine.

[b] Recalculated from the results of Miller (1955).

[c] β-Alanine peak obscured next to another unknown peak.

chromatograms in fact show several dark spots under short wavelength ultraviolet light. Precise characterization of these materials is now under way. The peak corresponding with the R_F of urea was observed in each run. However, the material has not been finally identified.

To check the possibility that the amino acids were due to microbial or other contamination, blank experiments were conducted under the same reaction conditions, but without heating. Only trace amounts of amino acids were detected by automatic amino acid analysis. The trace amounts of amino acids found in the blank runs were negligible compared with the quantities of amino acids synthesized thermally. Additional evidence that the amino acids are not from an organism is provided by the absence of cystine and methionine. The quantitative balance sheet (Table I) is also inconsistent with a microbial amino acid content.

The mechanism of the thermal reaction is undoubtedly complex. The Strecker synthesis is a likely part of the mechanism. However, glycine, alanine, and aspartic acid can be synthesized without the corresponding aldehyde as an intermediate, as was shown by Oró and Kimball (1961) and Heyns and Pavel (1957) and in the thermal synthesis on alumina (Table I). Harada (1963) has also shown that the heating of ammonium formate or of formamide produces the above-mentioned amino acids. To check on the possible mechanism, various kinds of study, including reactions using carbon monoxide, carbon dioxide, ethane, and acetylene, are under way.

Comparison of the thermal reactions with those energized by electric discharge suggests an unique significance to thermal energy in the synthesis of natural amino acids. Silent discharge (Miller, 1955) produces mainly sarcosine, glycine, and some amino acids not found in protein. Spark discharge reaction results in the synthesis of glycine, alanine, aspartic acid, and glutamic acid and produces several nonprotein amino acids. The thermal reaction described here, however, produces predominantly natural amino acids in a wide variety. These results call attention to the contribution of thermal energy in the spark discharge experiments, inasmuch as the electric spark is composed of heat and an electron stream (and some UV light). It may be worthwhile to compare the contents of sarcosine, aspartic acid, and glutamic acid in the silent discharge, spark discharge, and thermal syntheses of amino acids. In the silent discharge syntheses, sarcosine content was 45%, in the spark discharge reaction, sarcosine content was reduced to one tenth (4%), and in the thermal reaction sarcosine was not found in the reaction mixture. The contents of aspartic acid were 0.1%, 0.3%, and 3–15% in the silent discharge, spark discharge, and thermal syntheses, respectively. The glutamic acid contents were 0.3%, 0.5%, and 3–10%, respectively, in the syntheses by silent discharge, spark discharge, and heat. According to these results, the contents of the unnatural amino acids are depressed and the contents of natural amino acids enhanced by the use of thermal energy. Thermal reaction and the electric discharge reaction are both radical reactions in the formation of precursors of amino acids. However, the differences in the results indicate different mechanisms of the radical reactions in the thermal and electric discharge synthesis. The position of β-alanine in the automatic amino acid analysis is obscured by two other unknown peaks. β-Alanine was expected in relatively high proportion in the comparison described above. α-Aminobutyric acid was found in small amounts in the product synthesized on silica sand at 950°C. In addition to the four natural amino acids found in the reaction products of electric discharge, threonine, serine, proline, valine, alloisoleucine (unnatural), isoleucine, leucine, tyrosine, and phenylalanine were found by the thermal synthesis. The synthesis of aromatic amino acids is especially noteworthy.

The thermal energy of the primordial Earth seems to have been abundant. According to Sagan's (1961) estimate, the stabilization of Earth's mantle occurred about 4.5×10^9 years ago and the evolution of life on the Earth began $4.2 \pm 0.2 \times 10^9$ years ago. If life arose relatively shortly $(0.3 \times 10^9$ years) after the mantle of the Earth was settled as mentioned above, it seems reasonable that the thermal energy was abundant on the primitive Earth before life arose. When the mantle of the Earth was formed, the gravitational energy was converted to thermal energy and the temperature of the crust should have increased to a relatively high value (1000°C). Even after the crust was formed, the material inside the crust might erupt locally and some part of the Earth's surface might remelt and reform the crust. Volcanic actions also should have supplied thermal energy (Bullard, 1962). In the primitive atmosphere vigorous reaction might have occurred on the hot surface of the crust (Harada, 1961).

In summary, simple gases are thermally convertible to most of the amino acids common to protein in a way that is sequentially compatible with other aspects of the thermal theory of biochemical origins (Fox, 1960; Harada, 1961). The composition of the amino acids obtained varies significantly with temperature and with the nature of the solid surface on which the vapor phase reaction occurs. Aromatic amino acids are found in the products.

ACKNOWLEDGMENT

Contribution No. 025 from the Institute for Space Biosciences. Aided by grant NsG-173-62 of the National Aeronautics and Space Administration.

Manuscript received October 28, 1963.

REFERENCES

Bernal, J. D. (1951). "The Physical Basis of Life." Routledge and Kegan Paul Ltd., London.

194   KAORU HARADA AND SIDNEY W. FOX

Bullard, F. M. (1962). "Volcanoes in History, in Theory, in Eruption." Univ. of Texas Press, Austin, Texas.
Deschreider, A. R. (1958). Nature 182, 528.
Dose, K., and Rajewsky, B. (1957). Biochim. Biophys. Acta 25, 225.
Fox, S. W. (1960). Science 132, 200.
Fox, S. W., and Harada, K. (1960). J. Am. Chem. Soc. 82, 3745.
Groth, H. von Weysenhoff (1957). Naturwissenschaften 44, 510.
Harada, K. (1961). Tampakushitsu Kakuran Koso. (Protein, Nucleic Acid Enzyme) 6, 65.
Harada, K. (1963). Unpublished experiment.
Hasselstrom, T., and Henry, M. C. (1956). Science 123, 1038.
Hasselstrom, T., Henry, M. C., and Murr, B. (1957). Science 125, 350.
Heyns, K., Pavel, K. (1957). Z. Naturforsch., 12, 97.
Kotake, M., Nakagawa, M., Ohara, T., Harada, K., and Ninomia, M. (1956). Kogyo Kagaku Zasshi (J. Chem. Soc. Japan Ind. Chem. Sect.) 59, 121 and 151.
Miller, S. L. (1953). Science 117, 528.
Miller, S. L. (1955). J. Am. Chem. Soc. 77, 2351.
Miller, S. L. (1957). Ann. N.Y. Acad. Sci. 69, 260.
Miller, S. L., and Urey, H. (1959). Science 130, 245.
Oparin, A. I. (1938). "The Origin of Life." MacMillan, New York.
Oró, J., and Kimball, A. P. (1961). Arch. Biochem. Biophys. 94, 217.
Sagan, C. (1961). Radiation Res. 15, 174.
Urey, H. (1952). "The Planets, Their Origin and Development." Yale Univ. Press, New Haven, Connecticut.
Vermeil, C., and Lefort, M. (1957). Compt. Rend. 244, 889.

DISCUSSION

DR. SAGAN: I quite agree that the temperature regime may be reasonable on a local scale on the primitive Earth, but how do you avoid thermal dissociation of the amino acid products in your experiment?

DR. HARADA: I presume that by dissociation you mean decomposition.

DR SAGAN: In the experiment, you remove the amino acids from the high temperatures used in their formation. In nature, they are not so easily removed. It is not clear to me how such reactions help much in the prebiological synthesis of amino acids. If the destruction rate is very high, the steady state concentration will be very low.

DR. HARADA: I think thermal energy might have been so located as to yield products which were washed away or otherwise removed immediately.

My understanding of the interpretation of Miller's experiments is that amino acids are also produced under local conditions of electric discharge which would also result in rapid decomposition of amino acids. Miller's experiments employ circulation of water vapor so that the products are washed away from the destructive influence. The same principles of removal apply in the thermal syntheses.

DR. FOX: Another part of the answer is that methane, ammonia, and water are subjected to a vapor phase thermal reaction, and the products of that are reacted with aqueous ammoniacal solution. The amino acids, themselves, accordingly, are not subjected to this temperature.

The reaction is of the vapor phase type employed in industry, in which vapors in rapid motion are subjected to very high temperatures.

DR. SAGAN: That is the point. The short period of time spent at high temperature is a special situation and greatly limits the generality of this hypothetical reaction sequence to the primitive environment. Perhaps it would work where the ocean and a fumarole are in contact. Unless your high-temperature source turns on and off fairly frequently, most of your activated substances will be deactivated by the time they arrive in the water.

DR. ORÓ: Perhaps I can make an attempt to answer Dr. Sagan's question from a general point of view. As I discussed in my presentation, there are two major stages, namely preterrestrial and terrestrial, where the synthesis of organic compounds may have occurred with the help of thermal energy. Preterrestrially, perhaps a major synthetic process occurred in the quenching zones surrounding carbon star atmospheres. If the ejection of carbon particles from pulsating N stars occurs as proposed by Hoyle and Wickramasinghe, it is very likely that a number of organic compounds will be ejected along with the carbon particles. Such compounds will result from recombination of the reactive radicals normally present in the star's atmosphere. Such a general synthetic process presumably occurred and occurs on a cosmic scale. A less generalized synthesis may have also occurred in the more internal areas of the solar system by the shock waves coming sporadically from an active protosun.

On the Earth, there are several possibilities, and there are, as I pointed out, localized phenomena. Some examples are cometary and meteorite impacts. Another one has been suggested by Dr. Fox—volcanic processes.

Because of the nature of the foregoing phenomena (general or localized), conditions of chemical thermodynamic equilibrium rarely apply. The system is heterogeneous and in a state of rapid flux. There are interphases (carbon grains, inorganic particles, etc.) and sudden drops in the temperature. As a result, quenching will occur, allowing the recombination of radicals and stabilization of the synthesized compounds.

DR. SAGAN: The problem we're discussing is a very general one. We use energy sources to make organic molecules. It is found that the same energy sources can destroy these organic molecules. The organic chemist has an understandable preference for removing the reaction products from the energy source before they are destroyed. But when we talk of the origin of life, I think we should not neglect the facts that degradation occurs as well as synthesis, and that the course of reaction may be different if the products are not preferentially removed. In reconstructing the origin of life, we have to imagine reasonable scenarios which somehow avoid this difficulty. It is not enough to say that in a small fraction of cases degradation is avoided—for example, by a flash flood carrying the reaction products out to sea. We should seek general processes which produce the organic molecules of interest and, at the same time, avoid degradation. If you have one, that's splendid.

DR. Fox: Geolocales permitting vapor phase reactions are as common as volcanic and other thermal regions. Rapid motion of vapors is normal at such temperatures. Rain, also, is a general geochemical phenomenon.

DR. ORÓ: Perhaps another illustration of such a process is the formation of chondrules present in carbonaceous chondrites. Whether chondrules have been formed by thermal metamorphosis, collision, volcanism in the parent planetary body, or whether they have been formed in the solar nebula by shock waves coming from the protosun, the fact is that they are bodies formed at relatively high temperatures which have been subsequently cooled fast. Clear-cut evidence of rapid cooling is given by the fernlike microcrystalline structures found within some glassy chondrules. So at one time or another during their cooling, these small spheroidal bodies must have come in contact with the surrounding organic material present in the matrix of the chondrites at temperatures at which the organic compounds (e.g., amino acids) or their products (e.g., polypeptides) become stable. Perhaps such a process could give an explanation for the reported presence of combined amino acids on the chondrules of carbonaceous chondrites [Kaplan, I. R., Degens, E. T., and Reuter, J. H. Geochim. Cosmochim. Acta 27, 805 (1963)].

DR. Fox: One can approach this question factually. You can walk on the cinder cones on the island of Hawaii, for instance, in ordinary shoes, but two inches below the surface in some areas it is 160–200°C, three years after the eruption.

You have pretty sharp thermal gradients in many places, and I think you don't have to theorize about this. You can actually demonstrate it to your own satisfaction.

DR. SAGAN: I find a thermal gradient of 100 Kelvin degrees per inch astounding.

DR. FOX: It astounds some geologists. In orienting myself on this question last July, I had the company of a ranger from the Hawaiian Volcanoes National Parks, Mr. Raymond J. Geerdes, who read the temperatures with me.

DR. SAGAN: In any case, only a very small fraction of the Earth's surface will have such temperature interfaces at a given time.

DR. FOX: Theoretically, only one interface on the Earth's surface is necessary. But more than that, Dr. Sagan's assertion is not correct. Let me quote from Bullard's book on volcanoes (Univ. of Texas Press, 1962). On p. 55 Bullard says:

> The average person may think that lavas are something rather rare on the earth's surface. (I don't consider you an average person.) To dispel this idea he needs only to consider, in addition to the lava flows from individual volcanoes, the great plateau basalts, such as those which make up the Columbia River Plateau, of the Pacific northwest of the United States. Here, covering most of Oregon and parts of Idaho and Washington with an area of 200,000 square miles, are basaltic lavas reaching a thickness of 3,000 feet and representing hundreds of flows superimposed one upon another. When one realizes also that this is but one of many such areas of the earth he obtains some appreciation of the tremendous quantity of lava on the earth's surface.

Therefore, what we are discussing is not a very special kind of condition.

MR. STEWART: All that is needed to provide the processes which Dr. Sagan desires are hot surfaces, for the formation of organic materials, and rain for the subsequent cooling of the surfaces and the removal of the formed materials. As Dr. Fox said, rain is a common geological phenomenon.

DR. SAGAN: That is a very good point. But the temperature of the surface must then be cool enough for liquid raindrops to avoid vaporization before striking the surface. Also, if the rain is to remove the synthesized materials from the hot area of synthesis to some cooler area, the region in which synthesis takes place cannot be very extensive.

MR. STEWART: I believe that the hot regions in which organic materials could be formed and subsequently removed by rain were extensive enough to account for a great deal of the organic materials formed prebiologically.

DR. VALLENTYNE: I think there is another thing that should be mentioned here, too. If you want an analogy on the Earth for this, the best thing is probably to take lava. You have a temperature of about 1100°C and the same thing happens that Dr. Harada is talking about. The reactions in both, I think, are gas reactions, aren't they?

DR. FOX: The first step, prior to hydrolysis, is a gas reaction.

DR. VALLENTYNE: They come up and start cycles and do exactly the same as this system. All you have to do is put that heating element somewhere on the Earth, with a cooler place somewhere else and you've got what he is talking about.

DR. SAGAN: But there must be a liquid phase in Harada's reaction scheme. Don't the intermediates go into liquid solution?

DR. VALLENTYNE: The Sea.

DR. FOX: The water will evaporate above 100°C.

DR. SAGAN: Exactly. What about the extraction that Dr. Harada analyzed? In what phase were they—gas, liquid, or solid?

DR. HARADA: I don't do extractions. The reacted gas was absorbed in ammonia and later evaporated and hydrolyzed with hydrochloric acid, then this hydrolyzate was analyzed.

DR. SAGAN: The only liquid is hydrochloric acid? There is no water in the system?

DR. HARADA: Of course, water. The hydrochloric acid is used after the reaction, for analytical purposes.

DR. SAGAN: Okay, what happens if you don't use water?

DR. FOX: You don't have a trap.

DR. HARADA: We get cyanide.

DR. SAGAN: So you need liquid water. It is not a totally gaseous system, as Vallentyne suggested.

DR. HARADA: Yes, it is not a totally gaseous system. The reacted gas proposed this way forms a solution of chemical precursors of amino acids in a second stage after the first, or vapor phase, reaction.

DR. SCHRAMM: On what basis is the percentage calculated? Is it on the total input of ammonia or the percentage of amino acids?

DR. HARADA: The results are calculated as percentage of total amino acids.

DR. SCHRAMM: It seems to be highly specific in the case where you have 70% glycine.

DR. HARADA: Yes. Glycine forms easily under many conditions.

DR. FOX: But when higher temperatures are used (Table I of text) the per cent of glycine drops.

DR. PONNAMPERUMA: At the time Dr. Harada was writing this paper, we were setting up this experiment ourselves. We passed methane and ammonia through a Vycor tube at 800°C. The reactants were absorbed in water. We have preliminary evidence for the formation of amino acids and even peptides. We haven't analyzed the resulting material completely.

DR. SAGAN: After you've heated the surface, you have to get the products back into the water.

DR. VALLENTYNE: If you object to Dr. Harada's experiment, you object to everything that has been done. You object to Miller's experiment, because his temperature in the spark is at least equal to this.

DR. SAGAN: The spark temperatures are high. But the analogy in the primitive environment to the spark is atmospheric electricity. We know there was water. There must have been clouds. There must have been electrical discharges. The lightning bolt strikes once, the high-temperature phase passes, the reaction products are not destroyed, and amino acids are formed in water solution.

But here, we are talking about another model of the primitive Earth, in which the gases are heated by a hot surface, and the reaction products rapidly removed. In the primitive Earth environment, does this correspond to a general, or to a local phenomenon?

DR. VALLENTYNE: Quite a general one. Volcanic action in Pre-Cambrian may have been considerably in excess of what it is now.

DR. GROSSENBACHER: I want to call attention to something we have been worrying about. In addition to the thermal conditions in the discharge, there is a very real possibility that because of the nature of the gases in the arc, we have liberated in the arc very short wavelength radiation down to about 900 Å and if these get absorbed immediately in the cold gas in the surrounding atmosphere, the energy transfer may not be thermal but radiation and absorption of very short wavelengths. It is my prejudice that this probably explains a lot of what happens.

There is one experimental manipulation that throws some slight light on this. We were setting up apparatus to check this. That is the simple expedient of having a hot platinum filament, instead of an arc, so we have no arc, but have the heat, and we hope to have some more data.

DR. ORÓ: I wish to congratulate Drs. Harada and Fox for this additional information about the production of amino acids which fits with the general pattern of amino acid syntheses carried out in our laboratory.

I would like to make two brief comments, one concerning interpretation of analytical results and the other about possible mechanisms of aromatic amino acid synthesis. The criterion of the absence of sulfur-containing amino acids cannot be used to rule out contamination completely. Although it makes biological contamination unlikely, it does not rule out contamination from other sources such as the ion-exchange resins used in the analytical procedure. As I pointed out before in the discussion, some of the materials present in these resins can be transformed into amino acids and these will not necessarily be sulfur-containing amino acids.

One of the possible mechanisms of aromatic amino acid synthesis is suggested by the formation of styrene and other aromatic compounds from acetylene. As proposed some time ago [Oró, *J. Proc. Lun. Plan. Explor. Colloq.* 3, No. 2, 9, (1963)], the reaction of styrene with hydroxyl radicals could yield phenylacetaldehyde, which by a Strecker's condensation and subsequent hydrolysis would be converted into phenylalanine. The formation of tyrosine would only require an additional parahydroxylation.

Dr. Akabori: It is surprising to me that, in all the experimental reports, glutamic acid is formed in relatively high proportions. Do you have any idea of the mechanism of the formation of glutamic acid?

Dr. Harada: I don't know the mechanism. However, not only is the glutamic acid content high, the proline content is also high.

Dr. Akabori: Glutamic acid can be made from acrylonitrile as follows:

$$NC—CH{=}CH_2 + CO + H_2 \rightarrow NC—CH_2—CH—CHO$$

acrylonitrile   Strecker

DL—Glutamic acid

D   L

Dr. Oró: Similar observations have also been made in our laboratory.

Dr. Fox: Dr. Akabori, is that resolution by inoculation?

Dr. Akabori: Yes.

Dr. Fox: That fact has interest in the context here of spontaneous resolution [Harada and Fox, *Nature* 194, 768 (1962)].

Dr. Akabori: Yes, spontaneous resolution.

Dr. Haldane: I should like to ask whether there is not reason to think that at some stage the atmospheric pressure may have been considerably greater than it is now and, if so, whether any experiments of this type have been done under several atmospheres of pressure. I just don't know whether it is thought that at one time we had a lot more hydrogen than we have now.

Dr. Sagan: I will try to answer the first half of your question. From the relative underabundance of the terrestrial rare gases, we have good evidence that the initial atmosphere of the Earth has been almost entirely lost to space, except for a small fraction which reacted with surface material, or precipitated out, or was occluded in the interior. This initial reducing atmosphere very likely produced a greater surface pressure than exists on the Earth today. Any organic syntheses made in the initial atmosphere are not relevant to the question of the origin of life, because of subsequent thermal and other degradation. What the surface pressure was while the secondary atmosphere was forming, outgassing of the Earth's interior is a more difficult question. Opinions which have been expressed cover a wide range of pressures, both larger and smaller than one atmosphere. So the answer is, we do not really know.

DR. HALDANE: It might be worth trying a range of pressures.

DR. SAGAN: The partial pressures of hydrogen and helium could have been much greater, because the characteristic times for their escape from the Earth are short compared with 4.5×10^9 years. Heavier gases will not escape from the present terrestrial atmosphere, and it seems unlikely that they would have escaped during any epoch after the formation of the secondary atmosphere. The abundances of these other gases are determined by geochemical equilibria between their outgassing and their fixation. It seems unlikely that the sum of the partial pressures of all gases in the terrestrial atmosphere other than hydrogen and helium was greater than one atmosphere at any time since about four billion years ago.

Chairman's Remarks

E. E. SNELL

*Department of Biochemistry, University of California,
Berkeley, California*

We have heard a great deal about the synthesis of amino acids under probably prebiological conditions, and the chemical and physical conditions that give rise to the formation of these substances from methane, ammonia, etc., and the conditions under which these reactions can be observed.

For a person such as myself who has not previously been exposed to this field, these results are extremely striking and suggestive. At the same time, it seems that one area in the investigation of such possible reactions has been neglected and this is an investigation of the possible production under these conditions of vitamins, the primitive coenzymes, let us say, which might by their presence greatly reduce the activation energies needed for the formation of other essential compounds and therefore promote their formation under conditions much milder than those that have so far been used.

I gather, for example, that Dr. Sagan and others feel that the thermal instability of certain of the amino acids, such as threonine, serine, cysteine, etc., might well be a problem following their initial formation under primitive Earth conditions.

So it might be well to examine certain alternatives for the production of the thermally unstable amino acids. In this connection, I would like to discuss briefly some of the early work that we have done in quite a different context, namely, in an attempt to explain the mechanism of the reaction of certain pyridoxal-dependent enzyme systems *in vivo*, and mention some of the reactions that can be promoted by pyridoxal in the absence of any proteins.

This compound, as you all know, is one form of Vitamin B_6. Its structure is unimportant in this connection. Suffice it to say that in its presence glycine, which has appeared this morning as one of the most abundantly formed amino acids, can be induced to undergo a whole series of interesting reactions. For example, it can be caused to interact with almost any aldehyde, such as formaldehyde, to give the corresponding β-hydroxy

$$NH_2CH_2COOH + HCHO \overset{pyridoxal}{\underset{}{\rightleftharpoons}} CH_2OHCHNH_2COOH \qquad (a)$$
$$\text{glycine} \hspace{6.5cm} \text{serine}$$

amino acids, as illustrated in (a). This reaction can be carried further to give pyruvate by an α,β-elimination reaction (b) and the pyruvate then can transaminate with an appropriate amino donor (reaction c) to yield alanine:

$$CH_2OHCHNH_2COOH \overset{pyridoxal}{\longrightarrow} CH_3COCOOH + NH_3 \qquad (b)$$

$$CH_3COCOOH + RCHNH_2COOH \overset{pyridoxal}{\underset{}{\rightleftharpoons}} CH_3CHNH_2COOH + RCOCOOH \quad (c)$$

In closely analogous reactions, glycine plus acetaldehyde will yield threonine, α-ketobutyrate, and α-aminobutyrate; serine plus indole will yield tryptophan; serine plus hydrogen sulfide yields cysteine, etc.

All of these reactions, let me emphasize, will take place very rapidly in dilute aqueous solution at 100°C and within days at 37°C or even lower ambient temperatures in the presence of metal ions and the catalyst, pyridoxal.

So if threonine, for example, were to be destroyed by thermal reactions, a resynthesis of threonine from the much more stable glycine could readily be · effected in aqueous solutions at low temperature, providing one has present the compound pyridoxal, plus acetaldehyde.

Similarly, if the aldehyde is glyoxylic acid, one could get aspartate by this same series of reactions (a–c). Suffice it to say, there are some thirty known reactions and interconversions of the amino acids that are catalyzed by pyridoxal phosphate enzymes, many of which can be simulated with considerable exactitude simply by adding pyridoxal and metal ions to solutions of amino acids and allowing them to stand under very mild conditions.

It seems peculiar that, under these circumstances, no one has looked for a compound such as pyridoxal in these primitive reaction mixtures. It is quite probable, I think, that pyridoxal (or some catalytically similar analog) could be formed under these conditions, and by its presence many of the reactions leading to amino acids could be carried out under much milder conditions than presently appear necessary.

Leaving pyridoxal for a moment, we might consider some of the other vitamins which might function as "prebiotic enzymes" in catalyzing reactions at rates much lower than the proteins which now carry out these reactions. In this respect, a striking finding was made a year or so ago by Meister, when he showed that the amino acid oxidase, which is now known for its ability simply to remove the amino group of amino acids in the presence of oxygen, could function anaerobically in the reverse direction. Such a reaction is conceivably important if a reduced flavin compound, ammonia, and keto acids arise independently in an anaerobic environment. We could get amino acids formed in this way under the reducing conditions assumed to pertain on the primitive Earth. Since the reduced riboflavin would not be reoxidized by oxygen under these conditions, it could function in the amination of keto acids to yield amino acids rather than in the reactions that we now associate with flavins and flavoproteins.

Thirdly, the folic acid coenzymes which Dr. Buchanan has used in his research are important in a whole series of reactions involving one-carbon units at the oxidation level of formaldehyde, formic acid, or methanol. These coenzymes catalyze the addition, subtraction, and transfer of such one-carbon units from one compound to another, and in the presence of such a coenzyme, the activation energies necessary for such transfer are greatly reduced. Dr Oró mentioned this morning that pteridines were produced in his reaction mixtures which lead also to formation of purine bases, but the nature of these pteridines has not so far been investigated. Could such pteridines catalyze some of the reactions that we now associate with folic acid enzymes? The rates of such reactions need not be fast—I gather time is not a great factor here—rather, formation of certain specifically important compounds is what is needed.

If I am able to make any constructive suggestion at all to this con-ference, it would simply be that some attention be paid to the possible production under primitive Earth conditions of catalytic compounds (perhaps primitive analogs of today's compounds) which would reduce the stringency of the temperatures and other conditions that one needs to impose upon these systems in order to get the interconversions that we know to be of importance in present-day biochemistry and which might well have been important in a prebiotic chemical evolution toward biochemical systems.

DR. FOX: The heating of glucose and asparagine has yielded a mate-rial with nicotinic acid activity in bioassay (Fox, S. W., Vegotsky, A., Harada, K., and Hoagland, P. D., *Ann. N.Y. Acad. Sci.*, **69**, 328 (1957)).

PRIMORDIAL ULTRAVIOLET SYNTHESIS OF NUCLEOSIDE PHOSPHATES

CARL SAGAN

*Harvard University and Smithsonian Astrophysical Observatory,
Cambridge, Massachusetts*

Exactly one hundred years ago, Charles Darwin wrote, in a letter to Hooker: "It is mere rubbish thinking at present of the origin of life. One might as well think of the origin of matter."

Well, we *are* thinking of the origin of matter. The observed cosmic abundances of the elements are now explained by nuclear reactions of hydrogen and its products in stellar interiors. Stellar nucleogenesis became an active area of astronomical research at just the time that laboratory studies of the origin of life were initiated. Darwin's remark is not a negative prognostication, such as Auguste Comte's prediction, in the middle of the nineteenth century, that it would forever lie beyond man's ability to determine the chemical composition of the stars. (Just a few decades later, astronomical spectroscopy was flourishing.) It expressed, rather, his awareness that the origin of life was an extremely difficult problem. Many of the difficulties are with us still.

The logical starting place for any discussion of the origin of life lies in astronomy. After the astronomical background is laid, the problem of the origin of life becomes, I believe, somewhat simpler. We are then led, in a fairly direct manner, to certain specific events in the primitive environment. The following discussion will be of a theoretical nature. Afterward, Dr. Ponnamperuma will describe, in some detail, our joint experiments, performed in his laboratory, which successfully led to the synthesis of nucleoside phosphates under conditions which we feel in some respects reflect the primitive environment of the Earth.

The universe is made of hydrogen and helium. Everything else is a trace constituent. Of these trace constituents, only carbon, nitrogen, and oxygen are both reactive and relatively abundant. But even their abundances are about one-thousandth that of hydrogen. The abundance of something like phosphorus is several orders of magnitude less.

In any cold, nondilute gas of cosmic composition, the fully saturated hydrides of these most abundant atoms should form. We expect molecular hydrogen, methane, ammonia, and water in any primitive planetary environment.

The Earth we are standing on is not composed mainly of methane, ammonia, water, and hydrogen. Therefore it, and various other moons and planets, must be cosmically atypical. Yet an average cell is much closer to cosmic composition, and the size and gross composition of a dielectric interstellar grain is not much different from that of a bacterium. Why, then, is the Earth atypical and a cell more nearly typical of the cosmic abundances?

If we compare the relative abundances of the rare gases and silicon on the Earth with the corresponding cosmic proportion, we find that the terrestrial rare gases are greatly underabundant, and that the underabundance is more marked the lower the mass number. This is just the circumstance we would expect for the thermal escape of a mixture of gases from a planetary gravitational field, the least massive elements escaping most readily. This would then imply that the Earth's original atmosphere has escaped to space, and that therefore, the present atmosphere is of secondary origin. However, Jokipii (1964) has recently shown that the fractionation of the rare gases can also be understood in terms of ambipolar diffusion through the magnetic field of the solar nebula, the hypothesized cloud of gas and dust from which the planets are thought to have formed. Atoms which are easily ionized are trapped by the magnetic field, while atoms which are difficult to ionize move through the magnetic lines of force, and are removed from the vicinity of the sun. In this view, the fractionation of the elements occurred before the Earth itself was formed; but in either interpretation, our atmosphere is of secondary origin—that is, there was an initial distribution of the elements in the atmosphere surrounding the Earth (or the proto-Earth), it went away, and then, somehow or other, we acquired another atmosphere. Where did the secondary atmosphere come from? Accretion—for example, of the solar wind—seems to be entirely inadequate. The only likely remaining possibility is outgassing from the interior of the Earth.

As I have mentioned in the discussion earlier today, since the lightest gases—hydrogen and helium—can escape most easily by evaporation and relatively easily by ambipolar diffusion we have a ready explantation for the fact that the Earth has a much smaller proportion of these gases than the typical cosmic body. An object of somewhat larger mass—for example, the planet Jupiter—with an exosphere at the same temperature as the terrestrial exosphere would be entirely unable to lose hydrogen during geological time. If the secondary atmosphere arose by outgassing from the interior, and the interior was formed in a highly reducing environment, it is very natural to expect that the secondary atmosphere also had a reducing character originally. But then we must inquire how the transition took place from this secondary reducing atmosphere to our present oxidizing atmosphere.

We know of two processes which may have contributed to this transition. One is plant photosynthesis, which certainly dominates the oxidation state of the Earth's atmosphere at present. The contemporary rate of photosynthetic oxygen production is about 0.1 gm cm^{-2} $year^{-1}$. Since there are roughly 200 grams of molecular oxygen above each square centimeter of the Earth's surface, the mean equilibrium lifetime of an oxygen molecule in the atmosphere is slightly greater than 2000 years, a period of time much shorter than the billions of years available for the origin and evolution of life.

The other process, which may have been more important in primitive times, is the photodissociation of water vapor by ultraviolet light in the upper atmosphere. Because of its low mass, the hydrogen will escape; the heavier oxygen remains behind and selectively oxidizes the other reduced constituents of the atmosphere and lithosphere. This photodissociation process may have produced at least small amounts of oxygen in earlier times. But we do not know whether photodissociation or photosynthesis is responsible for the original production of the Earth's oxidizing atmosphere. The fact that no other planet in the solar system has free oxygen in its atmosphere suggests that plant photosynthesis is the original cause of our atmospheric oxygen. The calculations which have been performed on the water photodissociation rates are ambiguous. Some authors conclude that enough oxygen to account for the oxidation of the Earth's crust and the oxygen in the Earth's atmosphere can be produced by photodissociation; others reach a negative conclusion. The calculations have the fundamental difficulty that the present atmospheric structure is assumed for the primitive atmosphere, in computing the rate of water diffusion to the upper atmosphere and the subsequent rate of hydrogen escape. Accordingly, these computations do not yield an estimate of the date when the transition from reducing to oxidizing atmosphere occurred.

At this point, we can make a junction with the geological evidence for the evolution of the terrestrial atmosphere (see, e.g., Holland, 1962).

Holland recognizes three stages in the history of the secondary atmosphere of the Earth. Stage 1, in which the atmosphere was highly reducing, occupied perhaps 5×10^8 years after the formation of the Earth. This stage was marked by fairly extensive igneous activity, and possibly by the migration of iron from the mantle to the core. In Stage 2, the atmosphere is neither strongly reducing nor strongly oxidizing, and lacks both free hydrogen and free oxygen. Between Stage 1 and Stage 2 there has been a massive conversion of methane to carbon dioxide, and ammonia to molecular nitrogen. Stage 3 is our present oxidizing atmosphere. Some evidence on the oxidation states of uranium minerals from Precambrian sediments suggests that the transition from Stage 2 to Stage 3 occurred more recently than 1.8×10^9 years ago. This is probably a more reliable approach than others which previously had been made, involving the oxidation states of iron deposits, or the relative abundance of sulfur isotopes. The oldest known fossil, a calcareous alga found in the Rhodesian shield, has been dated at about 2.7×10^9 years.

The chronology then works out as follows: between 4.5×10^9 and about 4.0×10^9 years ago, the Earth had a reducing atmosphere; in this environment, the types of organic reactions which we are talking about at this conference occurred. Especially toward the end of this period, surface conditions were relatively milder, and a large-scale build-up of organic molecules can be expected. If we require extensive reducing conditions for the origin of life, then the origin of life must have occurred some time around 4.0×10^9 years ago.

By 2.7×10^9 years ago, evolution had already proceeded to organisms as complex as algae. The atmosphere was composed primarily of nitrogen, water, carbon dioxide, and argon: the oxidative degradation of organic compounds must have been much less prevalent than it is today. Finally, at some comparatively recent time, perhaps in the Paleozoic, enough free oxygen accumulated to give us our present atmosphere as a boundary condition on biological processes.

These considerations of the time scale involved in the origin of life are important. In the Precambrian, an epoch very recent in the 4.5×10^9-year history of the Earth, we believe that there were large numbers of what are ordinarily called simple, single-celled organisms. If we were to imagine that the evolution of complexity proceeds exponentially, it is clear that, four billion years ago, we had something enormously more simple than a cell. In the context of the origin of life, a single-celled organism is already extraordinarily complex. Therefore, we should not be surprised if the origin of life involves systems much simpler than single cells.

Now let us consider some events which must have occurred during Stage 1, when the secondary reducing atmosphere enveloped the Earth and when most of the events postulated in this conference could have taken place. If oxygen was absent, there also was no ozone, because ozone is produced by three-body collisions of O_2, O, and any other atom. The absence of ozone immediately raises the possibility that this primitive atmosphere was transparent to solar ultraviolet radiation. Methane, ammonia, water, and hydrogen are all transparent above about 2400 Å, even with the large amounts of these gases conceivably present on the early Earth. Such possible trace constituents as CO_2 and CO were also transparent in this region. So the ultraviolet opacity between 2400 and 3000 Å depends on the abundance of intermediate oxidation state molecules, in particular, the ketones and aldehydes.

In the simulation experiments which have been performed so far, where gas phase extractions have been made, the aldehyde or ketone found in highest yield is formaldehyde. Formaldehyde absorption extends longwards of 2900Å. Formaldehyde, then, still leaves a window between 2400 and 2900 Å in the primitive atmosphere of the Earth.

Some acetaldehyde should have been present, although it does not appear in high yield in these experiments, at least in the experiments that Stanley Miller and I did some years ago (Sagan and Miller, 1960). Perhaps later we can hear from some others who have done gas phase analyses. The acetaldehyde abundance is important, because it is a fairly strong absorber in the 2400–2900 Å region. The possibility that a sizable ultraviolet flux bathed the surface of the primitive oceans is, I believe, also consistent with some biological evidence.

There are several modes of damage produced by ultraviolet irradiation of contemporary cells. One is the production of peroxides, which oxidize things inside the cell. Another is thymine dimerization, which follows from the preferential absorption of ultraviolet photons by the nucleic acids. It is remarkable that contemporary cells have quite elaborate defenses against both these modes of ultraviolet damage. There are the very efficient enzymes catalase and peroxidase for the peroxide damage; there is photoreactivation for the thymine dimerization. This photoreactivation occurs only in the presence of long-wavelength ultraviolet light near 3700 Å, and in the presence of a photoenzyme. Why should contemporary cells have relatively sophisticated mechanisms to protect themselves against damage caused by short-wavelength ultraviolet light, which is not a pervasive feature of the contemporary environment?

It is certainly true that some peroxides are produced in the normal course of metabolism in some organisms, and could be usefully in-activated. Some ultraviolet light does trickle through our present atmos-phere, but it is essentially all at wavelengths longer than 3000 Å. It is also true that, occasionally, thymine dimerization should occur by barrier tunneling. But such events are relatively minor. Either they occur only in special varieties of organisms, or they happen very rarely; but ultraviolet defense mechanisms are widespread, both pheno-typically and temporally. These events would provide some low-level selection pressure to maintain the adaptations, once acquired, but it would seem remarkable indeed if the defense mechanisms were established simply to deal with these fairly unusual events. I think it makes much more sense to believe that organisms arose in an ultra-violet-rich environment. Ultraviolet defense mechanisms would then have had the highest evolutionary priority; they would be necessary to permit survival at all, and to keep the mutation rate down to toler-able levels. Otherwise, characteristics selected for would be immediately mutated away, and there would be no natural selection at all.

If it is true that the Stage 1 reducing atmosphere of the Earth was relatively transparent in the middle ultraviolet, we can then compute what the ultraviolet flux must have been. From models of the evolution of the sun—these models are now in a fairly good state—we can com-pute that the photon flux incident at the top of the Earth's atmosphere in the 2400–2900 Å region some 4×10^9 years ago was about 7×10^{14} photons cm^{-2} sec^{-1} (Sagan, 1961b). Such a flux delivers to many con-temporary organisms the mean lethal dose in about 1 second. The time to accumulate very high mutation rates is shorter.

Thus, we see that even with substantial atmospheric attenuation in the 2400–2900 Å region, the priority for ultraviolet protection devices would have been very high. You cannot ignore this flux; you must either deal with it, or escape it. Perhaps photoreactivation and other contemporary adaptations are the vestiges of attempts made to deal with the flux. Escape from this flux would have been possible, if organisms resided some tens of meters down, in oceans of pure liquid water. The ultra-violet flux would then be attenuated to a reasonable value. If the oceans were filled with organic matter that also absorbs ultraviolet light, smaller depths would have been acceptable.

The energy available for organic synthesis in such an ultraviolet flux is so much greater than the energies available from other expected energy sources in the primitive environment that the ultraviolet photo-products may have dominated the chemistry of the primitive oceans. If you know what the ultraviolet fluxes were, and what the quantum yield is for a given photochemical reaction, you can then compute how many molecules are formed in a column with a 1 cm-square base in any time period you want to consider. Using quantum yields for the ultraviolet production of hydroxy and amino acids obtained by Groth and von Weyssenhoff (1959) ($\sim 10^{-5}$), I find that the amount of organic matter produced in 10^9 years was so great that, if dissolved in the contemporary oceans, we would have a 1% solution of organic matter. This is a reasonable concentration for any hot, dilute soup, and gives us some idea of the kinds of concentration which are reasonable to consider in primitive Earth simulation experiments. We have to worry, as I mentioned earlier, about the ultraviolet dissociation of molecules which are produced by ultraviolet light. One ameliorating process which occurs in the upper atmosphere of the primitive Earth is that the heavier synthesized molecules tend to sink, and therefore move to regions in the atmosphere which are optically thicker.

The primitive oceans very likely had much less water than the contemporary oceans, since there is some contribution to oceanic water from outgassing and from accretion. But the continents have also grown in time. Since we do not know the relative rates of growth, it is difficult to state what the proportion of land to water was in primitive times.

With this as background, I would like to present for your criticism a hypothetical sequence of events. I will try to make some criticisms of the sequence myself, after it is presented. I believe that this sequence has at least heuristic value. The events, each following naturally from the preceding, do lead us in the direction of living systems.

Starting with the composition of the primitive atmosphere—methane, ammonia, hydrogen, and water—it has been shown, primarily by Miller, Oró, and Ponnamperuma, that the application of a variety of energy sources leads first to gas phase intermediaries—primarily cyanides, aldehydes, and hydrocarbons—and, subsequently, to purines, pyrimidines, ribose, and 2-deoxyribose, among other compounds of biological interest. Dr. Oró has already said something about this; Dr. Ponnamperuma will shortly tell us more. We may therefore expect a certain concentration of these substances in the primitive oceans. We also expect the presence of phosphorus compounds, although in what form or abundance, we are unfortunately not yet in a position to say.

At this point, it is important to emphasize that all energy sources are not equivalent. Ultraviolet irradiation of such mixtures should not yield the same results as, for example, heating them, or irradiating them with α-particles or high-energy electrons. The reason is that purines and pyrimidines have very large ultraviolet absorption cross sections in the

2600 Å region. Therefore, there will be preferential purine and pyrimidine reactions following 2600 Å ultraviolet irradiation which will not preferentially occur following the application of other energy sources. There is some non-zero probability for the formation of any organic molecule from methane, ammonia, water, and hydrogen in thermodynamic equilibrium. The application of heat as an energy source with no preferential removal of products should yield a good approximation to the thermodynamic equilibrium abundances of various organic molecules of interest; but the products of ultraviolet irradiation may differ significantly from such thermodynamic equilibrium abundances.

It is an extraordinary fact that purines and pyrimidines happen to have a relative maximum in their absorption cross sections at 2600 Å, just in the middle of the ultraviolet window which seems to have existed in the primitive terrestrial atmosphere. That is, by accident, solar radiation was pouring down into the seas at just the wavelengths where purines and pyrimidines happened to be absorbing. For this reason I suggested, in 1957 and again in 1961, that it would be nice to irradiate with ultraviolet light a mixture of, say, adenine and some pentose sugars and some phosphates, and see if adenosine triphosphate (ATP) and other nucleic acid precursors (which, even in 1957, were thought desirable to have around in the primitive oceans) could be synthesized.

This experiment has now been performed by Dr. Ponnamperuma, Miss Mariner, and myself, and recently published. We find that 2537 Å irradiation of a dilute solution of adenine, ribose, and phosphoric acid produces the nucleoside adenosine (Ponnamperuma et al., 1963a). Curiously enough, in these first experiments, adenosine did not seem to be formed in the absence of phosphorus, despite the fact that there is no phosphorus in adenosine. It is possible that this has something to do with the peculiar role which phosphorus plays in contemporary organisms—out of all proportion to its cosmic abundance—although I do not think that this is the whole story.

In a second series of experiments, we irradiated adenosine and phosphoric acid. There were no detectable yields of nucleoside phosphates. When, however, we used ethyl metaphosphate, a phosphorus source to which Schramm first called attention, nucleoside phosphates were successfully produced in quantum yields which in this business are fairly high. At the present time, I would prefer not to go into the question of a more suitable phosphorus source. It is clear that even if the metaphosphate was available in primitive times, it was probably not the most abundant form of phosphorus present in the primitive oceans. There are a number of other phosphorus compounds which bear exploring, and more experiments with phosphoric acid need doing. Using the metaphosphate, we have successfully produced adenosine, adenosine monophosphate (AMP), adenosine diphosphate (ADP), ATP, and even higher phosphates, directly from adenine and ribose (Ponnamperuma *et al.*, 1963b). I think the experiments are already sufficiently encouraging to support the contention that nucleoside phosphates were present, perhaps in large amounts, in the primitive oceans.

Suppose, now, that in place of ribose in these experiments, we had used deoxyribose; or in place of adenine, we had used guanine, thymine, cytosine, or uracil. It should be possible to produce the full range of deoxyribo- and ribonucleoside phosphates in this manner. Dr. Ponnamperuma will later have something to say about experimental work in which the deoxynucleoside phosphates have indeed been produced.

Suppose we have a primitive ocean which is filled with nucleoside phosphates. How likely is it that a polynucleotide will arise? Kornberg and Ochoa have found that a mixture of the appropriate kinds of nucleoside triphosphates can be made to copolymerize into polynucleotides in water solution, if appropriate cofactors, such as magnesium, and appropriate enzymes, such as deoxyribonucleic acid polymerase (DNA polymerase) or polynucleotide phosphorylase, are present. Both polymerizations can occur in the absence of a primer nucleic acid.

It is reasonable that inorganic cofactors such as magnesium ions were present in the primitive oceans, but the chance production of DNA polymerase or polynucleotide phosphorylase in primitive times seems very unlikely indeed. We need enzymes to make polynucleotides, and polynucleotides to make enzymes. As a possible way out of this quandary, I would like to suggest that we can trade geological time for DNA polymerase or polynucleotide phosphorylase. This problem is solved, if, in a time short compared with the age of the Earth, but long compared with the lifetime of an average contemporary organism, the spontaneous polymerization of the nucleoside triphosphates can occur in the primitive oceans.

After the production of the first polynucleotide—say, poly-AT—in a medium full of nucleoside triphosphates, a primer is now present, and the replication rate should go up very greatly. In time, the polynucleotides should acquire deletions, inversions, and substitutions, and eventually we may expect an ocean fairly full of self-replicating polynucleotides of various kinds.

I have found that this picture has a rather widespread appeal. Nevertheless, by no stretch of the imagination can we say that the origin of life has occurred at this point. Even if we had a medium which was full of self-replicating and mutating molecular systems, life has not necessarily come into being, because there is no mode for environmental control by these systems—or, put in another way, there is nothing analogous to the present DNA-messenger RNA-adapter RNA-enzyme transcription apparatus present.

I think we all very much appreciated Dr. Buchanan's attempt to outline how some of this apparatus might have been made. It would be very nice if we could reasonably expect such a transcription apparatus to be present in the primitive oceans. Perhaps it was. There are a number of alternative possibilities.

First of all, suppose, as Stent (1962) and Rich (1962) have suggested that the present triplet code is not the original transcription mechanism. Perhaps it is only a relatively recent acquisition, dating, say, from the beginning of Stage 3 in the evolution of the Earth's atmosphere. We may imagine that during Stage 2 we had a doublet code, and back in Stage 1, a singlet. Since amino acids and nucleotides have closely similar sizes when appropriately stacked, it is possible that the polymer of one can code the polymer of the other. In fact, this coincidence was the basis of the earliest attempts, in the 1940's to describe the code. When all the triplet code words have been found, it may even be possible to reconstruct any earlier doublet and singlet codes. The proposed singlet code could then be tested stereochemically. The catalytic properties of a protein composed of only four amino acids would be limited, but it would be a lot better than nothing. Perhaps the earliest code involved other purines and pyrimidines or other amino acids. Grossenbacher has pointed out that a broader range of amino acids may have been available in primitive times than are used by contemporary organisms.

There are other possibilities. Maybe there are polynucleotides which are weakly catalytic; maybe there are polypeptides which are weakly self-replicating. We should try to find out. There are still other aspects of the problem which remain muddy. Do the kinetics of spontaneous nucleoside triphosphate polymerization give substantial production in times short compared with 10^9 years? The kinetics can be examined, and the hypothesis can be tested. Does ultraviolet radiation enhance such polymerization? Has the purity of laboratory reagents obscured for us the true sequence of reactions in primitive, and less pure, times? Is it possible that DNA is itself a later sophistication, and that the earliest self-replicating molecular systems were based on another molecule entirely, perhaps RNA? There is clearly much more to be done than merely making nucleic acid precursors. Nevertheless, I believe that the fairly efficient production of the nucleoside phosphates supports the contention that the origin of life is at last becoming a tractable scientific problem.

There is another way of testing any model of the origin of life: look for independent organic synthetic sequences—that is, sequences which have not occurred on the planet Earth. One source of such molecules which is already at hand is the carbonaceous chondrites, meteorites already mentioned by Vallentyne, Oró, and others at this conference.

There are several other sources of organic matter, only indirectly accessible at the moment, but imminently more accessible—the exact moment of accessibility depending on various national budgets. They are the other natural objects in our solar system. Let me mention some of them, simply in order of their distance from the Sun.

We know directly of no organic molecules on Venus. There is a suggestion—it is no more than that, at the present time—that the lower atmosphere and surface of Venus contain large quantities of hydrocarbons. The suggestion follows from two independent arguments, one cosmogonical, the other spectroscopic, but both extremely indirect. Furthermore, recent thermodynamic calculations by Mueller (1964) suggest that hydrocarbons are thermodynamically extremely unstable in the expected environment of Venus. We must know much more about Venus before we can even say that it is moderately plausible that it contains organic matter. And even if it does, with its cloud-enshrouded surface at 700°K, we're going to have a hard time studying the molecules.

There is some possibility that organic matter exists buried beneath the lunar surface. The quantum yield calculation which I mentioned earlier for the Earth can be applied to the Moon during that epoch in its early history when its reducing atmosphere had not yet escaped to space. One derives characteristic total yields of about 10 gm of organic matter per square centimeter of lunar surface (Sagan, 1961b). Some of it may still be safely sequestered beneath the surface of relatively old and undisturbed regions of the Moon, such as the southern highlands.

Very likely, the Moon has undergone less melting than the Earth and, therefore, less thermal degradation of any organic molecules produced in its early history. Thus, if we find organic matter on the Moon, it may be more characteristic of the organic molecules produced in the very early history of the solar system, when the planets were condensing out of the solar nebula, than of molecules characteristically produced in secondary, outgassed atmospheres. The parent bodies of the meteorites are likely to share this characteristic with the Moon.

It seems clear, from the infrared reflection spectra of Mars obtained by Sinton (1959), that hydrocarbons and possibly aldehydes are present on its surface and in its atmosphere, particularly in the regions of the Martian dark areas. There is other, independent evidence for life on Mars, but it is not my place to describe it here. I feel that when all the evidence is weighed together, the chances not only for large amounts of organic matter on Mars, but even of living systems on that planet appear rather good.

Finally, I would like to mention the planet Jupiter. The possibility of organic matter on Jupiter is often rather airily dismissed, mostly because the observed bolometric temperatures are in the 150°K range. These temperatures refer, of course, to the cloud layer. The temperature increases below the clouds. According to recent calculations of Gallet (1963), there seems to be a region below the visible clouds of Jupiter where liquid water condensation occurs, where the atmospheric density approaches 0.1 gm cm^{-3}, and where the temperatures are in the 300–350°K range. This cloud is perhaps 10 km thick, would be the seat of electrical discharges, and perhaps would see some solar ultraviolet photons. I can't imagine a more likely medium for the production and large-scale interaction of organic molecules. In fact, the opportunities available during the 5×10^9 years that Jupiter has retained its primitive reducing atmosphere suggest that there may be more organic matter on Jupiter than there is in the entire terrestrial biosphere. We should seek spectroscopic tests of these possibilities. Jupiter is, in fact, an enormous laboratory, in which chemical experiments relevant to the origin of life are being performed today. The ultimate tests of many of our ideas may lie on that distant world.

Perhaps we have made a little progress, since Darwin wrote his letter to Hooker. In the next hundred years, it is very likely that we will have acquired something close to a real understanding of these fascinating problems.

Manuscript received October 28, 1963.

REFERENCES

Cited references, and references for much of the uncited material, follow:
Gallet, R. (1963). Private communication.
Groth, W., and von Weyssenhoff, H. (1959). *Ann. Physik* **4**, 69.
Holland, H. D. (1962). *In* "Petrologic Studies: A Volume to Honor A. F. Buddington," p. 447. Geological Society of America, New York.
Jokipii, J. R. (1964). RAND Corporation Memorandum RM-3977-PR.
Mueller, R. F. (1964). *Icarus.* In Press.
Ponnamperuma, C., Mariner, R., and Sagan, C. (1963a). *Nature* **198**, 1199.

Ponnamperuma, C., Sagan, C., and Mariner, R. (1963b). *Nature* **199**, 222; *Smithsonian Astrophys. Observ. Spec. Rept. No. 128.*

Rich, A. (1962). *In* "Horizons in Biochemistry" (M. Kasha and B. Pullman, eds.), p. 103. Academic Press, New York.

Sagan, C. (1957). *Evolution* **11**, 40.

Sagan, C. (1961a). *Radiation Res.* **15**, 174.

Sagan, C. (1961b). "Organic Matter and the Moon." Nat. Acad. Sci.–Nat. Res. Council Publ. 757, Washington, D. C.

Sagan, C. (1964). "Exobiology: A Critical Review." *In* "Life Sciences and Space Research," Vol. II (M. Florkin and A. Dollfus, eds.).

Sagan, C., and Miller, S. L. (1960). *Astronom. J.* **65**, 499.

Sinton, W. M. (1959). *Science* **130**, 1234.

Stent, G. (1962). Private communication.

ABIOLOGICAL SYNTHESIS OF SOME NUCLEIC ACID CONSTITUENTS

CYRIL PONNAMPERUMA

Exobiology Division, National Aeronautics and Space Administration, Ames Research Center, Moffett Field, California

In the experimental approach to the origin of life, the simplest working hypothesis holds that the molecules that are fundamental now were fundamental at the time of the origin of life. It is conceivable that the nucleic acids and proteins or at least their precursors appeared at a very early stage in the evolution of this planet. In our laboratory we are investigating the synthesis of the purines, pyrimidines, sugars, nucleosides, and nucleotides that are found in the nucleic acid molecule.

In Miller's (1955) electric discharge experiments, no ultraviolet-absorbing compounds were formed. Fox, however, had demonstrated the synthesis of uracil by the action of heat on malic acid and urea (Fox and Harada, 1961). Oró established very clearly the synthesis of adenine by the action of heat on a solution of ammonium cyanide (Oró and Kimball, 1961). More recently, he has described the possible pathways for the synthesis of the purines, guanine and xanthine, and the pyrimidines cytosine, uracil, and thymine by the interaction of their intermediates (Oró, 1963). The main purpose of our research was to see whether, starting from a mixture of primitive gases, we could in a stepwise manner synthesize the nucleic acid constituents.

The energies available for the synthesis of organic compounds under primitive Earth conditions have been reported (Miller and Urey, 1959) to be those shown in the accompanying tabulation.

Energy	kcal cm^{-2} yr^{-1}
Ultraviolet radiation from the sun	
2500 Å	570
2000 Å	85
1500 Å	3.5
Electric discharges	4
Ionizing radiation	0.8
Heat from volcanoes	0.13

All these forms of energy have been used by us in a series of experiments. In the first experiments methane, ammonia, and water were our starting materials. As hydrogen cyanide is one of the primary products of an electric discharge through a mixture of methane, ammonia, and water, this was chosen as starting material for the second series of experiments. In the third, we used formaldehyde as the raw material. Subsequently, attempts were made to link up the purines and sugars formed in the previous experiments to give nucleosides and nucleotides.

In the experiments with methane, ammonia, and water, electron irradiation was used as a convenient source of ionizing radiation, simulating the K^{40} on the primitive earth (Ponnamperuma $et\ al.$, 1963a).

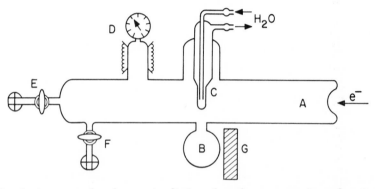

Fig. 1. Apparatus for electron irradiation of methane, ammonia, and water.

Mixtures of methane-C^{14}, $4\,N$ ammonium hydroxide, and hydrogen were irradiated in the glass apparatus shown in Fig. 1. The electrons entered the tube through the window at the concave end. The electrons had an energy of 4.5 Mev. The total energy absorbed was of the order of 7×10^{10} ergs per gram. The liquid in flask B was boiled during the irradiations. The boiling caused a continuous washing back into B of the condensation product on C. At the end of the reaction the liquid in B was removed for analysis.

Analyses for the nonvolatile products were carried out by means of paper chromatography. An aliquot of the product was placed on paper together with carrier adenine. The paper was developed with n-propanol–ammonia–water in one direction and with butanol–formic acid–water in the other. The area corresponding to the carrier adenine was cut out and eluted. The eluted material was rerun in two other solvent systems (n-butanol–water and isopropanol–HCl). The adenine was located on the chromatograms through the use of shadowgrams (Ponnamperuma *et al.*, 1962). The percentage of adenine formed from CH_4 was determined by elution of the adenine spots from the chromatograms and counting of the radioactivity in a liquid scintillation counter.

The results of this investigation clearly establish adenine as a product of the irradiation of methane, ammonia, and water (Fig. 2). It appears, furthermore, that the production of adenine is enhanced by the absence of H_2. This is not surprising since methane carbon must be oxidized in order to appear finally in purines.

The principal species affecting the oxidations are probably OH and NH_2 radicals and these radicals would revert to the starting materials

$$\cdot OH + H_2 \rightarrow H_2O + H\cdot$$
$$\cdot NH_2 + H_2 \rightarrow NH_3 + H\cdot$$

The first reaction is energetically favored since the H—H bond energy is 104.2 kcal and the HO—H is 119 kcal (Kerr and Trotman–Dickenson, 1962). The second is slightly unfavored (H_2N—H bond energy is 103 kcal) and may not occur. H_2 may also interfere with the production of purines through the back reaction.

$$\cdot CH_3 + H_2 \rightarrow CH_4 + \cdot H$$

Here the bond energies are very similar (H—CH_3, 104 kcal; H—H, 104.2 kcal). In any event, the high concentration of organic matter on the prebiotic Earth probably arose when most of the hydrogen had escaped from the atmosphere.

No guanine, cytosine, uracil, or thymine was detected on any of our chromatograms. Any one of these would have been detected if it had been present in $\frac{1}{100}$ of the amount of adenine. The apparent preference for adenine synthesis may be related to adenine's multiple roles in biological systems. In addition, molecular orbital calculations have shown that of all the biologically important purines and pyrimidines, adenine has the greatest resonance energy (B. Pullman and A. Pullman, 1960, 1962). This would not only make adenine's synthesis more likely, but would, in addition, confer radiation stability upon it.

Recent experiments completed on the eve of my departure for this symposium provide strong evidence for the formation of the two sugars, ribose and deoxyribose, during the electron irradiation of methane. ammonia, and water. While further experimentation would be necessary to substantiate this result on irrefutable grounds, the evidence available is compelling enough to warrant my presentation of the results at this meeting.

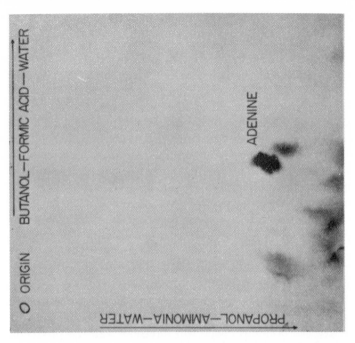

Fig. 2. Chromatogram showing the formation of adenine by electron irradiation of methane, ammonia and water.

224

The method of irradiation was identical with that in the previous experiment. The neutral portion of the reaction products was separated from the acidic and the basic fractions by the use of Dowex-50 and Amberlite C-400 ion-exchange resins. The total amount of C^{14} fixed in this experiment, as nonvolatile products, was 0.44%; of this, 14% was found in the neutral fraction.

Aliquots of D-ribose and 2-deoxyribose were then added to the neutral fraction and separated unidimensionally by paper chromatography using butanol–ethanol–water. The areas corresponding to the ribose and deoxyribose were cut out, eluted, and rerun in two dimensions using butanol–ethanol–water in one direction and n-propanol–ethyl acetate–water in the other. The nonradioactive carriers were detected by spraying the chromatograms with aniline-hydrogen phthalate and preparing their shadowgrams. In each of the chromatograms there was radioactivity coinciding with the bright areas of the shadowgram. This coincidence was identical in position and precise in shape. Ribose and deoxyribose, the sugars in ribonucleic acid (RNA) and deoxyribonucleic acid (DNA), thus appear to be formed during the electron irradiation of methane, ammonia, and water. The chromatography of the neutral fraction shows that a large number of other compounds are formed, possibly other sugars. Their identification and characterization is now under way.

The above result is perhaps not completely unexpected, as formaldehyde is one of the products of the effect of electric discharges on mixtures of primitive gases (El'piner and Sokol'skaya, 1959), and in basic solution polymerizes to give the higher sugars (Butlerow, 1861). In a further series of experiments, formaldehyde was, therefore, used as the starting material for our synthesis. The sources of energy used were ultraviolet (UV) and ionizing radiation in the form of cobalt-60 γ-rays.

Formaldehyde-C^{14} of specific activity 10 mc/mmole was used for the radiations at a concentration of 3×10^{-4} moles per liter. Dissolved oxygen was removed by bubbling a stream of nitrogen through the solution. For the ultraviolet light irradiations, the samples were sealed in Vycor tubes. Glass tubes were used for the γ-irradiation. Formaldehyde absorbs at a wavelength of 2880 Å. The Vycor glass of which the tubes were made transmitted 90% of light of this wave length. The γ-radiations were conducted with a 2½ kc cobalt-60 source which had a maximum intensity of 5×10^6 rads per hour. The reaction products were evaporated to near dryness. An aliquot was then chromatographed on paper in two dimensions. The solvents were butanol–pyridine–benzene–water, and butanol–acetic acid–water. A large number of discrete organic compounds are formed.

In a second experiment, an aliquot of each sample was chromatographed unidimensionally with nonradioactive ribose and deoxyribose alongside. The solvent used was butanol–ethanol–water. The nonradioactive ribose and deoxyribose were detected with the aid of aniline-hydrogen phthalate. The radioactivity was detected by means of X-ray film autoradiography. In both the UV and the ionizing radiation experiments, there were spots corresponding to the ribose and the deoxyribose (Fig. 3).

The areas corresponding to the ribose and deoxyribose were cut out, eluted, and rerun with the appropriate standards as carriers in a two-dimensional chromatogram using two different solvent systems (propanol–ethyl acetate–water; butanol–acetic acid–water). Shadowgrams and autoradiograms were prepared. The radioactivity exactly matched the spots on the shadowgram of the standards, in shape and location. Ribose and deoxyribose had been synthesized from formaldehyde by the action of UV or ionizing radiation.

A preliminary separation into groups of sugars seems to indicate that by far the highest yield is of the pentoses and hexoses. This is no doubt due to the inherent stability of the five- and six-membered rings.

It is interesting to note that the action of UV or γ-rays is somewhat similar in effect to the polymerization of formaldehyde by basic media, a reaction that has been known to organic chemists for over a hundred years. The reaction with UV or γ-rays, however, is not base catalyzed, as the pH of the solutions was approximately 4.5 before and after the irradiation.

In a third series of experiments, hydrogen cyanide was used as the starting material. This again is one of the primary products when a mixture of methane, ammonia, and water is exposed to electric discharges or ionizing radiation. Miller and Urey considered HCN as an intermediate in their synthesis of amino acids from primitive mixtures (Miller, 1955). Palm and Calvin (1962) identified HCN as a major product when a mixture of methane, ammonia, and water is irradiated with electrons.

The use of HCN as starting material is also strengthened by the theory that comets may have been responsible for the accumulation of relatively large amounts of carbon compounds on the primitive Earth (Oró, 1961). Some of these compounds are known to be transformed spontaneously into amino acids and other biochemical compounds. The CN band is generally the first molecular emission to appear on the tails of comets during the travel of these bodies toward the Sun (Swings and Haser, 1956). It is also the band with the largest degree of extension into the comets' heads. It is possible that the heads of comets contain frozen

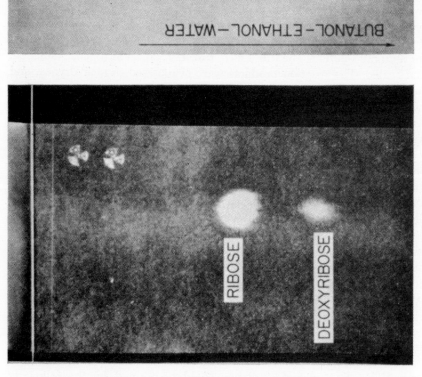

Fig. 3. Chromatogram showing the formation of ribose and deoxyribose from formaldehyde.

free radicals which are volatilized by radiant heat from the sun. It is also possible that they contain frozen molecules which are vaporized and photodissociated into radicals by solar radiation (Whipple, 1950).

A third reason for the use of HCN as starting material arises from the fact that aminocyanocarbene, an HCN dimer, has been postulated as an intermediate in the formation of proteins, purines and other compounds of biological significance (Kliss and Matthews, 1962).

$$2 \text{ HCN} \rightarrow (\text{H}\overset{\overset{\displaystyle NH}{\|}}{-\text{C}}-\text{C}\equiv\text{N}) \rightarrow \text{H}_2\text{N}-\overset{\cdot}{\text{C}}-\text{C}\equiv\text{N}:$$

Since the dimer is a substituted monocyanocarbene, it can also exist as a 1,1-biradical and as a 1,3-biradical. In its 1,3 form, this biradical could react to give the cyclic bases such as purines.

Hydrogen cyanide-C^{14} of specific activity 10 mc/mmole at a concentration of 10^{-3} moles/liter was used for the radiations. The samples sealed in quartz tubes were exposed to a battery of UV lamps for 7 days. Dissolved oxygen was removed by bubbling a stream of nitrogen through the solution. The tubes were frozen in liquid nitrogen, evacuated, and sealed. The reaction products were evaporated to near dryness and an aliquot chromatographed on paper in two dimensions. The solvents used were propanol–ammonia–water and butanol–propionic acid–water. Autoradiography with X-ray film revealed that a large number of discrete organic molecules were formed (Fig. 4).

In a second experiment, an aliquot of the reaction products was run on a two-dimensional chromatogram using non-radioactive guanine and adenine as carriers. The carriers were located as bright spots on the shadowgram. There was coincidence of the darkening on the X-ray film with the brightening on the shadowgram. This coincidence, perfect in location and precise in shape, was observed in four different solvent systems: propanol–ammonia–water, butanol–propionic acid–water, iso-propanol–HCl, and butanol–water. Material which was identical with known adenine and guanine had thus been synthesized from C^{14}-labeled HCN. By an extension of this technique, urea was also identified.

Approximately 6% of the starting material appears as nonvolatile products. About 1% of this material is adenine, 0.5% guanine, and 10% urea. The results do not appear to be dependent on pH.

Several mechanisms have been suggested for the synthesis of purines from HCN. For example, adenine could be formed by the following sequence of reactions suggested by Kliss and Matthews (1962). Hydrogen cyanide in its 1,3-biradical form reacts with 1 mole of HCN, to give the imidazole ring. Further addition of HCN and ring closure gives rise to the adenine. Oró has suggested the next series of reactions for the base catalyzed synthesis of adenine (Oró and Kimball, 1961). Formamidine and 4-aminoimidazole-5-carboximidine are formed spon-

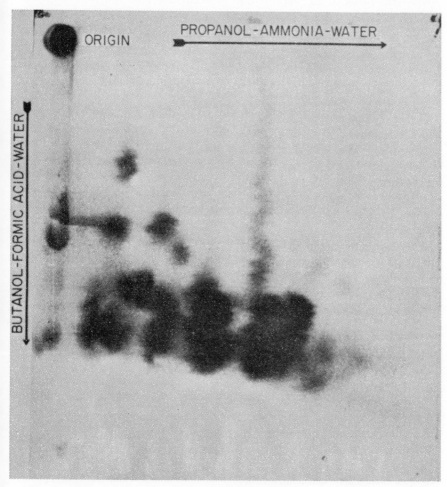

FIG. 4. Chromatogram illustrating the polymerization of hydrogen cyanide by ultraviolet light.

taneously. These are the key intermediates which in the final step give rise to adenine.

The experiment with hydrogen cyanide is of very special significance for the following reasons:

(1)   Adenine and guanine are the purine bases which occur in both RNA and DNA.
(2)   Both adenine and guanine are formed in the same reaction.
(3)   The concentration of starting material is extremely small—of the order of 10^{-3} moles/liter—comparable with the concentration of HCN under primitive Earth conditions.
(4)   The energy used is ultraviolet light which was the most abundant source of energy in primordial times.
(5)   Urea—an important biochemical intermediate—is formed in high yield.

In the series of experiments already described, we have established the formation of (1) the purines, adenine and guanine, and (2) the sugars, ribose and deoxyribose. It was, therefore, of interest to see whether the same sources of energy responsible for the synthesis of the purines, pyrimidines, and sugars could be instrumental in the synthesis of nucleosides and nucleoside phosphates. Two series of experiments have been conducted: (1) with ultraviolet light, and (2) with ionizing radiation.

As ultraviolet radiation from the sun is considered to have been the most abundant source of energy available on the primitive Earth, it is perhaps logical to assume that it had an important role in the production of the organic milieu associated with the origin of life. It has been suggested that the Earth's primitive reducing atmosphere was at least slightly transparent between 2400 and 2900 Å, and that the activation of UV-absorbing purines and pyrimidines was a possible step in the formation of nucleosides and nucleotides (Sagan, 1957, 1961).

Adenine-8-C^{14} of specific activity 23.4 $\mu c/mg$, adenosine-8-C^{14} of specific activity 7.2 $\mu c/mg$, and adenylic acid-8-C^{14} of specific activity 3.1 $\mu c/mg$ were supplied by Schwarz BioResearch (Orangeburg, New York). The nonradioactive adenosine, adenosine monophosphate (AMP), adenosine diphosphate (ADP), and adenosine triphosphate (ATP) used as carriers were supplied by C. F. Boehringer (Mannheim, Germany). The adenosine tetraphosphate (A4P) was a gift of Dr. John Moffatt (Syntex Ltd., Palo Alto, California).

The ethyl metaphosphate used in the experiment was prepared by dissolving 150 gm of phosphorus pentoxide in 300 ml of ethyl ether and refluxing the solution for several hours with chloroform (Schramm et al., 1962). The excess solvent was removed by evaporation under vacuum, leaving a syrupy residue of ethyl metaphosphate.

The method of irradiation and analysis was the following. Quantities of the labeled adenine, adenosine, and adenylic acid, varying from 1.5×10^{-6} to 1.5×10^{-5} mole in various experiments, were sealed in aqueous solution in Vycor tubes with approximately stoichiometric quantities of ribose, phosphoric acid, or polyphosphate ester, as outlined in Table I. The final concentration of base, nucleoside, and nucleotide in each solution did not exceed 10^{-3} mole per liter. The solutions were irradiated by four Westinghouse ultraviolet germicidal lamps (type 782H-10) which emit 95% of their light in the Hg resonance line at 2537 Å. The Vycor glass of which they were made transmitted 80% light at this wavelength. During a 1-hour irradiation, the sample absorbed a total of $\pm 10^8$ ergs. During the irradiation, the ambient temperature of the samples was $40 \pm 2°C$.

The reaction products were first analyzed by paper chromatography, autoradiography, and ultraviolet absorption studies. An aliquot of the reaction products was spotted on Whatman no. 4 paper and the chromatogram run in two solvents (butanol–propionic acid–water and isobutyric acid–ammonia). The positions of the carriers adenosine, AMP, ADP, ATP, and A4P were detected by shadowgrams. Coincidence both in position and in shape between the carriers on the shadowgrams and the radioactivity on the autoradiogram was the chromatographic basis for the identifications. A further aliquot was chromatographed in two other solvent systems (trichloroacetic acid–acetone and butanol–formic acid–water). Once again, there was coincidence between the carrier as outlined in the shadowgram and the radioactivity on the film.

Separations effected using thin-layer chromatography and ion-exchange chromatography confirmed the results obtained from paper chromatography.

Four different categories of experiments were performed. In the first, the starting material was adenine; in the second, adenosine; in the third, adenosine monophosphate; and in the fourth, adenosine diphosphate. The conversion of adenine to adenosine, adenosine to adenosine monophosphate, adenosine monophosphate to adenosine diphosphate, and adenosine diphosphate to adenosine triphosphate has been established (Ponnamperuma et al., 1963b). Experiments using adenine as the starting material have produced adenosine, AMP, ADP, and ATP (Fig. 5).

Adenosine is not produced in detectable amounts in the absence of a phosphorus compound. While adenosine is produced in the presence of both phosphoric acid and ethyl metaphosphate, the nucleoside phosphates were detected only with the use of ethyl metaphosphate. Phosphoric acid was chosen first in the attempt to synthesize the nucleoside

TABLE I
Synthesis of Nucleic Acid Constituents

Experiment	Adenosine	AMP	ADP	ATP	A4P
1.					
Adenine-C^{14} + ribose	–				
Adenine-C^{14} + ribose + phosphoric acid	+(0.01%)[a,b]	–	–	–	–
Adenine-C^{14} + ribose + ethyl metaphosphate	+(0.01%)	+(0.08%)	+(0.06%)	+(0.05%)	+(0.04%)
2.					
Adenosine-C^{14} + phosphoric acid		–	–	–	–
Adenosine-C^{14} + ethyl metaphosphate		+(0.5%)	+(0.2%)	+(0.1%)	+
3.					
Adenosine monophosphate-C^{14} + phosphoric acid			–	–	–
Adenosine monophosphate-C^{14} + ethyl metaphosphate			+(3%)	+(0.3%)	+(0.1%)
4.[c]					
Adenosine diphosphate + phosphoric acid				–	–
Adenosine diphosphate + ethyl metaphosphate				+	+

[a] Figures within parentheses show conversion as per cent of starting material.
[b] With the techniques used in this experiment the lower limit of detectability was 0.001%.
[c] In experiment 4 no quantitative estimates were performed, as unlabeled ADP was used. The ATP in this case was located by shadowgrams.

232

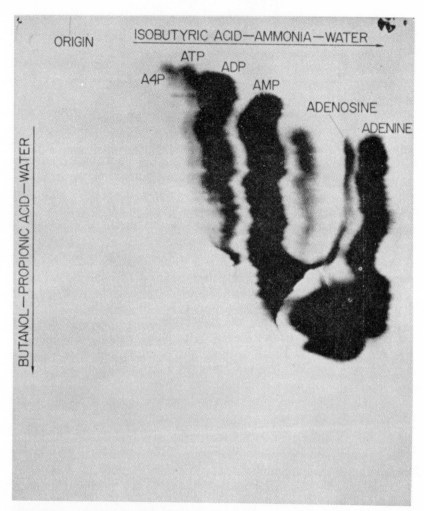

FIG. 5. Chromatogram illustrating the formation of ADP, ATP, and A4P from AMP by the action of ultraviolet light.

phosphates. Ethyl metaphosphate was selected as a possible reagent because of a recent report by Schramm *et al.* (1962) that it activates carbonyl, hydroxyl, and amino groups in organic synthesis. It can be expected that ethyl metaphosphate was probably not the most abundant source of phosphorus in primitive times. But we do not know how well other, possibly more abundant, phosphate salts may efficiently substitute for ethyl metaphosphate. At temperatures over 300°C, phosphoric acid occurs only in the forms of polyphosphate. It can, therefore, be assumed that when the crust of the Earth began to cool, a supply of polyphosphates was available which may have reacted with alkoxy compounds to form phosphate esters. Other phosphorus compounds may also be effective in this synthesis, but they have not yet been investigated.

Two general categories of control experiments were performed to assess two possible modes of biogenic contamination of the reaction products. To test the possibility that the relatively high temperatures $(40 \pm 2°C)$ attained by the Vycor tubes during ultraviolet irradiation stimulated the metabolic activities of microorganisms in the reactants, we placed control tubes at these same temperatures for comparable periods, but without ultraviolet irradiation. In all other respects they were handled and analyzed similarly to the irradiated samples. In no case was any yield detected.

An alternative hypothetical source of contamination is the presence in the labeled reactants of microorganisms which, under ultraviolet irradiation, are photolyzed, introducing their metabolic products into the medium. To test this possibility, we introduced into Vycor tubes that had been autoclaved for 45 minutes at 120°C reactants that had been passed through an autoclaved Seitz filter. These sterile samples were then irradiated with ultraviolet light and analyzed. No change in yield was observed. We conclude that the microbiological contribution to the observed yield was negligible.

The yields achieved in these experiments, as shown in Table I, are relatively high. In contrast, quite elaborate methods are ordinarily required for the laboratory synthesis of nucleoside phosphates (Baddiley, 1955). For the production of adenosine from adenine, ribose, and a phosphorus source, the quantum yield for a 1-hour irradiation is $\varphi \sim 10^{-5}$. For production of AMP, ADP, and ATP by the use of ethyl metaphosphate, the quantum yields are almost an order of magnitude greater.

To establish whether the ATP synthesized by us was biochemically active, a luminescence assay was performed using dehydrated firefly tails. The method described by Strehler and Totter (1962) was used. (Firefly tails were supplied by Schwarz BioResearch, Inc., Mount Vernon, New York.) The intensity of luminescence was measured by a Turner fluorometer. The decay curve of the luminescence was identical with that of an authentic sample of ATP. The concentration of ATP in the solution used, as determined by this method, corresponded within the limits of experimental error to the value obtained by spectrophotometric measurements.

The synthetic ATP was further tested for biochemical activity by Roberta Kupervas and Dr. Harold Klein of the Exobiology Division of the Ames Research Center, using yeast hexokinase. The synthetic product participated in this reaction in a manner equivalent to authentic ATP (obtained from the Sigma Chemical Co., St. Louis, Missouri).

In more recent experiments, attempts were made to synthesize deoxyadenosine and the deoxynucleotides using the same techniques. Preliminary evidence indicates that the deoxy compounds are formed in the same way. Deoxyadenosine, deoxy-AMP, -ADP, and -ATP have been identified in an irradiated mixture of deoxyribose, adenine, and ethyl metaphosphate.

The use of ionizing radiation appears to give even more satisfactory results. When a dilute solution of adenine and ribose in water is exposed to ionizing radiation, adenosine is formed. This result was detected even in the absence of a phosphate. With UV light, however, no adenosine was detected unless a phosphate was present. Preliminary data indicate that in the presence of an inorganic phosphate (phosphoric acid) the mono-, di-, and trinucleotides are formed.

The work in our laboratory thus far has demonstrated the synthesis of the purines, adenine, guanine; the sugars, ribose and deoxyribose, the nucleoside, adenosine, and the nucleotides, AMP, ADP, and ATP. These results are relevant to the problem of the origin of life, as the conditions of reaction are aqueous, and the concentrations of materials are very low, and the sources of energy used are those most likely to have existed under primitive Earth conditions.

Revised Manuscript received December 27, 1963.

REFERENCES

Baddiley, J. (1955). *In* "The Nucleic Acids" (E. Chargaff and J. N. Davidson, eds.) Vol. 1, p. 137. Academic Press, New York.

Butlerow, A. (1861). *Annalen* 120, 295.

El'piner, E., and Sokol'skaya, A. V. (1959). *Origin Life Earth Rept. Intern. Symp. Moscow 1957* p. 173.

Fox, S. W., and Harada, K. (1961). *Science* 133, 1923.

Kerr, J. A., and Trotman-Dickenson, A. F. (1962–63). *In* "Handbook of Chemistry and Physics," 44th ed., pp. 3519–20. Chem. Rubber Publ. Co., Cleveland, Ohio.

Kliss, R. M., and Matthews, C. N. (1962). *Proc. Natl. Acad. Sci. U.S.* 48, 1300.

Miller, S. L. (1955). *J. Am. Chem. Soc.* 77, 2351.

Miller, S. L., and Urey, H. C. (1959). *Science* 130, 245.

Oró, J. (1961). *Nature* 190, 389.

Oró, J. (1963). *Ann. N.Y. Acad. Sci.* 108, 64.

Oró, J., and Kimball, A. P. (1961). *Arch. Biochem. Biophys.* 93, 166.

Palm, C., and Calvin, M. (1962). *J. Am. Chem. Soc.* **84**, 2115.

Ponnamperuma, C., Lemmon, R. M., and Calvin, M. (1962). *Science* **137**, 605.

Ponnamperuma, C., Lemmon, R. M., Mariner, R., and Calvin, M. (1963a). *Proc. Natl. Acad. Sci. U.S.* **49**, 737.

Ponnamperuma, C., Sagan, C., and Mariner, R. (1963b). *Nature* **199**, 222.

Pullman, B., and Pullman, A. (1962). *Nature* **196**, 1137. (M. Burton, J. S. Kirby-Smith, and J. L. Magee, eds.)

Pullman, B., and Pullman, A. (1960). *In* "Comparative Effects of Radiation," pp. 111–112. Wiley, New York.

Sagan, C. (1957). *Evolution* **11**, 40.

Sagan, C. (1961). *Radiation Res.* **15**, 174.

Schramm, G., Grotsch, H., and Pollman, W. (1962). *Angew. Chemi.* (*Intern. Ed. Engl.*) **1**, 1.

Strehler, B. L., and Totter, J. R. (1952). *Arch. Biochem. Biophys.* **40**, 28.

Swings, P., and Haser, L. (1956). "Atlas of Representative Cometary Spectra." Univ. Liege, Astrophysical Institute, Louvain.

Whipple, F. L. (1950). *Astrophys. J.* **111**, 375.

DISCUSSION

DR. BERNAL[1]: I feel that Dr. Sagan's contribution is peculiarly valuable as introducing another of these conditions which we must take into account for any discussion of the origin of life, the abundance on a cosmic scale of the main elements, hydrogen, carbon, nitrogen, and oxygen. He implies that these would form the main constituents of any kind of life that might occur. The most significant deviation from this, it seems to me, is the underabundance of phosphorus, a key element for all biomolecular reactions and a pointer to the kind of conditions we may expect to have prevailed when life originated. This may be sufficient in itself to rule out any conception of life originating on meteorites or their parent bodies—the concentration of phosphorus is much too low—and at the same time point to its origin in a watery medium on the surface of an adequately heavy planet. Dr. Sagan's point about the destructive nature of ultraviolet light does go further and suggests that this was actually present when the ground work of biochemistry was being laid.

DR. HARADA: I would like to ask Dr. Sagan about the temperature of the primitive Sun.

Scientists have studied the formation and evolution of the Earth. According to your recent article in *Radiation Res.*, **15**, 174(1961), "The primitive reducing atmosphere was in existence for no longer than 1×10^9 years since the stabilization of the earth's mantle about 4.5×10^9 years ago," and "The event (origin of life) almost certainly occurred $4.0 \pm 0.5 \times 10^9$ years ago. A more narrowly circumscribed estimate,

[1] *In absentia*

based on the above remarks, is that life arose on earth $4.2 \pm 0.2 \times 10^9$ years ago." So until this time, the primitive atmosphere, methane and ammonia, etc., should have been converted to simple and complex organic molecules of biological importance by use of many kinds of energy, such as UV radiation, electric discharge, heat, etc. Ultraviolet light has been accepted among chemists as the most abundant form of energy on the primitive Earth. However, we chemists do not really know the surface temperature of the primitive Sun about 4.5×10^9 years ago. And the UV radiation energy is solely dependent on the surface temperature of the Sun.

The Earth has been considered to have a common origin with the Sun about 4.5×10^9 years ago. The Sun was also very young when life originated on the Earth about 4.2×10^9 years ago. The primitive Sun might have been an orange-colored star or a red-colored star or even a dark star, even if the thermonuclear reaction had occurred inside the primitive Sun's huge body. According to Stefan-Boltzmann's law and Wien's displacement law of radiation, the radiation energy (especially UV radiation) should be decreased considerably if the surface temperature of the primitive Sun is lowered. If the primitive Sun was orange colored, only long weak UV radiation was available. If the Sun was red, it would have been difficult to get UV energy from the primitive Sun. This is a discussion of the very early days when the atmosphere was still relatively transparent. The formation of an ozone layer should come later and this is not pertinent here.

Many chemists synthesized organic compounds of biological importance in the laboratory by use of artificial ultraviolet light. These works are very interesting and important. However, it seems to me that they assume *a priori* that UV radiation energy of the primitive Sun at the time when the life originated is the same as we observe today. Some chemists do not consider the UV radiation energy of the primitive Sun, or they misquote the astronomical studies. Other chemists discuss the primordial chemistry of the primitive Earth in terms of the kinds and amounts of energy which are observed today.

I think that the evolution of the Sun has to be considered in conjunction with the evolution of the primitive Earth. In summary, the surface temperature of the primitive Sun (4.5–4.2×10^9 years ago) is very important in connection with the formation of organic compounds by UV irradiation. So the surface temperature of the Sun should be discussed. And what was the surface temperature of the primitive Sun (4.5–4.2×10^9 years ago)? If the temperature of the primitive Sun was high enough to permit radiation of short UV light, this makes the chemist (including me) happy, because we chemists get an authorized playground.

Dr. Sagan: The photon flux shortward of some characteristic wavelength λ_0 at the top of the Earth's atmosphere in primitive times can be written as

$$Q = \frac{kT}{\hbar\lambda_0^2}\left(\frac{R}{a}\right)^2 \exp\{-hc/\lambda_0 kT\}$$

where k is Boltzmann's constant, $\hbar = h/2\pi$, h is Planck's constant, T is the equivalent solar blackbody temperature in the ultraviolet, R is the radius of the solar photosphere, and a is the semimajor axis of the Earth's orbit. c is the velocity of light. k, h, c, and a very likely had the same values some 4×10^9 years ago as they do today. Therefore, if we choose our characteristic wavelength λ_0, we can determine the photon flux, Q, in photons cm^{-2} sec^{-1}, if we know R and T.

Present models of solar evolution indicate that during the time that the Sun was contracting from an interstellar cloud of gas and dust, it was moving approximately vertically downward in the Hertzsprung-Russell diagram toward the main sequence. Thus, earlier than about 5×10^9 years ago, the temperature of the Sun's surface was almost as great as it is today, while its radius was much larger. Therefore, there is some possibility that the ultraviolet flux was even greater than it is today. However, this contraction to the main sequence occurred before the planets were formed, and, therefore, this is probably not the ultraviolet flux relevant to the problem of the origin of life.

Since reaching the main sequence, the Sun has been relatively stable, increasing in luminosity by only about half a bolometric magnitude in 5×10^9 years. Models of solar evolution indicate that the radius of the solar photosphere some four billion years ago was about 0.90 the present value. If we assume that the effective ultraviolet temperature is proportional to the mean bolometric temperature, the effective ultraviolet temperature was about 0.98 the present value, or slightly less than $5000°K$. With this information, the following table can be constructed, giving approximate values of the solar ultraviolet photon flux shortward of wavelength λ_0 available at the top of the Earth's atmosphere about 4×10^9 years ago.

λ_0 (Å)	Q (cm^{-2} sec^{-1})
2900	7×10^{14}
2600	4×10^{14}
2400	9×10^{13}
2000	2×10^{13}

I believe such figures clearly demonstrate the dominant role which ultraviolet light played among primitive energy sources relevant to the origin of life. It is for this reason that the use of ultraviolet energy sources may be more relevant in primitive Earth simulation experiments than some other energy sources which have been used—to take only one example, high-energy α particles.

MR. PIRIE: Could I ask Dr. Sagan to enlarge a little on Jupiter, because I don't remember the figures, but I thought the density was extremely low, the figure is less than 1, and therefore, some part of its body must be made up of some extremely light products, such as liquid hydrogen or ammonia. Is this compatible with the temperatures of which you spoke?

DR. SAGAN: From its mass and radius, we know that the mean density of Jupiter is about $1\frac{1}{3}$ gm/cm^3. It's Saturn which would float on water, if there were enough water. The motion of the Jovian satellites shows that there is a strong central condensation of mass inside Jupiter. Therefore, the bulk of the planet is gaseous. The physical state of the Jovian interior requires it to be composed primarily of metallic hydrogen, a form of hydrogen having high thermal and electrical conductivities, and which is not in ordinary use.

The possibilities I referred to, which followed from Gallet's thermodynamic calculations, describe a region in the atmosphere, perhaps 100 km below the visible cloud tops. The solid body of Jupiter is much farther down.

MR. PIRIE: Therefore, you would be thinking of synthesis in some sort of a fog on Jupiter.

DR. SAGAN: The atmospheric density is already approaching that of liquid water. While the atmosphere is not a liquid in the ordinary sense, it is still dense enough to replace, in part, liquid water as an interaction medium for the production of large organic molecules. In addition, of course, the cloud contains water.

DR. MORA: Dr. Ponnamperuma, did you try phosphorous acid in place of phosphoric acid with adenine in your radiation experiments? You might find that since phosphorous acid has a low dissociation constant for the third hydrogen, it might act very well as a push-pull catalyst.

DR. PONNAMPERUMA: No. There is a chance of phosphorous acid being a possibility.

DR. MORA: See Swain and Lowry with regard to this possible push-pull mechanism. [Swain, C. G., and Brown, J. F. (1952). *J. Am. Chem. Soc.* 74, 2534; Lowry, T. M., and Smith, G. F. (1927). *J. Chem. Soc.* p. 2539.]

DR. PATTEE: I have a question in regard to what Dr. Sagan suggested, but anyone can answer it, I suppose. In your statement you said that you are glad to trade geological time for polymerase. Whether you can do this or not depends on two numbers, which I don't know. One is the half-life of nucleotide and the other is the catalytic power of polymerase —the order of magnitude. Is this a reasonable trade?

DR. SAGAN: I don't know the answer. It's a problem in kinetics, which I hope can be solved.

DR. HALDANE: DNA is surprisingly stable, even RNA maybe.

I should like to ask Dr. Sagan, however, whether he doesn't think it is possible on Jupiter, and perhaps further out in our system, there may be a chemistry, what one might call a Franklin chemistry, based on ammonia rather than water, with considerable alternative possibilities.

DR. SAGAN: I certainly do think that such replacements of OH by NH_2 are possible. On Jupiter, we must expect a liquid ammonia cloud layer below the observed ammonia cirrus cloud layer and above the hypothesized liquid water cloud layer. So it's possible that both the Franklin type and the ordinary type of organic chemistry exist on Jupiter.

DR. FOX: I would like to respond to Dr. Mora's question by pointing out with respect to the question of the plausibility of phosphorous acid that Addison Gulick [*Am. Sci.* 43, 479 (1955) and *Ann. N.Y. Acad. Sci.* 69, 309 (1957)] has, in two reviews, presented the plausibility of both phosphorous acid and hypophosphorous acid in the primitive earth. Gulick suggested that life originated under conditions in which phosphorus was only partially oxidized.

DR. SAGAN: Gulick's point was that the only forms of phosphorus which would be stable under the reducing conditions that he *assumed* were the phosphites and hypophosphites; but you can have phosphoric acid under reducing conditions as well. The reducing conditions which Gulick assumed are much more highly reducing than we today believe plausible for the secondary atmosphere. Phosphoric acid is an entirely reasonable phosphorus source in primitive times.

DR. FOX: This leads to the point I was going to make in addition, that we might have a paper not only on the folly of probability, but one on the folly of plausibility.

DR. ORÓ: Dr. Ponnamperuma was wondering why he was not able to find pyrimidines in his experiments as we have found in ours. I would like to suggest two possible explanations. Perhaps the proper C_3 intermediates were not formed in his experiments or the temperature used was lower than the one used in our experiments, which was 135°C.

DR. SCHRAMM: It should be possible to convert the adenosine to adenosine phosphate without radiation. Have you tried that?

DR. PONNAMPERUMA: At the temperatures we were working with, about 40°C, we didn't detect any nucleotides in the absence of ultraviolet light.

DR. CHARGAFF: Is there any evidence that, for instance, such a thing as hydrazine or hydroxylamine is formed in these various primitive soups? If hydrazine was formed, this would explain the absence of pyrimidines very nicely because they are easily destroyed by it. I have been wondering whether hydrazines or hydroxylamine do appear.

DR. PONNAMPERUMA: We haven't looked for them.

DR. ORÓ: Hydrazine is formed in large amounts by the action of electrical discharges on ammonia or ammonia–water mixtures. However, in the presence of methane the synthesis of hydrazine will decrease appreciably at the expense of the formation of amino acids and amines. The chemistry of hydrazine is not very well understood.

DR. CHARGAFF: That is why I asked.

DR. SCHRAMM: The splitting of the pyrimidines is caused only by high concentrations of hydrazine.

DR. ORÓ: I may add that we have observed that formaldehyde and hydrazine lead to the formation of a number of interesting compounds. In addition to the amino acids mentioned in my presentation, acetaldehyde and pyridines are also formed. Since some coenzymes are pyridine derivatives, it might be of interest to suggest how pyridines could be formed from formaldehyde and hydrazine. In the presence of hydrazine, formaldehyde undergoes an aldol base-catalyzed condensation to form monosaccharides which eventually are cyclized into pyranoses (or furanoses). Addition of ammonia—which is formed by reduction of hydrazine—to the carbonyl group of the sugar, will cause the replacement of the oxygen in the pyranose ring with an imino group. Final dehydration of the resulting compound will yield a pyridine. Perhaps by a similar sequence of reactions one could also expect the formation of pyrroles from furanose intermediates.

DR. ORÓ: Purines can also be synthesized from amino acids, such as glycine and other common biosynthetic precursors, as originally shown by Horbaczewsky and more recently by other investigators (Bredereck, Oró, Ponnamperuma). However, temperatures of about 500°K are needed in this case. Usually the amounts obtained decrease as one proceeds from the more to the less oxidized purines, in the following order: uric acid, xanthine, hypoxanthine, adenine. The yield of adenine is small but comparable to that obtained from hydrogen cyanide.

From another point of view, it is also possible that a synthesis of purines resembling more closely the enzymatic pathway could take place in hydrogen cyanide mixtures at room temperature. This is based on earlier observations made by the application of the Gerlach-Döring test. The Gerlach-Döring test is specific for adenine and adenine-containing compounds. Well, then, in addition to adenine we found in our chromatograms another compound which gave also a positive Gerlach-Döring test. On the basis of its slower movement on the chromatograms and other properties we felt that it was an acyl or glycosyl derivative of adenine and reasoned that the formation of a nucleosidic intermediate probably took place before the cyclization of the imidazole and pyrimidine rings of the adenine moeity, in a similar manner as it occurs enzymatically.

DR. SAGAN: Dr. Buchanan has suggested that the primitive synthesis of purines and pyrimidines may parallel the contemporary biosynthetic pathways. However, it is very likely that carbon dioxide was always a minor constituent of the Earth's atmosphere, because of what is called the Urey equilibrium, in which outgassed carbon dioxide reacts with silicates to form carbonates and sand. The reaction is controlled at a partial pressure which depends almost only on the ambient temperature. This partial pressure is within an order of magnitude of the contemporary carbon dioxide partial pressure, so if primitive and contemporary pathways are analogous, the primitive syntheses would have been hampered by the requirement of an underabundant gas as a precursor.

DR. BUCHANAN: It is possible that a compound like oxalacetic acid might break down to yield CO_2 in sufficient quantity. In fact, in the enzymatic reaction, it is difficult to determine whether oxalacetic acid is a better precursor of purines than CO_2 itself.

DR. PONNAMPERUMA: Dr. Fox stated earlier that malic acid and urea give uracil. This might probably be the answer.

DR. FOX: This is done in the presence of polyphosphoric acid, which is dehydrated. The mechanism is a plausible mechanism which includes loss of a molecule of water.

DR. PONNAMPERUMA: We have examined proteinoid prepared by heating amino acids together and found traces of guanine. This may be similar to a biosynthetic process in which amino acids act as precursors.

I could not tell definitely from where the guanine came. By using labeled aspartic and glutamic acids, we have shown that the guanine does not come from the aspartic acid nor from the glutamic acid. It may come from one or more of the other amino acids.

PROBABLE SYNTHESIS OF PORPHINE-LIKE SUBSTANCES DURING CHEMICAL EVOLUTION

ANTON SZUTKA

Department of Chemistry, University of Detroit, Detroit, Michigan

Introduction

It is already a well established theory that chemical evolution, i.e., evolution on the molecular level, preceded the appearance of the first living cell on the Earth. Current concepts suggest that a relatively simple primitive atmosphere consisting of methane, ammonia, water, and probably some molecular hydrogen under the influence of ultraviolet radiation, electrical discharges, and high energy radiations was transformed into more complex compounds (Oparin, 1957, 1962; Urey, 1952; Haldane, 1954). It has been generally accepted that the temperature at the time of this transformation was less than 100°C. The raw material thus produced accumulated in pools of water, forming an organic milieu, i.e., the nonliving mixture of carbon compounds which is generally considered a prerequisite for the origin of life. Some estimates made by Urey (1952) indicate that the concentration of organic compounds dissolved in the primitive oceans might have been as high as 10%. The synthesis of these raw materials continued until a state of equilibrium was reached, in which the action of available energy sources destroyed as much of the raw material as it produced. In this period of time only relatively simple molecules could be formed because the more complicated and labile ones would be destroyed by the energetic ultraviolet radiation reaching the surface of the Earth, unscreened by the ozone layer which now protects the Earth.

The foregoing theories of Oparin (1957, 1962) and Urey (1952) have been subjected to rigid laboratory tests by Miller (1953, 1955, 1957a), Miller and Urey (1959), Pavlovskaya and Pasynskii (1959), Abelson (1956), Oró (1961), Hasselstrom and Henry (1956), Hasselstrom et al. (1957), Paschke et al. (1957), and others (Bahadur, 1954; Bahadur and Srivastava, 1961; Palm and Calvin, 1962). These experiments have pro-

243

duced various products of biochemical importance, such as amino acids, aliphatic acids, polyhydroxy compounds, aldehydes, and urea. Subjecting these simple molecules to further action of ultraviolet radiation or mild heating produced a variety of complex organic molecules. Such higher order reactions, for example, result in production of polypeptides from amino acids, as demonstrated by Fox (1956, 1960), Fox and Harada (1960), and from polyglycine by Akabori (1959).

In the reviewed literature, most of the authors (Oparin, 1957, 1962; Gaffron, 1960; Calvin, 1959, 1961, 1962a,b; Sagan, 1961) dealing with the problem of the origin of life are convinced that at some stage of chemical evolution porphyrins must have developed. However, until recently there was no experimental evidence that porphyrins or porphine-like substances could be synthesized from precursors which were available during the period of chemical evolution on Earth.

This paper presents observations having direct bearing on the formation of the organic milieu, namely, the synthesis of porphine-like substances from simple precursors.

Experimental Procedures

It has been known that pyrrole and benzaldehyde when heated to about 180°C condense to form α, β, γ, δ-tetraphenylporphine (Rothemund, 1936) (Fig. 1) and α. β, γ, δ-tetraphenylchlorin (Ball et al., 1946). The same system, with 5 ml of pyrrole, 10 ml of benzaldehyde, 10 ml of pyridine (all freshly redistilled), and 5 gm of zinc acetate, was used in our first experiments (Szutka et al., 1959). The pyridine serves as a solvent. Zinc acetate was found to increase the yield (Ball, et al., 1946; Priesthoff and Banks, 1954). The mixture was placed in a screw-cap Pyrex tube with approximately 2 ml of air space above the liquid and was irradiated with Co^{60} γ-rays for 10 hours at the rate of approximately 0.5 megaroentgens per hour. The solution removed from the irradiation vessel, reddish in color, was diluted with chloroform, treated with an equal volume of 6 N hydrochloric acid, and stirred vigorously for 3 hours. The acidic solution was then neutralized with ammonia. The chloroform solution, separated from the aqueous layer, was washed several times with distilled water and chromatographed on activated alumina, as suggested by Priesthoff and Banks (1954), with fresh chloroform as the eluent. Three chromatographic separations removed most of the tarry products from the chloroform solution, which was subsequently subjected to chromatography on a Magnesol column. The dark-green band was repacked into a second column, wetted with ether, and eluted with chloroform. The procedure was repeated until a single, clear band was obtained on the column.

In recent experiments (Szutka, 1963), a system consisting of 3 ml of freshly distilled pyrrole, 6 ml of benzaldehyde, and 4 ml of water, was placed in a 250 ml beaker and then irradiated, at a distance of 25 cm with ultraviolet light, using a 100 Watt Hanovia Utility model lamp. The radiation transmitted through the filter was 45% at 2500 Å and 90% at 3000 Å; the output of the lamp was 1.5×10^{15} quanta per second cm^2 or 5×10^{16} quanta per second per area of the mixture exposed to radiation. The doses were measured by chemical actinometry, using an uranyl

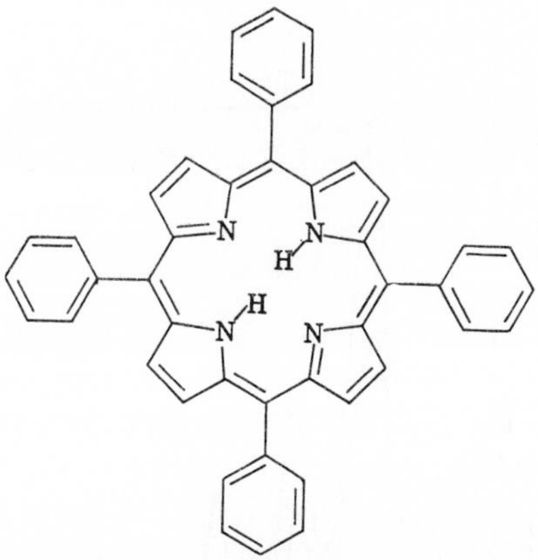

FIG. 1. α, β, γ, δ-Tetraphenylporphine molecule.

oxalate actinometer according to Forbes and Heidt (1934). After exposure, the reddish-brown solution was diluted with approximately 20 ml of chloroform and washed with 20 ml of distilled water. After separation in a separatory funnel, the aqueous layer was discarded, and the chloroform layer was transferred into a beaker charged with approximately 20 gm of anhydrous sodium sulfate to remove any dissolved water. The sodium sulfate was removed by filtration and discarded, while the filtrate was diluted to 50 ml volume with chloroform and stored for the quantitative determination of porphines.

The final product was isolated by column chromatography, using activated alumina (F-20) and Florosil (60–100 mesh) as adsorbents and fresh chloroform as eluent. Two chromatographic treatments on alumina and three to four chromatographic separations on Florosil yielded a pure product. The porphines appeared in the effluent, and collections of effluent were continued until no Soret band was detected.

The same mixture of pyrrole, benzaldehyde, and water, when placed in the dark without irradiation, also produced porphines. The isolation and quantitative determination of porphines was done by the same methods used for irradiated mixtures.

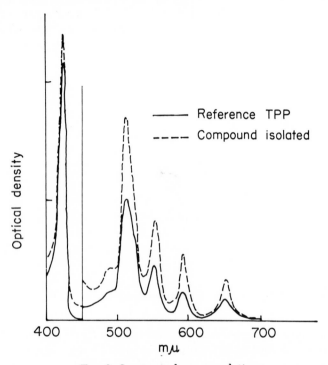

——— Reference TPP

– – – – Compound isolated

FIG. 2. Spectra in benzene solution.

If, instead of water, pyridine was used as a solvent in the system, and the mixture was then irradiated for 2 hours, no porphine-like substances could be detected by previously used methods. Aging of the mixture for 10 days produced only traces of porphines.

A typical spectrum of a compound isolated from an irradiated mixture and the reference spectrum of the compound synthesized by the method of Ball et al. (1946), are presented in Fig. 2. Both spectra are identical with those obtained by Thomas and Martell (1956) and Dorough et al. (1951). For quantitative estimation of the yield, the molar extinction coefficient of 18.7×10^3 at 515 mμ maximum was used, as suggested by Thomas and Martell (1956). Identity of the compound was further established by the formation of a zinc chelate, according to the procedure of Rothemund and Menotti (1948) and Dorough et al. (1951). The spectra of the reference zinc chelate and the chelate of

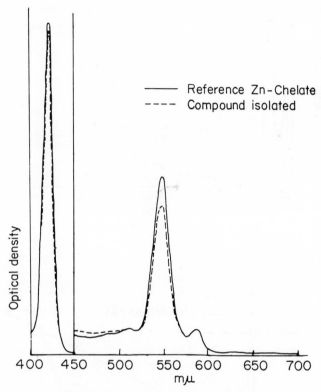

FIG. 3. Zinc chelate spectra in benzene.

the compound isolated from the irradiated mixture are identical, as shown in Fig. 3.

It is also well known that acid salts of α, β, γ, δ-tetraphenylporphines exhibit a characteristic spectrum (Rothemund and Menotti, 1948; Banks and Bisque, 1957). Therefore, part of the benzene solution of the reference compound and part of the benzene solution of compounds isolated from irradiated mixtures were evaporated to dryness and treated with glacial acetic acid. Upon recording the spectra (Fig. 4),

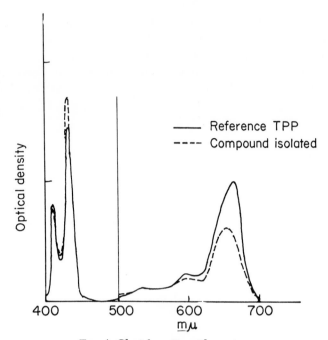

FIG. 4. Glacial acetic acid spectra.

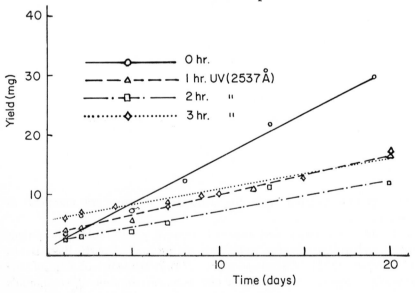

FIG. 5. Plot of total yield versus time of storage in chloroform after irradiation with tungsten lamp.

they were found to be identical with those listed in the literature (Rothemund and Menotti, 1948; Banks and Bisque, 1957).

Although the amount of porphines isolated after γ-irradiation was in the microgram range, this quantity was sufficient to make positive identification.

Figures 5 and 6 represent the total yields of porphines isolated from the stored mixtures, plotted against time of storage in the chloroform

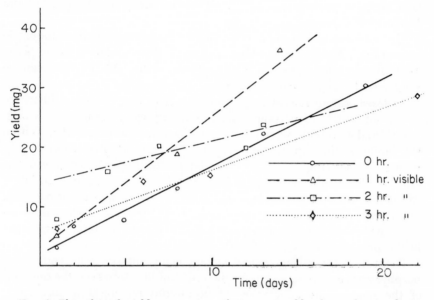

FIG. 6. Plot of total yield versus time of storage in chloroform after irradiation with ultraviolet light.

solutions. Each line in these graphs represents different irradiation conditions.

Discussion

In our present study we have shown that porphine-like structures can be synthesized in the presence of oxygen from precursors which were available in the very earliest stage of chemical evolution. Aldehydes were found in products of the action of electrical discharges on the Urey atmosphere in Miller's experiment (1953, 1955, 1957a). Pyrroles and pyrrolidines were easily formed from ammonia, acetylene, and other unsaturated hydrocarbons by simple catalysis or under influence of ultraviolet radiation (Oparin, 1957). In addition, Tsukamoto and Lichtin

(1960, 1962) found pyrroles as the major product of the reaction of active nitrogen with 1,3-butadienes.

The results of this study also indicate that the presence of water, or rather the suspension of the organic matter in water, increases the yield of porphine-like substances considerably. Oparin (1957, 1962) and Haldane (1954) have already indicated the possibility of evolution of living matter from the pools rich in organic matter, rather than on solid surfaces. The concentration of organic matter could be quite high, if part of the water solvent evaporated, as the case might be in lakes and lagoons.

The increase in the yield of porphine-like substances, on standing in chloroform solutions, shows that a process of autocatalysis takes place. This process, postulated by Calvin (1959, 1961, 1962a), now can be supported by experimental evidence.

A closer examination of Figs. 5 and 6 reveals that there is a difference in the total yield of porphines after standing when the mixture is originally irradiated with different kinds of electromagnetic radiation. Within the limits of the experimental method, the rate of production of porphines in the sample initially exposed to the tungsten lamp was the same as that in the nonirradiated sample. On the other hand, an initial irradiation with ultraviolet light has a lower rate of increase of porphine production under identical conditions of storage. This comparison has been made on aqueous suspensions of the starting materials irradiated in the presence of oxygen.

There is a general agreement among many authors that synthesis of porphyrins is a necessary step for the origin of life. However, the question of the time of the appearance of porphyrins is subject to discussion. Gaffron (1960) and Calvin (1959, 1961, 1962a) support the idea that porphyrins were already active in the very earliest quasi-living organic structure. Miller and Urey (1959), consider this as not necessary and suggest that porphyrins may have arisen during the evolution of primitive organisms. Strughold and Ritter (1962) consider preexisting stores of oxygen, produced by photochemical dissociation of water, as a prerequisite for the formation and development of chlorophyll, whereas the heme types of porphyrins were formed about 1–1.5 billion years later.

Although at the present time it seems to be impossible to determine with absolute confidence at what stage of chemical evolution porphine-like substances developed, certain deductions can be based on the experimental evidence now available. It can be argued that after the stores of simpler organic compounds reached their saturation point, in the first stage of chemical evolution, there was a reduction of the energy level of the source that enabled the continuation of the chemical evolution to a more complicated nature. The photolysis of water and the formation of an ozone layer cut out short ultraviolet radiation completely, leaving only a mild energy source of longer ultraviolet and visible radiation.

In addition, an evolutionary need arose for the synthesis of porphine-like substances as soon as the reductive atmosphere was converted into an oxidative one. Since the short-wave ultraviolet radiation was no longer available as an energy source, the appearance of porphines and especially their metal chelates at this stage was important in that they provided a mechanism for the efficient utilization of lower energy radiation. Their aid in chemical transformations such as hydrogen transfer or oxidation is well established.

Simultaneously, with the change of reductive atmosphere to an oxidative one due to the photolysis of water, hydrogen peroxide appeared. If it remained in contact with organic substances, extensive oxidation would have occurred. Therefore, for chemical evolution to continue, a mechanism for the destruction of these large amounts of hydrogen peroxide had to be available. Calvin (1959) has already pointed out that incorporation of ferric iron into a heme-type molecule would increase the catalytic activity of iron for the destruction of hydrogen peroxide by a factor of 10^3, while the addition of certain proteins increases this destruction rate by an additional factor of 10^5.

These last two arguments indicate that with the transition of a reductive atmosphere into an oxidative one, an immediate need was created for the formation of the porphine-like substances.

ACKNOWLEDGMENT

This work is supported in part by grant NsG-226-62 from the National Aeronautics and Space Administration.

Revised Manuscript received January 6, 1964.

REFERENCES

Abelson, P. H. (1956). *Science* **124**, 935.
Akabori, S. (1959). *Origin Life Earth Rep. Intern. Symp. Moscow 1957* pp. 189–196.
Bahadur, K. (1954). *Nature* **173**, 1141.
Bahadur, K., and Strivastava, R. R. (1961). *Zh. Obshch. Khim.* **31**, 3017.
Ball, R. H., Dorough, G. D., and Calvin, M. (1946). *J. Am. Chem. Soc.* **68**, 2278.
Banks, C. V., and Bisque, R. E., (1957). *Anal. Chem.* **29**, 522.
Calvin, M. (1959). *Science* **130**, 1170.
Calvin, M. (1961). *Chem. Eng. News* **39**, 96 (May).
Calvin, M. (1962a). *Perspectives Biol. Med.* **5**, 147.

Calvin, M. (1962b). *Perspectives Biol. Med.* **5**, 399.
Dorough, G. D., Miller, J. R., and Huennekens, F. M. (1951). *J. Am. Chem. Soc.* **73**, 4315.
Forbes, G. S., and Heidt, L. J. (1934). *J. Am. Chem. Soc.* **56**, 2363.
Fox, S. W. (1956). *Am. Scientist* **44**, 347.
Fox, S. W. (1960). *Science* **132**, 200.
Fox, S. W., and Harada, K. (1960). *Arch. Biochem. Biophys.* **86**, 281.
Gaffron, H. (1960). *Perspectives Biol Med.* **3**, 163.
Haldane, J. B. S. (1954). "Collection of Essays on the Origin of Life." Penguin Books, London.
Hasselstrom, T., and Henry, M. C. (1956). *Science* **123**, 1038.
Hasselstrom, T., Henry, M. C., and Murr, B. (1957). *Science* **125**, 350.
Miller, S. L. (1953). *Science* **117**, 528.
Miller, S. L. (1955). *J. Am. Chem. Soc.* **77**, 2351.
Miller, S. L. (1957a). *Ann. N.Y. Acad. Sci.* **69**, 260.
Miller, S. L. (1957b). *Biochim. Biophys. Acta* **23**, 480.
Miller, S. L., and Urey, H. C. (1959). *Science* **130**, 245.
Oparin, A. I. (1957). "The Origin of Life on the Earth" (translated by A. Synge), 3rd ed. Academic Press, New York.
Oparin, A. I. (1962). "Life, Its Nature, Origin and Development" (translated by A. Synge). Academic Press, New York.
Oró, J. (1961). *Nature* **191**, 1193.
Oró, J., and Guidry, C. L. (1961). *Arch. Biochem. Biophys.* **93**, 166.
Oró, J., and Kamat, S. S. (1961). *Nature* **190**, 442.
Palm, A., and Calvin, M. (1962). *J. Am. Chem. Soc.* **84**, 2115.
Paschke, R., Chang, R. W. H., and Young, D. (1957). *Science* **125**, 881.
Pavlovskaya, T. E., and Pasynskii, A. G. (1959). *Origin Life Earth Rept. Intern. Symp. Moscow 1957* pp. 151–157.
Priesthoff, J. H., and Banks, C. V. (1954). *J. Am. Chem. Soc.* **76**, 937.
Rothemund, P. (1936). *J. Am. Chem. Soc.* **58**, 625.
Rothemund, P., and Menotti, A. M. (1948). *J. Am. Chem. Soc.* **70**, 1808.
Sagan, C. (1961). *Radiation Res.* **15**, 174.
Strughold, H., and Ritter, C. L. (1962). *Aerospace Med.* **33**, 275.
Szutka, A., Hazel, J. F., and McNabb, W. M. (1959). *Radiation Res.* **10**, 597.
Szutka, A. (1963). *Radiation Res.* **19**, 183.
Thomas, D. W., and Martell, A. E. (1956). *J. Am. Chem. Soc.* **78**, 1338.
Tsukamoto, A., and Lichtin, N. N. (1960). *J. Am. Chem. Soc.* **82**, 3798.
Tsukamoto, A., and Lichtin, N. N. (1962). *J. Am. Chem. Soc.* **84**, 1601.
Urey, H. C. (1952). "The Planets." Yale Univ. Press, New Haven, Connecticut.

DISCUSSION

DR. OPARIN: I wish to communicate relevant work carried out at the A. N. Bakh Institute of Biochemistry by A. A. Krasnovskii and A. V. Umrikhina. They have shown that the synthesis of porphine from pyrrole and formaldehyde is facilitated by the presence of oxygen and that the synthesis is accelerated in the presence of silica and similar compounds.

This is of interest in connection with the possibility of abiogenic formation of porphines.

It has been found that porphine acts as a photosynthesizer in reactions of hydrogen transfer. As an example, this occurs when one uses ions of ferrous oxide as electron donors and methyl red as an acceptor.

DR. SZUTKA: I am very grateful for the communication. I am familiar with some of the work of Professor Krasnovskii related to porphines and porphine-like substances, but not this particular one. It actually confirms the findings that I obtained in my laboratory.

DR. SAGAN: It seems plausible that the major biological utilization of porphines and porphyrins did not occur until after the transition from the reducing environment occurred. At that time, the "free" production of organic matter by ultraviolet light was effectively turned off, and a premium was placed on alternative energy utilization mechanisms. This was a major evolutionary crisis. I find it remarkable that any organisms survived it. But if porphines and porphyrins had already been utilized for another function, back in the times of the reducing environment, then it would be easier to understand their rapid utilization after oxidizing conditions arose. Perhaps they were utilized in primitive photoreactivation mechanisms, which would have had high evolutionary priority because of the great ultraviolet fluxes at the surface in earlier times. Certainly, there must be some visible photon acceptor for any kind of photoreactivation to work. My question is this: Do you know if there is any radiation protection device in contemporary organisms which uses porphines or porphyrins as photon acceptor?

DR. SZUTKA: The absorption spectrum of porphines has a wide range and therefore they are also absorbers of visible light. They are photosensitizers, as Professor Krasnovskii found out. Therefore, they could facilitate certain photochemical reactions utilizing either ultraviolet or visible quanta.

DR. SAGAN: I understand. In contemporary photoreactivation, what is the visible photon acceptor?

DR. SZUTKA: I don't know. It depends on the system.

DR. MORA: In the early stages, when the atmosphere was penetrated by ultraviolet, could not the visible light also have had a role?

DR. SAGAN: Yes, it would also be transmitted by the atmosphere.

DR. MORA: What was the probability of porphyrin having function at the same time?

DR. SAGAN: Perhaps porphyrins were used. It would be nice to know what the contemporary acceptors are.

DR. BLOIS: One would have to inquire into the photoreactivation or photoreversal of the dimerization. The dimer is the absorber.

DR. SAGAN: Does the dimer absorb in the visible?

DR. BLOIS: Yes.

DR. HALDANE: I didn't quite understand Dr. Sagan's question. It seems to me that photosynthesis by porphine compounds through this ozone curtain gave a way out simultaneously.

DR. SAGAN: I was thinking of the possibility that the original production of free oxygen and ozone occurred abiogenically.

DR. HALDANE: Another alternative being biogenically.

Part III

MACROMOLECULES

(Including a general paper by Dr. Fritz Lipmann)

Chairman's Remarks

A. E. MIRSKY

Rockefeller Institute for Medical Research, New York City, New York

At this point we are in the middle of our program, and I think there is a certain change taking place. We have been dealing on the whole with the conditions on the planet that made the origin of life possible. From now on, some of the discussion will take the form of going a little closer toward the primitive forms of life that then began to appear. It seems to me that there is a very big difference in the position of the investigator here. In considering the conditions on the planet, it is possible to arrive at a very plausible conception of the "primordial soup." What we are depending on is, of course, some knowledge of living cells, but also a very considerable backlog of organic chemistry. The speakers in the past day or two have been pointing out that much of the organic chemistry that is involved here had its origin far back in the 19th century. This is not to underestimate the value of documenting it all and indicating the significance in the way that has been done. I think that is of very great value indeed. The fact is that we have a great backlog of very precise organic chemistry, so that even when there are gaps in our knowledge, when we don't understand certain things, we can have a feeling, some intuition of the nature of our ignorance because we have a feeling for the whole subject.

Now, coming to this other part of the discussion, the part having to do with the earliest forms of life, here again of course we pay a good deal of attention to living cells as we know them. It seems to me, judging from the comments that were made on the first day of this symposium, that the very latest information about living things plays a much more important part here in speculation about the first living things than it does in speculation concerning the environment on Earth at that time.

A good deal of what has been said about the earliest living form is based on what has been learned only in the last five or ten years, indeed often in the last year or two. This induces one to extrapolate a bit and think of how much is going to be learned in the next five, ten, or twenty years, and to consider how significant the information which is coming in the next generation is for these speculations that are taking place.

This could be said of every branch of science, of course. It is however, especially significant, for the problem under discussion today, that what we don't know can be decisive. In this connection, we should remember that not so many years ago nucleic acids would not have been mentioned in speculation about the origin of life. It may be, Dr. Mora, that you were alluding to this background of ignorance about living systems when you spoke the other day. Perhaps you were saying other things as well, but I had the feeling, after a while, that you wanted to emphasize the fact that much of our knowledge in this field is very recent indeed, and that we actually don't have a great deal of what in the course of time we probably will have.

Projecting Backward from the Present Stage of Evolution of Biosynthesis

FRITZ LIPMANN

The Rockefeller Institute, New York City, New York

My basic motivation for entering into this discussion is an uneasy feeling about the apparent tenet that a genetic information transfer system is essential at the very start of life. All efforts seem to be fixed exclusively on using presumably available energy sources, e.g., electric discharges, for synthesizing nucleotides and amino acids and, therefrom, polynucleotides and polypeptides from various carbon-nitrogen sources. As I interpret it, the fascination with the two classes of compounds indicates the assumption that they are essential at the very outset. Being dissatisfied with this fixation on starting with the hen rather than with the egg, I have attempted to find alternatives. I am afraid what I have to say will be just as much natural philosophy as necessarily most discussion on the origin of life need be at present. But try we must.

I. Need for More Data on Bacterial Evolution

If we take our departure by projecting back as far as possible within the limits of experimental verification, we find our start in microbial life. Microbial evolution has been very little touched upon, the main reason being that there are no fossils, which leaves us nothing to build on. We only have the organisms that are alive now; what there was before is not readily available. I have looked for schemes of microbial evolution and found the best to be one presented by Kluyver and van Niel (1936) (Fig. 1). This scheme is constructed on the assumption that the most primitive structures of cocci precede more sophisticated ones which are expected to branch off from the cocci. Such more complex microorganisms develop organelles, and so on. As far as I can see, metabolically the cocci are quite complete. Some microbiologists even dislike to talk about higher organisms, the reason being that the microorganisms, metabolically speaking, are often more interesting. They offer

enormous variety, and they have a spectrum of metabolism which the
higher organisms have largely discarded or taken only parts of.

This microbial stage of evolution is the plateau from which one now
is forced to move backward in time. It is at this stage that most of the
metabolic carriers, which we generally call vitamins, had already developed; we have the information transfer from deoxyribonucleic acid
(DNA) to ribonucleic acid (RNA) to protein; the stage is fully set for
further development, and yet these primitive organisms have not truly
reached the stage of individualization. When one looks at a culture of

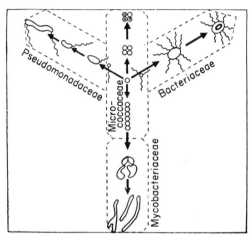

FIG. 1. A hypothetical scheme of the evolution of the bacteria (from Kluyver and
van Niel, 1936).

microorganisms growing exponentially, one realizes that they are not
individuals in the true sense. There is continuous duplication and one
is practically unable to distinguish individuals; there is a chain of growing. This, however, does not have direct relevance to our present concern. In most microorganisms, large intracellular structures are still
missing—they appear first in higher organisms—and, particularly, there
are no mitochondria in many lower microorganisms. The only structures
are ribosomes, and the microorganisms are loaded with them as they are
necessary for rapid growth, i.e., protein synthesis.

Now, in attempting to map evolutionary steps, I prefer to assume
that polynucleotides and proteins are late developments. Let us step
aside for a moment and consider the evolution of our understanding of
the mechanisms of replication. We have been able lately to move so

fast in our understanding because we could build on what had been learned from intermediary metabolism about energy utilization in biosynthesis and energy derivation. Metabolically speaking, the replication mechanism is relatively unsophisticated, except for protein synthesis which, although energetically reasonably simple, requires a complex arrangement for putting the twenty different amino acids into sequence. The energy-yielding metabolism on which all this feeds is more complex in its chemistry and it will serve us well to consider it first.

II. Two Principles of Biosynthesis

Our understanding of metabolism has yielded two things, which I find stand out. One, the organism builds its organic material from scratch; it builds it up chemosynthetically from small units. Two, these units are glued together by using an enormously versatile condensing reagent, adenosine triphosphate (ATP). Sketching tentatively a chemical evolution, carbon dioxide, and $CO_2 + H_2$ = formate are used as the carbon starters; these condense reductively to larger C—H—O derivatives, with carbohydrate a likely candidate for one of the earliest aggregates. One two-carbon unit, acetate, becomes the ancestor of the large group of fats and lipids. Then ammonia feeds in through various channels to yield amino acids followed by nucleosides, nucleotides, and so on to greater complexities. Energy is needed to put these bits together. Throughout, the condensing force—used largely for intermolecular dehydration—is drawn from the phosphoanhydride bond such as that carried in ATP. We have here a chemical potential in phosphate bond energy that is universally translatable into biosynthesis. It is also fed into other energy-requiring facets such as concentration, contraction, nerve function, and so on. One is now reasonably well acquainted with mechanisms of chemobiosynthesis, and this is what will mainly concern us here since at the early stages in organismic development we are essentially working in a phase of chemobiosynthesis.

We turn now briefly to a discussion of the manner by which the organism can obtain its condensing reagent, the phosphoanhydride bonds. We find that it can get them by an energy-coupling mechanism. Primarily, it draws from an electron transfer potential, a redox potential. The redox potential is converted into group potential, an expression I proposed to measure the free energy derivable from energy-carrying bonds (Fig. 2). In the initial stage of chemical-metabolic evolution one might omit oxygen as a hydrogen acceptor, but consider instead ferric ion, sulfate, or a nitrogenous hydrogen acceptor. One has to visualize some kind of coupling mechanism which, in its more intricate form, is developed in the mitochondria. The problem is to convert electron flux potential into phosphate bond potential with inorganic phosphate lifted up to the anhydride level of phosphate group potential.

III. Suggestion of Chemical Coupling as a Start to Life

I propose now to assume that coupling by crossover of two forms of chemical energy might have been the first event on the way to life. From

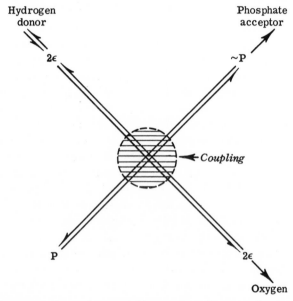

FIG. 2. Crossover scheme for reversible coupling between electron transfer and generation of energy-rich phosphate. The shaded area indicates the unknown mechanism of the intermediate step. (Hoch and Lipmann, 1954).

the late appearance of photosynthesis in bacterial evolution, I conclude this type of energy derivation to be a late comer. We will go into details shortly, namely, that it appears acceptable that inorganic pyrophosphate, presumably present early on Earth, precedes the nucleotide triphosphates as an energy carrier.

Clearly, the Earth, like a living organism, is what one calls a thermodynamically open system because it draws on a constant influx of the Sun's energy. One finds energy cycles here on Earth quite independent of life. I propose to consider them parallel with or as precursors of organismic energy transformations. A system that attracted my attention is the water cycle, shown schematically in Fig. 3. Here, heat from the sun is used to lift water by evaporation, mainly from the sea, to mountain tops or clouds. As in a reflux condenser, the water condenses in the colder upper atmosphere and runs down to the plain and back to the

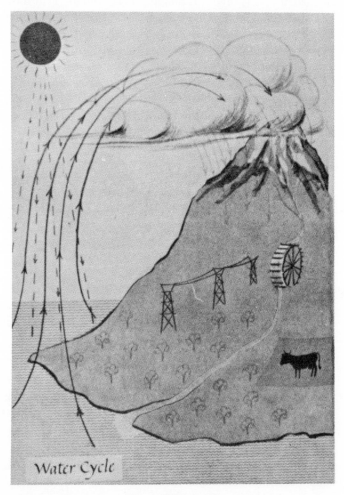

FIG. 3. Water cycle.

sea. In this manner, heat is converted to mechanical energy by lifting water through evaporation. The extensive use of this energy for the production of hydroelectric power is a good example of the working of this energy coupling, i.e., cycling of energy from heat to mechanical work.

Parenthetically, we note that on land organismic life developed dependent upon this water cycling.

We now compare this inorganic cycle to the energy cycle in an organism. Its most striking features are described in Fig. 4 in a scheme I proposed some years ago (Lipmann, 1941) when I introduced the metabolic wheel to symbolize the system that transforms externally avail-

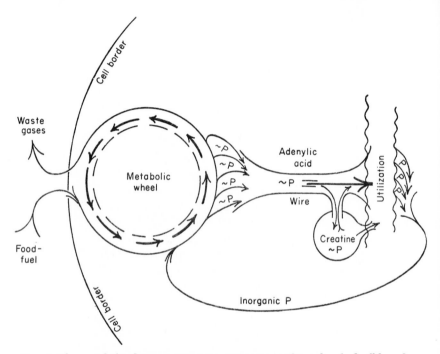

FIG. 4. The metabolic dynamo generates ~P-current. This is brushed off by adenylic acid, which likewise functions as the wiring system, distributing the current. Creatine ~P, when present, serves as P-accumulator. (Lipmann, 1941.)

able energy to internal use by converting redox potential into the phosphate group potential that feeds into biosynthesis. If we compare this with Fig. 3, the similarity may be seen—the extrabiotic physical energy conversion cycle, with heat yielding gravitational energy. It is legitimate therefore, to presume that, in some way, a chemical energy cycle is developed by converting the redox potential available on Earth in various systems into the phosphate bond energy that is eminently useful for all kinds of chemical condensations. As a redox donor, hydrogen, for example, could react with sulfate, as we know it does in microorganisms where this reaction is used to generate phosphate bond energy; or, hydrogen or H_2S may couple to ferric oxide, to mention only some primitive possibilities.

Deviating briefly, I find it possibly of relevance that hydrogen activation, which would be involved here, is mediated by one of the more primitive catalysts, the recently discovered ferredoxin (Lovenberg et al., 1963). This is a small protein with 50 amino acid residues and containing only about two thirds of the 20 amino acid species now found in a normal protein. It has 7 moles of iron bound through a curious linkage involving equivalent amounts of loosely bound H_2S, connecting probably with 7 molecules of cysteine present in the protein. The iron shifts from ferrous to ferric when functioning catalytically. It is significant, considering an evolution of catalysts from primitive to complex, to find here a primitive catalytic assembly made up of a small protein "deficient" in many amino acids, with ionic iron loosely bound through H_2S. This may be the ancestor of the complex hematoporphyrins used abundantly in later metabolic evolution. In parenthesis, the likewise rather complex magnesium porphyrins, the chlorophylls, could scarcely be early in chemical evolution; if not for other reasons, this suggests that photosynthesis came relatively late, preceded by the chemosynthesis already highly developed in anaerobic clostridia. We have to remember that we have to begin metabolic evolution with a primitive stage. The microbial world as we look at it today is still dominated largely by anaerobic metabolism in contrast to that found in most animals. Many metabolically highly developed organisms such as the clostridia are strict anaerobes, and many among them do not contain hematoporphyrin catalysts.

IV. Pyrophosphate as Energy Carrier

On the phosphate side, it may be reasonable to assume that generation of the phosphate group potential might have originated with inorganic pyrophosphate as the primitive group carrier. In many microorganisms, and in some higher organisms, one finds large amounts of polyphosphates (Juni et al., 1948). Part of these polyphosphates appears as insoluble metaphosphate, possibly for storage; however, more soluble short-chain polyphosphates, metabolically more active, also seem to be present. A recycling of these polyphosphates into the metabolic pool has been difficult to show. The Kornbergs (Kornberg et al., 1956) could show a sluggish reincorporation of polyphosphate into ATP. They concluded that the phosphate group potential in polyphosphates was lower than that in ATP, which does not exclude polyphosphate from being a primitive carrier. The discovery of a very interesting reaction by Harland Wood and his colleagues (Siu and Wood, 1962) seems relevant to such a question. As shown in the scheme of Fig. 5, they found inorganic phosphate serving as an acceptor for energy-rich phosphate from phosphoenolpyruvate (PEP), this transfer being coupled with CO_2 fixation. In reverse, CO_2 is liberated while phosphate is being transferred from pyrophosphate to yield PEP. The more common type of reaction is written underneath for comparison. Here guanosine diphosphate (GDP) is phosphate acceptor or, in the reverse, guanosine triphosphate (GTP) is the phosphate donor. Wood's reaction is an example of the

$$\text{Oxaloacetate} + PP_i \rightleftharpoons P - \text{enolpyruvate} + CO_2 + P_i$$
$$\text{Oxaloacetate} + GTP \rightleftharpoons P - \text{enolpyruvate} + CO_2 + GDP$$

Fig. 5. Functioning of pyrophosphate in biosynthesis (from Siu and Wood, 1962).

$$ATP + H_2O \rightleftharpoons \text{adenosine} + PPP_i, \ \Delta F° - 6.7 \pm 2 \text{ kcal}$$
$$ATP + \text{L-methionine} \rightleftharpoons S - \text{adenosyl methionine} + PPP_i, \ \Delta F° - 0.6 \pm 3 \text{ kcal}$$

Fig. 6. Functioning of tripolyphosphate in biosynthesis (from Mudd and Mann, 1963).

possibility that inorganic phosphate can act as a phosphate acceptor to yield pyrophosphate; quite importantly, this is a reversible reaction and pyrophosphate thus acts as donor of energy-rich phosphate.

Another analogous and intriguing reaction has recently been developed by Harvey Mudd (Mudd and Mann, 1963) in the study of the mechanism of synthesis of active methionine. He showed that when ATP reacts with methionine, inorganic tripolyphosphate is liberated, also a reversible reaction; the reaction scheme is shown in Fig. 6. We have a rather amusing reaction here, in which triphosphate is glued to the carbon-5 of the adenosine ribose by a displacement of methionine. Another case of a very similar mechanism is the reaction of ATP with vitamin B_{12} when Barker's coenzyme is formed (Barker, 1961). Here, carbon-5 of the adenosine ribose joins with the central cobalt by displacing triphosphate.

V. Evolving of Microbial Life

Now we come to the more difficult task of seeing how we can bridge the gap between a possible early creation of an energy cycle and the existence of the fully developed microorganism as we see it now. We know from the later history of organisms that every development has gone in steps; I am attempting, therefore, to project such a stepwise metabolic evolution from the very first stages when some preorganismic system developed. Our task is to fill the gaps in between. First, and most difficult, is to suggest the course of development before the organism fenced itself in, or rather, before it truly became an organism. After this, the development of internal structures seems to have been slow. As mentioned briefly, in more primitive microorganisms with walls already around them, we find relatively simple ribosomes as the only internal structures. At that phase we expect them to be probably exclusively or largely anaerobics. Those more familiar with the development of the phosphorylation picture will recall that we distinguish between two types of phosphorylation. The first is fermentative phosphorylation, presumably developed early in evolution. In laboratory slang, this is called "extract" phosphorylation because it is independent of complex structures, is substrate bound, and is stoichiometric. It easily impresses one as being a predecessor of the second and now more common, more efficient, but more complex system of oxidation-chain phosphorylation, which developed when respiration entered the picture. This mechanism yields three or more phosphoryls for every pair of hydrogens transferred through a chain of hydrogen carriers from substrate to oxygen. Fermentation needs much less machinery, but there remains the problem which Oparin recognized early on, that is, how do we get the catalyst? We need catalysts, and we have to find primitive ones of many forms to promote such reactions as we have discussed. We have already considered an inorganic type of fermentation such as hydrogen transfer to sulfate, or H_2S to Fe^{+++}. One may remember here ferredoxin as a primitive catalyst.

VI. Gradual Chemosynthetic Evolution

We now have to consider the evolvement of complex carbon structures. As a first approximation, I propose that the earliest carbon chains should have been of a carbohydrate type. Hexoses and pentoses together with two-carbon acetate are substrates to and products of many fermentations. Thus, fatty acid synthesis is forecast in the rather common type of fatty acid-yielding fermentations, most frequently of the butyric acid type. These seem to present us with a phase of evolution of fat from carbohydrate metabolism. The scheme in Table I may serve to confirm this direction in a brief survey of amino acid structures evolving secondarily from methodologies developed in carbohydrate fermentation. The 20 amino acids from top to bottom are in order of increas-

ing chemical complexity. Here one might add that although ketoglutarate
and oxalacetate are generally thought of as respiratory intermediates,
they seem to appear also in complex fermentations. Many amino acids,
it appears, originate more or less directly from carbohydrates and fatty
acids through initial condensation followed by ammonia fixation largely
through transamination to α-keto acids. The description is fragmentary

TABLE I

AMINO ACID DERIVATION (PRESENT EVOLUTIONARY STAGE)[a]

No.	Source	Amino acid	Precursor fragments
1	Carbohydrate	Glycine	C_2
2		Alanine	C_3; $C_2 + C_1$
3		Serine	
4		Cysteine	
5		Aspartic acid	$C_3 + C_1$
6		Asparagine	
7		Threonine	
8		Methionine	
9		Phenylalanine	$[(C_4 + C_3) - C_1] + C_3 = C_6 \cdot C_3$
10		Tyrosine	
11	Carbohydrate + fatty acid	Glutamic acid	$(C_4 + C_2) - C_1 = C_5$
12		Glutamine	
13		Proline	
14		Arginine	
15		Lysine	Complex
16	Predominantly fatty acid	Valine	Complex
17		Isoleucine	
18		Leucine	
19	Complex	Tryptophan	Similar to nucleotide synthesis
20		Histidine	

[a] For details, consult Fruton and Simmonds (1958).

but the survey is inserted to substantiate evolution of more complex
molecules from small fragments by way of only a few basic biosynthetic
principles that have evolved in the course of fermentations. No attempt
is made to translate such a molecular evolution into possible pre-enzy-
matic events developing toward a premicrobial phase.

VII. Biosynthesis of Purines and Pyrimidines

This brief review is to paraphrase the thesis that chemical potential
in the form of phosphate bond energy is eminently suited for construction of complex chemical edifices. The difficulty of projecting such

schemes backward, while neglecting the complex enzymology, is appreciated. The emphasis is more on the simplicity of ingredient molecules and uniformity of the dehydration procedure through polyphosphates.

Purine rings, as summarized in Fig. 7 (Buchanan, 1960), are constructed from small units, ammonia and one-carbon derivatives, with glycine as the only 2-carbon compound. The sugar, ribose, is the foundation on which the whole ring system grows. The main point I want to

$$
\begin{aligned}
&\text{Ribose-5-P} \\
&4 \quad NH_3 \\
&2 \ HCOOH \\
&CO_2 \\
&CH_2 \cdot NH_2 \cdot COOH \\
&10 \ ATP \\
\hline
&\text{Adenylic acid } (C_{10}N_5P)
\end{aligned}
$$

Fig. 7. Purine biosynthesis.

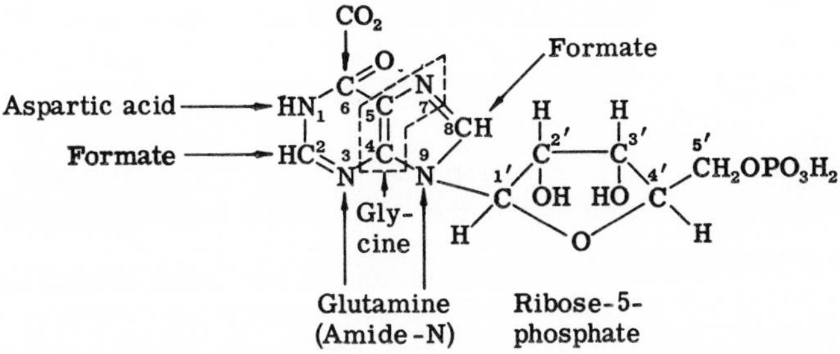

Fig. 8. Origin of purine nucleotide atoms (from Buchanan, 1960).

make is that these small fragments are glued together by drawing energy from $10 \sim P$. This is what makes me wonder why it should be necessary to use radiation energy and not think, right from the beginning, of chemical energy for condensation. A more detailed scheme of the synthetic process, progressing from left to right, appears in Fig. 8.

Pyrimidine synthesis is depicted in some more detail in Fig. 9 (Buchanan et al., 1959); it starts differently and with an interesting variance. Here, aspartic acid is the nucleus on which the ring structure grows. Aspartic acid appears as the prominent member of the synthetic "team." The only small bit that is put in here is carbamyl phosphate (CMP), which condenses on the amino group of aspartic acid. Carbamyl

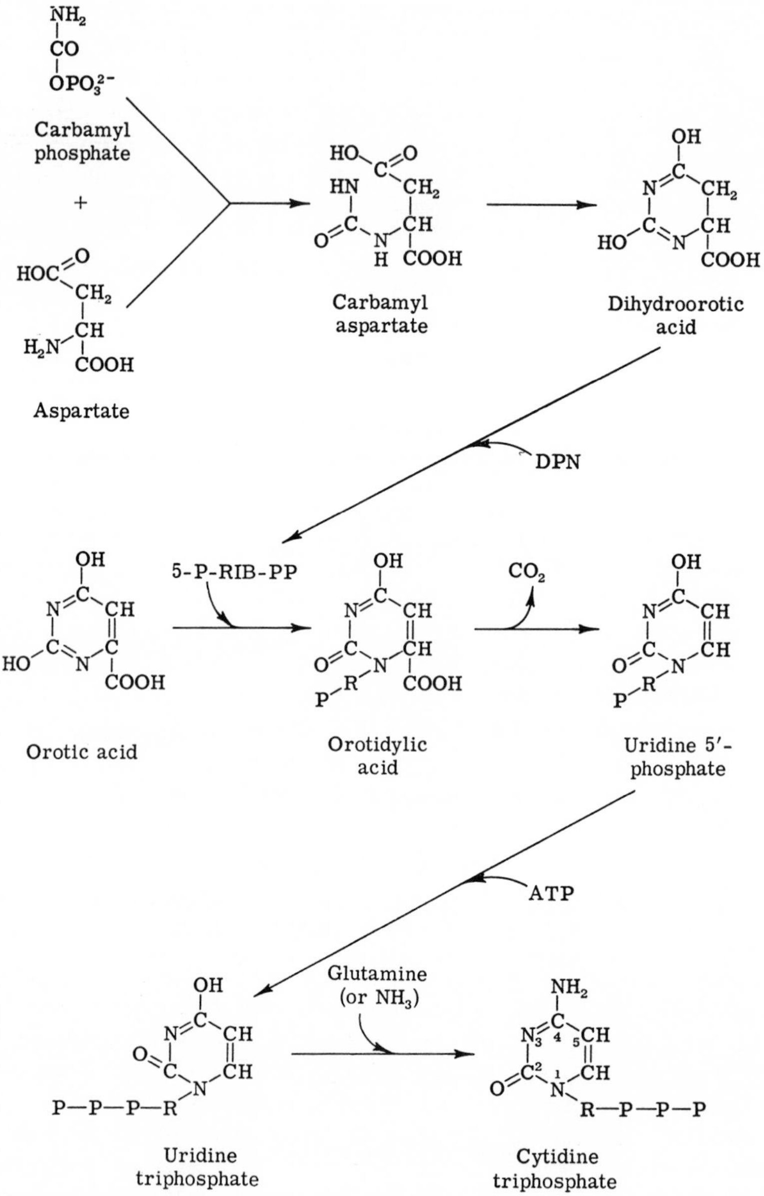

FIG. 9. Enzymatic synthesis of pyrimidines.

aspartate then yields orotic acid by spontaneous closure to the six-membered ring. And from there on, the path to uridylic acid is obvious. Parenthetically, I should add here a few words about CMP (Jones and Lipmann, 1960), which has been mentioned as a candidate for the "primordial" energy-rich phosphate (Bernal, 1957). This choice is attractive because CMP forms spontaneously from cyanate and inorganic phosphate and seems to be the only organismically used energy-rich compound formed at low temperature spontaneously. I think, however, that CMP is not well suited to be the progenitor of this class of compounds. I have already indicated that I prefer inorganic polyphosphate as a primitive energy carrier; it is the amazingly versatile condensing capacity of the phosphoanhydride bond that is so remarkable throughout biosynthesis.

VIII. Remarks on the Evolution of Polypeptide Synthesis

I have deliberately neglected here the essential question of catalysts. I have concentrated on ingredients. One surely needs catalysts, but at the moment I would prefer not to enlarge on that aspect. The eminent suitability of polypeptide structures for catalysts makes me want to add just a few words about possible primitive stages of polypeptide formation. Considering the possibility of a primitive method of sequentialization, one should consider polypeptide synthesis in cell wall precursors. This occurs in nontemplate fashion. Strominger and his group (Ito and Strominger, 1960) have shown that, by consecutive addition through specific enzymes, up to six amino acids may be condensed to a polypeptide in a specified sequence without a template. This is some kind of information transfer in which RNA does not enter into the picture. And thus it seems possible to propose that primitive polypeptides could be made without a complex information transfer scheme. It may be significant that this is the mode of fabrication in cell wall synthesis and possibly illustrates one of the earliest appearances of a protein-like substance. Once polypeptides were formed, then they might have shown right away their suitability as catalysts, particularly in conjunction with metal ions as mentioned previously with ferredoxin.

IX. Evolution of Information Transfer

Many people now think that the information transfer initially may not have started with DNA and that DNA is actually a later development. Such a course is suggested since RNA in the RNA viruses is sufficient to carry information; actually, mutation rates with RNA viruses seem rather high, which would be of advantage in the early stages of development to create greater variety. Projecting backward from there, one could consider that initially only one pair of hydrogen-bonding bases, e.g., adenine and uridine, may have sufficed as a beginning. Table II shows that with this one pair we have eight variants for triplets. Taking a list from compounded Nirenberg-Ochoa data (Jones and Nirenberg, 1962; Gardner *et al.*, 1962), one finds that, of the eight, six combinations so far have been found to have a singular meaning as amino acids. A wide variety of side chain chemistry would be available,

TABLE II

AMINO ACID TRIPLETS CORRESPONDING TO THE ADENYLIC
ACID-URIDYLIC ACID PAIR[a]

No.	Triplet	Amino acid
1	AAA ⎫	Lysine
2	AAU ⎭	
3	AUA	Asparagine
4	AUU	Tyrosine
5	UAA ⎫	Isoleucine
6	UAU ⎭	
7	UUA	Leucine
8	UUU	Phenylalanine

[a] Possible number: $2^3 = 8$.

with these amino acids for a formation of protein. A fictive selection of UA alone yields two phenolic groups in phenylalanine and tyrosine, two hydrophobic side chains in leucine and isoleucine, a basic one in lysine, and the dicarboxylic acid type represented by asparagine. This would present a nucleus that could serve as initial proteins for catalytic purposes.

X. Summary

This survey was prompted by a feeling for the unlikelihood of a discontinuous evolution. This led to the attempt to discover a continuous trend from preorganismic, largely chemical development to reach eventually the microbial plateau from which all presently known evolution appears to take off. I have attempted to recast the development of an organism in the manner in which we know evolution to have gone forward, namely, in orderly sequence from more primitive to more complex situations. Projecting backward makes it necessary to make assumptions which seem difficult or perhaps impossible to verify. I think it might be possible to find links by looking more attentively for primitive evolutionary stages within the metabolic picture in the hope to apprehend there surviving metabolic "fossils." As an important premise, the coupling of chemosynthesis to electron transport was proposed as an early event in parallel with nonbiological energy-coupling mechanisms on Earth, such as the water cycle. Polyphosphate was preferred as the primeval energy carrier, with encouragement from recent observations on pyrophosphate and tripolyphosphate appearing in reversible energy transfer reactions. In protein evolution, such primitive structures as the iron-containing, amino acid-deficient hydrogen carrier, ferredoxin, may be representative. Searching still further back, cell wall peptides synthesized in a primeval fashion could represent a very early sampling of a pretemplate period. Receding into the dimmer past, a sketch of metabolic evolution was attempted, largely by borrowing from present information.

Revised manuscript received March 18, 1964.

REFERENCES

Barker, H. A. (1961). *Federation Proc.* **20**, 956.
Bernal, J. D. (1957). *Origin Life Earth Rept. Intern. Symp. Moscow 1957* p. 132.
Buchanan, J. M. (1960). *In* "The Nucleic Acids" (E. Chargaff and J. N. Davidson, eds.), Vol. III, p. 303. Academic Press, New York.
Buchanan, J. M., Hartman, S. C., Herrman, R. L., and Day, R. A. (1959). *J. Cell. Comp. Physiol.* **54**, Supp. 1, 139.
Fruton, J. S., and Simmonds, S. (1958). "General Biochemistry," 2nd ed. Wiley, New York.
Gardner, R. S., Wahba, A. J., Basilio, C., Miller, R. S., Lengyel, P., and Speyer, J. F. (1962). *Proc. Natl. Acad. Sci. U.S.* **48**, 2087.
Hoch, F. L., and Lipmann F., (1954). *Proc. Nat. Acad. Sci. U.S.* **40**, 909.
Ito, E., and Strominger, J. L. (1960). *J. Biol. Chem.* **235**, PC5.
Jones, M. E., and Lipmann, F. (1960). *Proc. Natl. Acad. Sci. U.S.* **46**, 1194.
Jones, O. W., and Nirenberg, M. W. (1962). *Proc. Natl. Acad. Sci. U.S.* **48**, 2115.
Juni, E., Kamen, M. D., Reiner, J. M., and Spiegelman, S. (1948). *Arch. Biochem.* **18**, 387.
Kluyver, A. J., and van Niel, C. B. (1936). *Zentr. Bakteriol. Abt. II*, **94**, 369.
Kornberg, A., Kornberg, S. R., and Simms, E. S. (1956). *Biochim. Biophys. Acta* **20**, 215.
Lipmann, F. (1941). *Advan. Enzymol.* **1**, 99.
Lovenberg, W., Buchanan, B., and Rabinowicz, J. C. (1963). *J. Biol. Chem.* **238**, 3899.
Mudd, S. H., and Mann, J. D. (1963). *J. Biol. Chem.* **238**, 2164.
Siu, P. M. L., and Wood, H. G. (1962). *J. Biol. Chem.* **237**, 3044.

DISCUSSION

DR. STEINBACH: I would not like to cloud the comments that Dr. Lipmann made, because to me they were very trenchant and very clear. The discussions that we have had have clearly illustrated that a large number of things could have developed in our prebiotic world. This large collection of materials does, in fact, just represent prebiotic materials. Any meaningful shift to the biotic world would come only when there was some sort of an organized system in which the information would be transferred to some sort of machinery to do something. It is, I think, worth while keeping in mind that the first organizing system might well have been the organization of layers, interfaces, or what-have-you, to give rise to what is certainly one of the ubiquitous characteristics of all living cells—an energy gradient across a limiting layer.

I am not at all sure that the prototype of an organism is not to be visualized as a set of energy gradients by which the materials that have been collected through the various mechanisms that have been talked about here are drawn into orbit.

DR. LIPMANN: I don't see an easy connection to energy gradients. In the scheme I discussed, the conversion of redox potential to group potential was put at the top to feed condensing energy to make more complex chemicals. I would find it difficult to draw energy for such a purpose from what you allude to. We know that we ourselves, our present organisms, make the material with their own energy. They have to. They don't get it from outside, except if it is made by other organisms.

DR. STEINBACH: How do they know where to go, your bits of machinery, your soluble stuff that you get out. Don't they need something to bring them together?

DR. LIPMANN: Not essentially. You have a soup anyway. You start out with a soup.

DR. SCHRAMM: I understood that gylcolysis might be a more primitive form of energy supply than oxidation. It would be interesting to design a nonenzymatic scheme that resembles the glycolysis and which could be considered as a precursor to this enzymatic process. In a reducing atmosphere, an aldehyde is a reactive compound possessing a high energy. Aldehydes could be formed in the primordial atmosphere by combination of hydroxy radicals with alkyl radicals. By reversion of the aldol condensation and a series of oxidoreductions or chemically catalyzed disproportions of the aldehyde groups to carboxylic and alcoholic groups, a model system could be constructed for glycolysis, which might have provided the energy for the prebiological syntheses. Later

on these processes could have been improved by specific protein enzymes for each step. I could imagine that this primordial energy transfer was already at that stage mediated by phosphate esters similar to
ATP.

DR. LIPMANN: I am quite open to suggestion. Hydrogen was around.

DR. BUCHANAN: I have two questions. The first involves the period of
evolution with which your remarks on the development of an oxidative
metabolism are concerned. Have you assumed that evolution has prog-
ressed so far that the major energy source, ultraviolet light, has now
been lost?

DR. LIPMANN: I must confess that I am not familiar enough with the
ideas about primitive Earth environment, but have been wondering
lately how well established they are [cf. discussion by Fowler *et al.*
(1961), *Am. J. Physics* **21**, 393) of the unlikelihood of a reducing atmosphere and the probability of oxidizing conditions which I presume would
keep out the ultraviolet light after the formation of the Earth.]

DR. BUCHANAN: In your discussion you have considered, very possibly
quite correctly, that an inorganic polyphosphate might have been the
storage of chemical energy. Dr. Sagan and Dr. Ponnamperuma have
shown that adenosine and possibly even adenosine triphosphate could
have been formed under prebiological conditions. If ATP could have
been formed in sufficiently great yields, would you consider that it could
have been the energy storage system in early times rather than inorganic
polyphosphates?

DR. LIPMANN: That is what I am not going along with. I feel that
evolution goes further backward. You don't throw something in which
is premade so to say, and then develop.

DR. BUCHANAN: Why not?

DR. LIPMANN: Because, in the first place, if you really look, if you put
it into the ocean, it is so enormously diluted that you have to make so
much that it is impossible.

DR. BUCHANAN: That is true, but would your polyphosphates be
present in sufficiently high concentrations?

DR. LIPMANN: I don't say that life developed there. The higher
organisms, the animals, seem to have developed in the sea, but not the
microorganisms.

DR. SAGAN: In response to Dr. Buchanan's query, the numbers work
out as follows. With our laboratory quantum yield, $\varphi \sim 3 \times 10^{-5}$, and
with the expected ultraviolet photon flux in the 2400–2900 Å window
in primitive times, the ATP production rate becomes 5×10^{-12} gm cm^{-2}
sec^{-1}. This is enough to support a population of 20,000 *Escherichia coli*

cells per square centimeter column of ocean, assuming a doubling time of 1 hour, and an equivalent death rate (Ponnamperuma, Sagan, and Mariner, Nature 199, 222, 1963). The calculation is primarily of heuristic interest, but it does suggest that the abiologically synthesized ATP in primitive times may have been adequate to support fairly sizable populations of microorganisms.

I have a question for Dr. Lipmann. I wonder if perhaps you would make a few comments on why it is that the element phosphorus is so heavily involved in biological energy transport. Is there a fundamental physical reason, or may it have been an historical accident? Can we expect some congener of phosphorus in the periodic table to supplant it in extraterrestrial life forms?

DR. LIPMANN: In a symposium at Johns Hopkins [Lipmann, 1951, in "Phosphorus Metabolism" (W. D. McElroy and B. Glass, eds.), Vol. I, p. 521, Johns Hopkins Press, Baltimore, Maryland], I compared the free energy of hydrolysis, i.e., the acetyl potential, of acetic anhydride with that of acetyl phosphate or ATP. This comparison shows their free energies of hydrolysis, i.e., thermodynamic potentials, to be about equal for acetic anhydride, acetyl phosphate, and phosphoanhydride. What is enormously different, however, is their stability in the system in which living organisms exist, namely, dilute solution at pH 7. Here, acetyl phosphate is reasonably stable and the phosphoanhydride in ATP nearly indefinitely so, but acetic anhydride is destroyed in seconds, or at best in a few minutes, in water. The reason why the phosphoryl derivatives are so much more stable appears to be a shielding of the energy-loaded anhydride link by the negative charges in phosphoryls. The difference is that water or OH^- groups are free to approach in the absence, i.e., acetic anhydride, but not in the presence of the repellent screen of negative charges. That is the great advantage of ATP; it carries a reasonably large package of energy in POP links, shielded and safe until drawn off by proper catalysts. It appears, furthermore, that a phosphoryl as energy carrier confers stability to available energy when joined to an organic residue. This emphasizes a most important function of phosphate, namely, to transfer kinetically protected energy to an organic residue in order to activate it and prime it for transfer in biosynthesis.

DR. OPARIN: I would like to ask Dr. Lipmann's opinion as to whether he represents correctly the stages of energy transfer. The mitochondria in higher organisms are a good arrangement to get maximum energy yield by means of phosphorus relations. But, as Dr. Lipmann correctly pointed out, in aerobic bacteria mitochondria are absent, and energy transfer is collected as a lipoid lipo-protein membrane.

This, in my opinion, is a more primitive evolutionary stage of development of energy metabolism. But let us go still further down. In anaerobes the energy metabolism is realized without any structure, simply in solution.

But even the obligate anaerobes sometimes consume molecular oxygen. To be sure, this does not lead to any useful effect and, on the contrary, leads to the breakdown and death of the organism. Such anaerobes contain enzymes, flavin pigments, which are participating in the process, and these enzymes can function in well-centrifuged solutions. Those are the same enzymes which are transfer participants, and participate in transfer of hydrogen to the organic acceptors, e.g., pyruvic acid. The same enzymes can transfer hydrogen to oxygen molecules. But this leads to no positive effect. And in order for this process to produce a useful effect, it has to be included in an arrangement connected with the membrane.

This, then, is an example of the existence of a process which is present, but cannot be utilized without introduction of an electron transport chain.

Dr. LIPMANN: Dr. Oparin's comment gives an exposition of what I would call a primitive metabolic stage of anaerobic fermentation from which is developed, as he indicated, the more complex one of respiration. Respiration, therefore, is not essential although it leads to better utilization of the available food, but anaerobic organisms may grow as well as aerobic organisms.

Dr. GROSSENBACHER: I wondered if this simple protein formation might have something to do with the formation of early membranes in the origin of living machinery, and the presence of membranes then would be part of this other discussion of how you develop a more effective energy machine.

Dr. LIPMANN: Your guess is just as good as mine.

Dr. GROSSENBACHER: Would it be possible that this primitive protein formation might have played a role in primitive wall formation?

Dr. LIPMANN: I really can't say. I have taken it more as an example of a protein or specific polypeptide that originates without a template. Antibiotic polypeptides may be formed similarly since they seem to be related to the cell wall. As far as I can see, this may be the best example of a formation of polypeptide chains without a template, i.e., without an information transfer chain.

Dr. BUCHANAN: Don't you think that reactions such as polypeptide formation take place simply because they are chemically feasible? No information in the form of a "template" is needed, only that one molecule affects the next with which it will join.

Dr. Mirsky: It might be hard to make a disinction.

Dr. Lipmann: I might say that when there is a primitive information transfer through sequential enzyme specificity, it is likely to be a polypeptide formation feeding on the terminal phosphate in ATP. This appears generally as the more primitive stage of energy transfer.

Dr. Szutka: A question has been raised if whether the alternative high-energy bonds will supply enough free energy for certain reactions. Dr. Lipmann elaborated on this topic. I would like to suggest (and I don't know if any work has been done) polyvanadate as an alternate high energy bond. Polyvanadates have some properties which are similar to those of polyphosphates. Did somebody use polyvanadates instead of polyphosphates?

Dr. Lipmann: I am doubtful about this possibility of substitution of vanadate for phosphate. In all cases we know about, the similar heavier analogs, for reasons which I believe are not well understood, seem to form compounds very unstable in water. This is best known for arsenate which, in many enzyme reactions, has been shown to substitute for phosphate but only to disrupt the reaction and act as an energy leak by forming the analog links, opening it to the attack of water. A similar relationship was found by Bandurski [Wilson, L. G., and Bandurski, R. S. (1958) *J. Biol. Chem.* **233**, 975] for chromate, molybdate, and tungstate with the enzymatic reactions involving sulfate. Again, chromate, molybdate, and tungstate were found to substitute enzymatically in the activation step but only to labilize the energy-carrying link to sulfate and cause a waste of energy. I am not familiar, however, with any extensive study using vanadate, but I would not be surprised if it, likewise, would form labile compounds with organic residues.

Mr. Pirie: Any organism that depended on the use of amounts of vanadium comparable to the amounts of copper or zinc generally needed, would find itself severely restricted because it is such a rare element. That is the basic obstacle to its use.

But, to continue in a somewhat cynical and operational tone, scientists, by and large, find the sort of things they are looking for. We have had good methods for determining phosphorus for about 50 years; you can teach a student to estimate it easily. As a result, perhaps 100,000 times as many manhours have been spent studying phosphate as studying, for example, sulfate.

So I suggest that part of the importance of phosphate in our knowledge of metabolism is simply operational. Evidence for that is that we knew little about sulfate exchanges until radioactive sulfate became readily available and made it possible to teach students to determine it too. So we now have quite a vigorous growth of sulfate-based systems.

Therefore, although I agree with most of what Dr. Lipmann has said, we should also bear in mind the practical issue that it is easier to follow the metabolism of one element than the other.

DR. SAGAN: Arsenic and molybdenum, as well as vanadium, have low cosmic abundances, compared with phosphorus. Sulfur has a higher cosmic abundance, and could not be excluded on such grounds.

I have a question regarding Dr. Lipmann's suggestion that perhaps RNA was an evolutionary predecessor of DNA, that DNA may be a later sophistication. It has been my understanding (perhaps I am wrong) that molecular oxygen is essentially a poison in the cell nucleus and that, in fact, some fairly elaborate biochemical mechanisms exist which have as their function the protection of nuclear organelles from oxidation by molecular oxygen. I also understand that in aerobic cells, oxygen does have access to ribosmal and soluble RNA and not only to the mitochondria. If it were true that DNA has a greater oxygen lability than RNA, we might be tempted to suggest that DNA arose in the primitive reducing atmosphere, and that RNA is a later sophistication. Which nucleic acid is more stable in an oxygen atmosphere?

DR. MIRSKY: I don't know where you got that about the nucleus. The nucleus requires ATP for its activities. The nucleus makes its own ATP and it cannot make it in the absence of oxygen. It doesn't get it from the mitochondria. Osawa, S., Allfrey, V. G., and Mirsky, A. E. (1957), *J. Gen. Physiol.* **40**, 491; Allfrey, V. G., and Mirsky, A. E. (1957), *Proc. Natl. Acad Sci. U.S.* **43**, 589, (1958), **44**, 981; McEwen, B., Allfrey, V. G., and Mirsky, A. E. (1963), *J. Biol. Chem.* **238**, 758, 2571, 2579.

DR. LIPMANN: I don't know either. DNA has greater stability than RNA. It has a greater resistance because in ribose you have two adjacent hydroxls in 2' and 3' positions; there is, then, a "glycolic" situation around the phosphate bridges that is labile and might be considered a soft spot. Deoxyribose has lost the 2'-hydroxyl and the phosphate bridges are neighbored by CH_2 instead of $\cdot CHOH$. This chemically stabilizes against attack. That is what we feel is the advantage of DNA over RNA. It is more stable. I don't know where you get this oxygen business.

DR. SAGAN: In a paper by H. Stern, published in *Science* **121**, 144 (1955).

DR. MIRSKY: I am aware of that paper, but the most recent and most thorough work is in the references I just gave you.

DR. BERNAL[1]: I feel that Dr Lipmann's paper has gone a long way to resolving some of the difficulties raised by Dr. Mora. The fact that we

[1] *In absentia*

have in existing life a highly complex and efficient system of information transfer and its variation through mutation, should not blind us to the fact that this is not the only way in which such functions may be carried out. Dr. Lipmann's hypothetical simplified RNAs with only two nucleotides may represent one of the steps, and the invention or discovery of DNA may have been a turning point only in the negative sense, preventing further biochemical evolution on that level. Once four or five nucleotides had been fixed, there seemed no point in adding any others as these are already redundant enough. Further evolution had to take place using this system as a unit and combining it in a more complex way to move from simple nucleic acids to complex linearly arranged genes. In a similar way, there are indications that once ATP had been found as a useful proton transferer, this has blocked the evolution of channels to develop other possible coenzymes.

Random Polycondensation of Sugars

PETER T. MORA

National Institutes of Health, Bethesda, Maryland

I would like to show that probability considerations are useful in predicting the structure of polysaccharides obtained by polycondensation of certain carbohydrates (aldoses) at elevated temperatures. Namely, the resulting structures are random, but they depend on the nature of monomers and on the reaction conditions employed.

The following parameters will be considered, as they control the reaction mechanism and the structure of the polymer formed: functional groups of the monomers, their relative reactivities, and the influence of activation energy (heat) and catalyst.

Let us take first the aldohexose glucose. Its most reactive hydroxyl is on carbon number 1 (C-1). It was demonstrated that mutarotation of glucose proceeds by a concerted displacement mechanism (Swain and Brown, 1952) on C-1 and that both acid and base must be present (Lowry and Smith, 1927). Mutarotation must include a temporary opening of the glucopyranose ring (Fig. 1).

Let us take an acid, such as phosphorous acid, which can fulfill a dual role in a concerted push-pull mechanism. It has a low dissociation constant for the third hydrogen (4.8×10^{-13}). Other similar catalysts (phosphoric acid, boric acid, etc.) can also reduce the activation energy. The twice ionized phosphorous acid is a relatively nucleophilic reagent as compared with the undissociated acid, which is the electrophilic reagent. When mutarotation occurs, the intermediate carbonium ion at C-1 reacts preferentially with the hydroxyl at C-5 in dilute aqueous solution. Because of steric restrictions, this hydroxyl is most probably in the neighborhood of the C-1 hydroxyl.

When high concentrations of monomers are present, such as in a melt, the carbonium ion will easily react with any hydroxyl of another glucose. The C-6 hydroxyl, being a primary hydroxyl, is more reactive than the secondary hydroxyls C-2, C-3, C-4, and C-5. The latter may be present

281

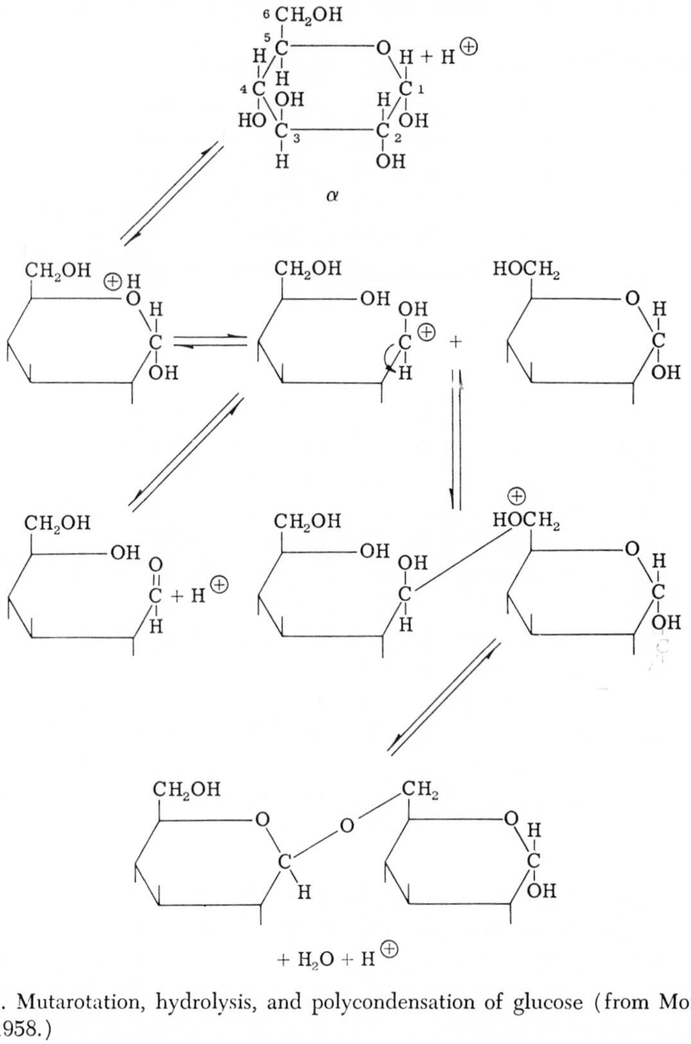

FIG. 1. Mutarotation, hydrolysis, and polycondensation of glucose (from Mora and Wood, 1958.)

in case the open chain carbonium ion at C-1 first reacts with the C-4 hydroxyl on the same molecule to form a glucofuranose ring. Of course, the carbonium ion at C-1 can react with a C-1 hydroxyl on another molecule, in which case the dimer product (trehalose) shall not have a C-1 group any more and shall not be able to form a carbonium ion. A polymerization reaction initiated by these units would terminate because of such linkages, were it not for the fact that the polycondensation and hydrolysis steps are in equilibrium and eventually a C-1—C-1 linkage will open up, making the two participant units again reactive.

If the water of condensation is removed by vacuum (Mora and Wood, 1958) or by a water-binding reagent (phosphorus pentoxide in ether), the condensation will continue. The frequency of the type of linkages which result in the polymer at the end of the equilibrium reaction should

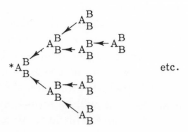

etc.

Fig. 2. Reason for the absence of gel in the condensation of polyfunctional carbohydrates. From the AB_{f-1} monomer, if linkage is restricted to $A \rightarrow B$ the (fraction of B reacted) $P_B = \alpha$ (the branching probability)

$$(f - 1)P_B = P_A$$
$$P_B = \frac{P_A}{f - 1} = \frac{P}{f - 1} = \alpha$$

P always < 1; critical (gel) $\alpha = \frac{1}{f - 1}$

Thus, the gel point can be approached but never reached. Notice that there is only one free A group (marked by asterisk) in the polymer. This is the reducing end group (after Flory, 1953.)

be a function of the relative reactivities of the hydroxyls under the conditions of polycondensation.

Since the relative reactivity of the C-1 (glucosidic) hydroxyl (A) is much greater than any of the others and if the activation energy is sufficient to cause condensation only through this hydroxyl, it will be always a participant in a reaction.

This means that the monomer will follow the polycondensation kinetics of the type of monomers AB_{f-1} as was discussed by Flory (1953), when reactions between solely B (nonglucosidic hydroxyls) are forbidden. In this case, the formation of insoluble gel is impossible, since the branching probability may approach but never reach the critical value for incipient formation of infinite structures (Fig. 2). This is actually the case in our polycondensation conditions when we kept the

temperature just above the melting point of sugars; under such conditions no insoluble gel is formed. However, at slightly higher temperature
a considerable amount of insoluble gel is produced, which still hydro-
lyzes back quantitatively to glucose, proving that no side process but
actually the B-B linkages are responsible for the cross-linking. Another
proof that we follow the AB_{f-1} type of reaction scheme was that there
is only one A group (glucosidic hydroxyl) per polymer. This was
demonstrated by the agreement of reducing end group number average
molecular weight with physical number average molecular weight
determination by osmotic pressure (Mora, 1957). One may keep in mind
that when A-A linkages reopen because of equilibrium, in the two parts
of the polymers which they connected the number of B groups available
must have increased with growth in molecular size (by grafting of
monomers through their A groups to B groups on the polymer). Therefore, the probability that an A-A link will be formed again will be lower
than it was when it originally formed. This leads to a statistically insignificant number of A-A linkages. Thus, at a high enough molecular
weight there should be only one A group in each molecule. This again is
proved by the agreement in the two types of molecular weight
determination.

The relative reactivities of the nonglucosidic hydroxyls C-2, C-3, C-4
(C-5), and C-6 at acid pH in condensation with the C-1 hydroxyl was
studied by Frahm (1944). He found that at moderate temperatures the
primary hydroxyl C-6 is about three times as reactive as the others,
which are more similar in their reactivities.

The frequency of particular linkages in various synthetic polysaccharides, as determined by the methylation technique, generally bore
out this relative reactivity relationship (Dutton and Unrau, 1962a,b).
Actually, we predicted much of the structure, and were able to check the
main features by periodate oxidation of the polysaccharides (Mora et al.,
1958). In periodate oxidation one mole of periodic acid is consumed in
oxidation between neighboring hydroxyls, and one mole of formic acid
is produced if there are three such adjacent hydroxyls (Fig. 3).

If we increase the polycondensation temperature we reduce the required activation energy, and also reduce the differences in reactivity
between the C-6 and the other (C-2, C-3, and C-4) hydroxyls. What
we have then is a more equal probability for reaction through any of
the hydroxyls of a monomer, and a greater chance that in addition to
C-6, one or more other hydroxyl will also be in a polymer linkage on the
same monomer. Then the consumed periodate or the produced formic
acid will be lower when comparing corresponding polymer fractions pre-

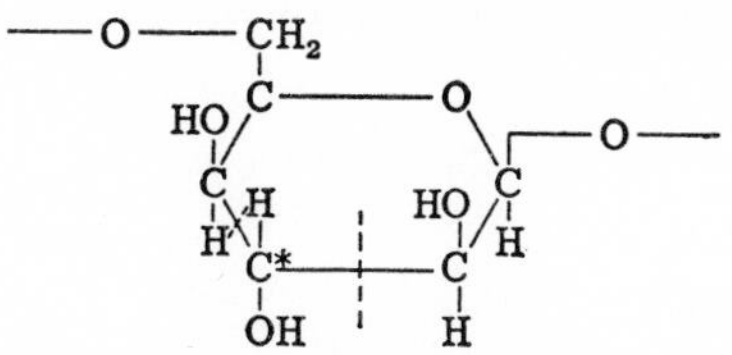

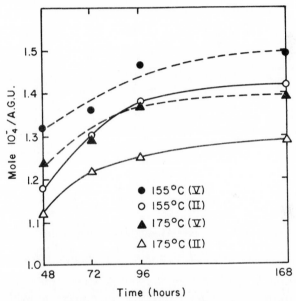

FIG. 3. Periodate oxidation of a glucose monomer. In this $1 \to 6$ linked gluco-pyranose unit, two moles of periodate are reduced for splitting (broken lines) and one mole of formic acid is produced (at asterisk) with the reduction of a third mole of periodate.

FIG. 4. Periodate consumption by polyglucoses. The polymerization temperatures are given in the insert. The roman numerals denote fractions characteristic of each polymer. Lower Roman numerals denote higher molecular weight fractions. Oxidation at 4°C in the dark for various times. A.G.U. = anhydroglucose unit. (From Mora *et al.*, 1958).

pared at higher temperatures, or comparing higher molecular weight fractions as obtained by alcohol fractionation of a polymer prepared at a given temperature. This anticipation was also substantiated (Mora *et al.*, 1958), as shown in Figs. 4 and 5 and Table I.

As I mentioned, a glucofuranose monomer can be formed when the C-4 hydroxyl reacts first intramolecularly. Such units, when they have free C-5 and C-6 hydroxyl groups will provide formaldehyde upon

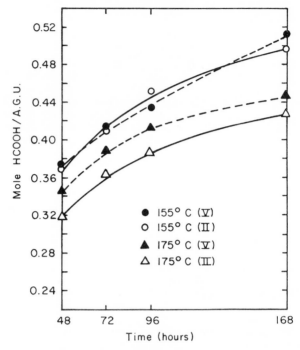

FIG. 5. Formic acid production by polyglucoses upon periodate oxidation.

periodate oxidation (Fig. 6). About 50% of them are expected to be in this position. We indeed found about the expected amount of formaldehyde produced after oxidation (Mora *et al.*, 1959).

The periodate oxidation results on polymers prepared from other aldoses (Mora *et al.*, 1960) were also in agreement with the general

TABLE I
PROPERTIES OF POLYGLUCOSE FRACTIONS[a]

Temperature (°C)	Fraction	$\bar{M}_n$	$[\eta]$	HCOOH
155	II	16,200	0.03	0.674
	V	8,250	0.01	0.721
175	II	32,800	0.03	0.622
	V	20,000	0.01	0.647

[a] Symbols: $\bar{M}_n$ = number average molecular weight; $[\eta]$ is given in deciliters per gram; HCOOH = formic acid produced after 120 hours. Oxidation as defined in Fig. 4.

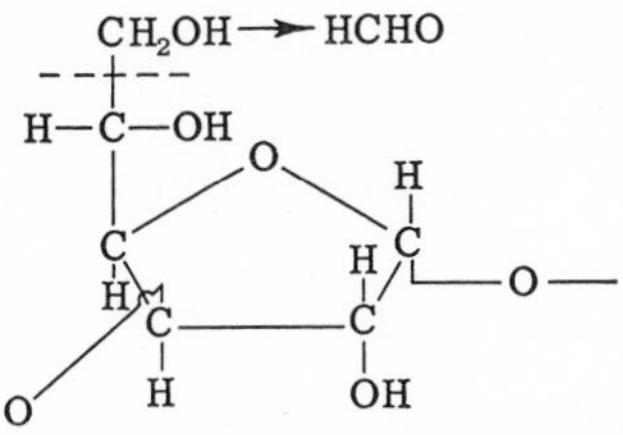

FIG. 6. Formation of formaldehyde from periodate oxidation of a glucofuranose residue.

principle elaborated above for glucose namely, that the number, the type, and the relative reactivities of the functional groups and the activation energy fully predict the frequency of the different linkages (Table II). We have not found any evidence of deviation from randomness in the distribution of different linkages.

TABLE II

PERIODATE OXIDATION (4°C, 72 HOURS) OF VARIOUS SYNTHETIC POLYSACCHARIDES[a]

Polysaccharide	Moles/anhydro sugar unit	
	IO_4^-	HCOOH
D-Glucose	1.22	0.45
D-Galactose	1.34	0.37
D-Mannose	1.79	0.81
2-Deoxyglucose	0.49	0.04
L-Arabinose	0.69	0.13
D-Xylose	0.89	0.34
D-Ribose	0.79	0.22
L-Rhamnose	1.11	0.38
Maltose	1.12	0.40

[a] For discussion of the meaning of these results see Mora et al. 1960.

The foregoing was presented to show that in polycondensation, probability considerations are useful, and that they lead to the necessity of a random structure, which was experimentally verified. Of course this type of randomness is a complicated randomness, which depends on parameters changing under various conditions. In the acid-catalyzed polycondensation of aldohexoses by heat, there is no sign of deviation from randomness, provided we are sophisticated in considering what type of randomness we should expect. This is just to illustrate my thesis that there could be no more "order" expected in polymerizations than the "information put in."

ACKNOWLEDGEMENT

Much of the above results is based on years of careful, patient research work by my deceased colleague John W. Wood.

Revised Manuscript received December 16, 1963.

REFERENCES

Dutton, G. G. S., and Unrau, A. M. (1962a). *Can. J. Chem.* **40**, 1196.

Dutton, G. G. S., and Unrau, A. M. (1962b). *Can. J. Chem.* **40**, 1479.

Flory, P. J. (1953). "Principles of Polymer Chemistry," pp. 347–398. Cornell University Press, Ithaca, New York.

Frahm, H. (1944). *Ann. Chem.* **555**, 187.

Lowry, T. M., and Smith, G. F. (1927). *J. Chem. Soc.* p. 2539.

Mora, P. T., (1957). *J. Polymer Sci.* **23**, 345.

Mora, P. T., and Wood, J. W. (1958). *J. Am. Chem. Soc.* **80**, 685.

Mora, P. T., Wood, J. W., Maury, P., and Young, B. G. (1958). *J. Am. Chem. Soc.* **80**, 693.

Mora, P. T., Merler, E., and Maury, P. (1959). *J. Am. Chem. Soc.* **81**, 5449.

Mora, P. T., Wood, J. W., and McFarland, V. W. (1960). *J. Am. Chem. Soc.* **82**, 3418.

Swain, C. G., and Brown, J. F. (1952). *J. Am. Chem. Soc.* **74**, 2534.

Thermal Polycondensation of Free Amino Acids with Polyphosphoric Acid

KAORU HARADA AND SIDNEY W. FOX

Institute for Space Biosciences, The Florida State University, Tallahassee, Florida

The thermal polycondensation of amino acids to yield proteinoids (polymers containing most to all of the eighteen amino acids common to protein) has been reviewed many times (Fox and Harada, 1960; Fox, 1960, 1963; Harada, 1961; Fox et al., 1962, 1963). The essential conditions are the use of sufficient aspartic acid and glutamic acid or of lysine, temperatures above the boiling point of water, and relatively dry reaction mixtures. These reactions are aided by the presence of such phosphates as orthophosphoric acid (Fox and Harada 1960), adenosine triphosphate (ATP) (Vegotsky and Fox, 1959), calcium phosphate (Vegotsky, 1960), and polyphosphoric acid (Harada and Fox, 1960). The practical temperatures necessary for condensation in the laboratory are lowered, by the use of phosphates, to values below the boiling point of water in some cases.

The occurrence of amino acids on the preorganismic Earth has been explained by many published syntheses, including the newly described thermal syntheses from primordial gases (p. 187). Phosphates of course occur in the crust of the Earth, and many variations can be visualized easily. We know, for instance, that ordinary phosphate would be converted to polyphosphate by temperatures of 300°C or less in volcanic zones. The firmness of such inferences is comparable to those which suggest a primitive atmosphere of methane, ammonia, and water.

Some of the studies which led to synthesis of proteinoid at 100°C and below are detailed in this paper.

Polyphosphoric acid in this work may act in a way similar to orthophosphoric acid and, moreover, it is a stronger dehydrating agent. Recently, polyphosphoric acid has been used in many organic reactions (Kenard, 1957). Galinsky et al. (1957) reported the synthesis of some diketopiperazines from free amino acids by use of polyphosphoric acid.

It was found possible here to obtain polymers by heating free amino acids containing sufficient aspartic acid with polyphosphoric acid at temperatures well under 100°C, whereas temperatures around 170°C are required for rapid polycondensation in the absence of polyphosphoric acid.

The conditions used in the thermal polycondensation are temperatures in the range of 70–130°C and a reaction time of 50–250 hours. Analyses of amino acid composition, N-terminal amino acid composition, and molecular weight of the reaction products were studied. In this work, either polyphosphoric acid (PPA) prepared by Victor Chemical Company or thermally prepared PPA obtained by heating orthophosphoric acid at different temperatures was used (Galinsky et al., 1957).

I. Experimental

The methods employed were closely similar to those described earlier (Vegotsky et al., 1958; Harada and Fox, 1958; Fox and Harada, 1958, 1960), except low temperatures and longer reaction periods were employed.

A. Polyphosphoric Acid (PPA)

PPA was prepared by heating 85% orthophosphoric acid for 2 hours at different temperatures such as at 200°C (200 PPA) 250°C (250 PPA), 300°C (300 PPA), and 350°C (350 PPA). The major components of such thermally prepared PPA were orthophosphoric acid, pyrophosphoric acid, and a small amount of triphosphoric acid (Ohashi and Sugatani, 1957). On the other hand, the Victor PPA (Victor Chemical Co.) contained some material of much higher molecular weight.[1]

B. Polycondensation with 200 PPA

Orthophosphoric acid (85%, 2 ml) was heated in an open test tube in an oil bath at 200°C for 2 hours under nitrogen. Water vapor evolved and volatile materials were expelled. To the thermally prepared PPA,

[1] The approximate composition of this acid at 83% P_2O_5 is:

Orthophosphoric acid	5.7%	Heptaphosphoric acid	7.1%
Pyrophosphoric acid	21.4	Octaphosphoric acid	6.9
Triphosphoric acid	18.0	Nonaphosphoric acid	
Tetraphosphoric acid	13.4	Higher polyphosphoric acid	6.5
Pentaphosphoric acid	11.4		
Hexaphosphoric acid	9.6	*Total*	*100%*

From the Bulletin of Victor Chemical Co.

0.02 mole of amino acid mixture[1] was added. This mixture was heated under an atmosphere of nitrogen at 70, 100 and 120°C for 100 hours in a constant-temperature air bath. The reaction mixture dissolved to form a yellow or amber transparent solution. After cooling, 15 ml of water was added to form a granular precipitate. The mixture was then dialyzed for 100 hours. Yields are listed in Table I.

C. Polycondensation with Victor PPA

Amino acid mixtures (0.02 mole) were mixed with 3 ml Victor PPA, and were heated at 100°C for 100 hours under an atmosphere of nitrogen in a constant-temperature air bath. The reaction materials were stirred with a glass rod after heating had started. The reaction mixtures were colored yellow to brown after 100 hours. After cooling, reaction mixtures were treated with 20 ml water and were dialyzed for 100 hours as described above.

Polymers were prepared by use of many kinds of PPA as above. Amino acid compositions were determined by a colorimetric method using column chromatography (Harada and Fox, 1958). N-Terminal amino acid composition and molecular weight were also determined by the DNFB method (Harada and Fox, 1958). Phosphate content was determined by the Fiske-SubbaRow method (Fiske and SubbaRow, 1925).

II. Results and Discussion

Table I shows the effect of 200 PPA in the polycondensation of six different combinations of amino acids, at 70, 100, and 120°C. Higher reaction temperatures result in higher yields in each case. Aspartic acid gave the highest yield; and aspartic acid-glutamic acid, aspartic acid-lysine gave the lowest yield of the six amino acid combinations. The yield and the amino acid composition marked with an (*) show the results in polymers prepared with orthophosphoric acid. The amount of polymer obtained at 100°C with orthophosphoric acid is less than that obtained at 70°C with 200 PPA. In composition, aspartic acid is a major component; the second amino acid content ranges from 10 to 23%.

Figure 1 shows the yield of polymers prepared with different kinds of PPA. The literature (Ohashi and Sugatani, 1957) shows that PPA prepared at higher temperatures contains material of higher molecular weight than the PPA obtained at lower temperatures. Polycondensation with Victor PPA gave the best yield. The yield decreased with 350 PPA,

---

[1] In the polycondensation, 0.02 mole of aspartic acid, Asp-Gly (1:1), Asp-Ala (1:1), Asp-Val (1:1), Asp-Glu (1:1), Asp-Lys HCl (1:1) were used. In each case the reacted form of aspartic acid was DL. The other amino acids used were as follows: DL-alanine, DL-valine, L-glutamic acid, and L-lysine monohydrochloride.

300 PPA, 250 PPA, and 200 PPA in that order. The higher molecular weight PPA (prepared at higher temperatures) appears to be the stronger agent in the thermal polycondensation of amino acids.

Figure 2 shows the effect of reaction time on the yield in the polycondensation of amino acid with Victor PPA at 90°C. It can be seen

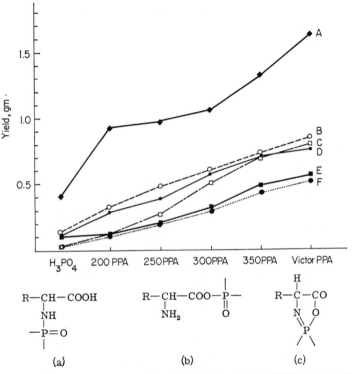

Fig. 1. Yields of polymer prepared with different kinds of PPA in reactions at 100°C for 100 hours. A: polyaspartic acid (0.02 mole of aspartic acid); B: copoly (aspartic acid, valine); C: copoly (aspartic acid, glutamic acid); D: copoly (aspartic acid, alanine); E: copoly (aspartic acid, glycine); F: copoly (aspartic acid, lysine). Mole ratios = 1.0:1.0.

that longer heating—up to 3 or 4 days—results in higher yields. After 3 or 4 days, the yields remain relatively constant. In these studies, also, aspartic acid gives the highest yield; the yield is almost quantitative after 3 days.

Table II shows the analysis of polymers prepared with 300 PPA. (Yields were shown in Fig. 1.) Amino acid determination shows that

TABLE I
YIELD AND AMINO ACID COMPOSITION OF POLYMERS PREPARED AT DIFFERENT TEMPERATURES WITH 200 PPA[a]

Polymer	At 70°C			At 100°C			At 120°C		
	Yield after dialysis (gm)	Amino acid composition		Yield after dialysis (gm)	Amino acid composition		Yield after dialysis (gm)	Amino acid composition	
		Asp (%)	2nd amino acid (%)		Asp (%)	2nd amino acid (%)		Asp (%)	2nd amino acid (%)
Asp	0.55	—	—	0.99(0.37*)[b]	—	—	1.84	—	—
Asp-Gly	0.04	86	14	0.13(0.12*)	83(83*)	17(17*)	0.67	77	23
Asp-Ala	0.25	82	18	0.30(0.12*)	81(82*)	19(18*)	0.82	80	20
Asp-Val	0.24	86	14	0.34(0.12*)	88(87*)	12(13*)	0.69	87	13
Asp-Glu	0.08	90	10	0.18	90(86*)	10(14*)	0.35	—	—
Asp-Lys	0.09	85	15	0.14	89	—	0.16	—	—

[a] Amino acid mixtures [0.02 mole Asp:2nd amino acid (1:1)] were heated with 200 PPA for 100 hours at 70, 100, and 120°C.

[b] Asterisked numbers denote the yield and the analysis of products prepared with 2 ml of orthophosphoric acid (85%) and the equimolar amino acid mixture (same as above).

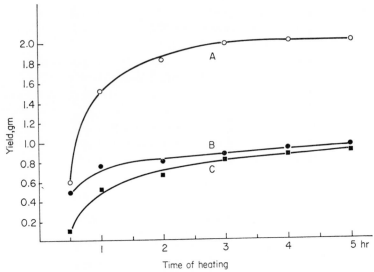

FIG. 2. Effect of reaction time on yields. A: polyaspartic acid (0.02 mole aspartic acid); B: poly (aspartic acid, alanine); C: poly (aspartic acid, glutamic acid). Mole ratios = 1.0:1.0.

aspartic acid is the main component and the second amino acid content falls in the 10–20% range. The molecular weight of these polymers are relatively high, especially the aspartic acid homopolymer and the (Asp-Glu) copolymer which are about 15,000. In the N-terminal amino acid composition of these polymers, the aspartic acid content decreases. For example, in the (Asp-Glu) copolymer, the N-terminal glutamic acid is

TABLE II

CHARACTERIZATION OF POLYMERS PREPARED WITH 300 PPA AT 100°C
FOR 100 HOURS[a]

| Polymer | Amino acid composition | | Molec-ular weight | N-Terminal composition | | |
	Asp (%)	2nd Amino acid (%)		Asp (%)	2nd Amino acid (%)	H₃PO₄ (%)
Asp	—	—	15,000	—	—	0.30
Asp-Gly	85	15	6,200	71	29	0.34
Asp-Ala	83	17	9,200	74	26	0.35
Asp-Val	81	19	5,800	66	34	0.28
Asp-Glu	91	9	15,000	46	54	0.50
Asp-Lys HCl	86	14	—	74	26	0.47

[a] Total amino acid: 0.02 mole; amino acid ratio = 1:1.

54%, whereas the glutamic acid is only 9% in the total amino acid composition. The phosphate content, as H_3PO_4, is about 0.3–0.5%. The value is almost the same as in casein, a phosphoprotein.

Table III shows the results of characterization of polymers prepared with Victor PPA at 100°C for 100 hours. (Yields were given in Fig. 1.) The amino acid composition is almost the same as in Table II. Aspartic acid is the major component and the second amino acid content is about 10–20%. The molecular weight is again high, especially in the aspartic acid homopolymer (13,000) and the (Asp-Glu) copolymer (14,000). The N-terminal amino acid composition is also similar to that shown in Table II. The aspartic acid content at the N-terminus is much less than

TABLE III

CHARACTERIZATION OF POLYMERS PREPARED WITH POLYPHOSPHORIC ACID
(VICTOR) AT 100°C FOR 100 HOURS[a]

Polymer	Amino acid composition		Molec-ular weight	N-Terminal composition		
	Asp (%)	2nd Amino acid (%)		Asp (%)	2nd Amino acid (%)	H_3PO_4 (%)
Asp	—	—	12,700	—	—	0.30
Asp-Gly	84	16	6,100	55	45	0.47
Asp-Ala	82	18	9,000	63	37	0.32
Asp-Val	86	14	6,100	59	41	0.33
Asp-Glu	89	11	13,800	34	66	0.41
Asp-Lys HCl	86	14	—	85	15	0.33

[a] Total amino acid: 0.02 mole; amino acid ratio = 1:1.

the content of this amino acid in the polymer. This is especially true in the case of the (Glu-Asp) copolymer. The phosphate content, as H_3PO_4, is 0.3–0.4%.

Glutamic acid and aspartic acid copolycondense with fourteen neutral and basic amino acids in the presence of PPA by heating at 100°C for 100–150 hours. The amino acid analysis of the proteinoid (by the Stein-Moore method) shows that it contains 51% aspartic acid, 13% glutamic acid, 7% basic amino acids, and 24% neutral amino acids (Table IV). The amino acid proportions of the proteinoid are similar to those of protein except for the fact that aspartic acid is more prevalent in the synthetic polymers. The properties of the low-temperature proteinoid are similar to those of proteinoid prepared at higher temperatures without PPA.

PPA acts as a solvent and a dehydrating agent and possibly also as an acid catalyst in the polycondensation reaction. Although the mechanism of the reaction is uncertain, it is conceivable that (a) N-phosphorylamino derivatives or (b) mixed acid anhydrides are formed during the reaction.

Free energy of phosphorolysis of PPA may contribute to the endothermic condensation of free amino acids. The PPA prepared by heating orthophosphoric acid is composed only of linear polyphosphoric acid as in ATP. The synthetic PPA does not contain cyclic products (Ohashi and Sugatani, 1957).

Racemization of L-aspartic acid was followed during polycondensation. The aspartic acid was isolated from the hydrolysate of the aspartic acid homopolymer prepared from L-aspartic acid. This amino acid has no

TABLE IV

AMINO ACID COMPOSITION OF PROTEINOID PREPARED WITH 200 PPA[a]

Thr	0.55%		Lys	2.79%	
Ser	0.63		His	2.53	7.15%
Pro	1.04		Arg	1.83	
Gly	2.93				
Ala	1.31		Asp	51.9	
Val	1.33	27.6%	Glu	13.3	65.2%
Met	0.86				
Iso	0.71				
Leu	3.44				
Tyr	3.87				
Phe	5.87				
NH₃	5.02				

[a] Asp:Glu:basic and neutral amino acid ratio = 2:1:3; 100°C, for 150 hours.

rotatory power. Such loss of optical activity during the polycondensation may be explained by the formation of azlactone-type intermediates (c) which can enolize (Schramm and Wissman, 1958).

On the other hand, sulfuric acid is also a good solvent for amino acids and peptides: it may act as an acid catalyst, and it is a strong dehydrating agent. However, sulfuric acid does not yield any amino acid polymers under the reaction conditions described for PPA. The fact that the results with the two mineral acids are so different is interesting in view of the importance of polyphosphate in the biological synthesis of protein.

Diketopiperazine was prepared by Galinsky et al. (1957) by use of PPA. However, in this study, the dialyzed product does not contain diketopiperazine. The polymers dissolved completely in 5% sodium bicarbonate solution at room temperature, and no insoluble diketopiperazine remained. The diketopiperazine formed in the reaction would escape during the first dialysis of aqueous solution with PPA.

Infrared absorption spectra of these polymers show strong bands at 1720 and 1780 cm^{-1} which indicate anhydroaspartyl residues, and also show bands at 1630 cm^{-1} (amide I), 1530 cm^{-1} (amide II) which indicate the presence of peptide bonds.

ACKNOWLEDGMENTS

This paper is contribution no. 030 of the Institute for Space Biosciences. The study was aided by grant NsG-173-62 of the National Aeronautics and Space Administration. The technical assistance of (Mrs.) Hatsuko Harada is appreciated. Most of this subject matter was presented at the 137th meeting of the American Chemical Society in Cleveland, Ohio, April, 1960.

Revised Manuscript received April 10, 1964.

REFERENCES

Fiske, C. H., and Subba Row, Y. (1925). *J. Biol. Chem.* **66**, 375.

Fox, S. W. (1960). *Science* **132**, 200.

Fox, S. W. (1963). *Symp. Protein Nutrition Metabolism* p. 141. *In* "Symposium on Protein Nutrition and Metabolism" (J. Kastelic, H. H. Draper, and H. P. Broquist, eds.), Special Publication No. 4 p. 141, University of Illinois College of Agriculture, Urbana.

Fox, S. W., and Harada, K. (1958). *Science* **128**, 3333.

Fox, S. W., and Harada, K. (1960). *J. Am. Chem. Soc.* **82**, 3745.

Fox, S. W., Harada, K., and Rohlfing, D. L. (1962). *In* "Polyamino Acids, Polypeptides, and Proteins" (M. A. Stahmann, ed.), p. 47. Univ. of Wisconsin Press, Madison, Wisconsin.

Fox, S. W., Harada, K., Woods, K. R., and Windsor, C. R. (1963). *Arch. Biochem. Biophys.* **102**, 439.

Galinsky, A. M., Gearien, J. E., and Smissman, E. E. (1957). *j. Am. Pharm. Assoc.* **46**, 391.

Harada, K. (1959). *Bull. Chem. Soc. Japan* **82**, 1008.

Harada, K. (1961). *Protein, Nucleic Acid, Enzyme (Tokyo)* **6**, 65.

Harada, K., and Fox, S. W. (1958). *J. Am. Chem. Soc.* **80**, 2694.

Harada, K., and Fox, S. W. (1960). *Abstr. 137th Meeting Am. Chem. Soc., Cleveland, Ohio* p. 28c.

Kenard, K. C. (1957). *Org. Chem. Bull.* **29**, No. 1.

Ohashi, S., and Sugatani, H. (1957). *Bull. Chem. Soc. Japan* **30**, 864.

Schramm, G., and Wissman, H. (1958). *Chem. Ber.* **91**, 1073.

Vegotsky, A. (1960). Ph.D. dissertation, Florida State University, Tallahassee, Florida.

Vegotsky, A., and Fox, S. W. (1959). *Federation Proc.* **18**, 343.

Vegotsky, A., Harada, K., and Fox, S. W. (1958). *J. Am. Chem. Soc.* **80**, 3361.

DISCUSSION

DR. BUCHANAN: Could I please have just a brief statement of the enzyme activity that has been studied in which the rate of reaction of the proteinoids is greater than what the catalysis of the unpolymerized amino acids would be in a model system?

MR. ROHLFING: The reaction that has been studied in detail is the acceleration of the hydrolysis of p-nitrophenyl acetate; approximately 100 proteinoids have been tested in this system. All have been more active than the equivalent amount of histidine or, when tested, the hydrolysate of the polymer. The most active ones are in the neighborhood of fifteen times as active as the equivalent amount of histidine. These can be almost completely inactivated by heating in a buffered solution at pH 6.8.

DR. FOX: Inactivation is accompanied by an opening of imide linkage. The two structural features of imide and histidine must both be present, in presumably a special arrangement, for the most active polymers which have been found.

MR. ROHLFING: We have also studied compositionally simple co-polymers of histidine and aspartic acid; these also are more active than histidine. They are not as active as most of the proteinoids. They can be inactivated by heat, which indicates that the simultaneous presence of anhydroaspartyl residues and histidine residues results in an enhanced level of catalytic activity in these polymers, as in proteinods.

DR. FOX: I would like to make one statement relative to "randomness" in proteinoids.

The preconception that I have encountered most often in many discussions is the one that no order could result from the seemingly brutal process of heating amino acids together. This preconception states essentially that eighteen kinds of amino acids, like beads of eighteen colors, must be distributed randomly along a chain. This concept fails to take into account the fact that the eighteen amino acids differ not superficially as in a shade of color, but fundamentally in conformation and distribution of electric charge, etc.

If beads differed one from the other in such a fundamental and pervasive way as amino acids do, their distribution in a chain, however assembled, could not be assumed to be uniform. In this way we can understand the kinds of analytical disparities between total composition and terminal compositions such as shown in this last paper. This is consistent with a concept of *nonrandomness* or "favored bonds," to borrow a phrase used by Dr. Mora in another context. Our use of the word *random* is like that of the statistician in his reference to "random sample." In a random arrangement in a set of peptide chains, each amino acid of the total composition would be proportionally represented alike in each position in the chains.

Synthesis of Nucleosides and Polynucleotides with Metaphosphate Esters

GERHARD SCHRAMM

Max-Planck-Institut für Virusforschung, Tübingen, Germany

If studies on the origin of biological systems should be a part of science, we have to avoid deductions a priori and rely on experimental data.

What kind of experiments can be done? One approach is the analysis of existing living organisms in order to find out the most fundamental principles of life. This is a difficult task and different investigators may come to different conclusions. Therefore, this analytical way needs to be supplemented by a synthetical approach. Regarding the geological conditions in the early history of Earth, and if necessary on other planets, too, we should try to construct a model which operates according to the principles found by the analytical way. By careful measurements we have to study whether such an experimental system deserves the name "prebiological" or even "biological." It can never be proved definitely that such a model system is the only possible one, but the difficulties in transcending from the physical world to living organisms are so tremendous that a demonstration of just one transition would be of the greatest importance for the development of human thinking.

I. Biological Multiplication

Our present knowledge about living organisms has already been presented by the previous speakers. I would like to mention only a few points which are so obvious that they can easily be overlooked.

In my opinion the most fundamental property of a living organism is its ability to multiply. The structure of the parents has to be reproduced in the progeny, but it is important that the process be flexible and allow mutations and, therefore, evolution. Evolution is in fact a very complex process, which is not yet fully understood. However, evolution is the key to understanding the extreme improbability of life.

I would like to present some figures for this improbability of biological structures. The ribonucleic acid (RNA) of the tobacco mosaic virus (TMV) contains 6000 nucleotides. The probability that this special molecule results by random combination of the four nucleotides is $\frac{1}{4}^{6000} = 10^{-2000}$. Since the whole cosmos has an estimated weight of 10^{80} protons, it is practically impossible to obtain such a ribonucleic acid in 10^9 years, the age of the world, even if the whole world would consist of a reacting mixture of nucleotides.

The situation is quite different in a population of multiplying molecules or organisms. Improbable alterations of such an entity leading to a higher multiplication rate will survive, and finally the whole population will be replaced by these faster multiplying entities. In this great number of better adapted entities, another change may lead to an even higher multiplication rate. One mole of a substance contains 6×10^{23} molecules in a volume not larger than a few liters. In such a great population of multiplying molecules, mutations with a probability of 10^{-20} can occur, which according to the higher multiplication rate lead to a substitution of the whole slower multiplying population in a certain period. If this period is not too long, 100 substitutions can lead to a structure the probability of which, compared with the original one, is 10^{-2000}.

Therefore a model of a prebiological system is necessarily able to multiply and undergo evolution. In other words, we have to design a system which contains the information for its own reproduction, transferable to another system, in which the information can be stored, modified, and the most favorable one selected.

The human imagination is too poor to invent such a complicated process, but fortunately such a system is verified by the nucleic acids in the living organism. These molecules contain the genetic information and can transmit blueprints for their construction from one generation to the next. In the cell this information transfer is connected with a metabolic system which provides the energy and the substances necessary for this transfer. Viruses, on the other hand, can be considered as information transfer units without metabolism. For this reason it seems easier to construct a model which resembles a virus; that means a system which can multiply by using the energy sources of the environment.

The information for the construction of a virus is stored in its core which contains either deoxyribonucleic acid (DNA) or (RNA). The reproduction of the genetic material occurs by means of a template mechanism, in which a matrix, formed by nucleotides, controls the catalytic assembly of other nucleotides to a complementary strand, which in turn serves as a matrix for the original strand. The most primitive precondition for biological multiplication is a template which can direct the assembly of nucleotides. Further, a mechanism is needed to separate the two templates and enable them to start reproduction again. The problem is whether such a system can be set up without enzymes. In order to find an answer to this question I shall at first discuss the nonenzymatic formation of nucleotides from sugars, bases, and phosphate, and the condensation of these nucleotides to long chains of polynucleotides.

II. The Origin of Nucleic Acids

The biosynthesis of polynucleotides and many other biological macromolecules is based on a series of condensations, by elimination of the OH group from one and the H from the other molecule. This combination is in general achieved by a procedure shown in Table I. The

TABLE I
Syntheses of Biological Macromolecules

Condensation	Product
⟨℗^{a} O H R :O	Polyglycoside; R = C Polynucleotide; R = P Aminoacyl RNA ⟶ Polypeptides
℗OR ◄— :NH	Nucleosides
℗OR ◄— :SH	Acetyl-CoA ⟶ Fatty acids
℗OR ◄— :CH	Polyisoprene R = Isopentenyl

^{a} ℗: phosphate, pyrophosphate or pyrophosphate ester.

hydroxyl group of one component is substituted by phosphate, pyrophosphate, or pyrophosphate ester in such a way that the electrons are withdrawn from the central atom and a nucleophilic attack of the other component is made possible. The activating group is then eliminated together with the proton of the attacking molecule. The initial phosphorylation is achieved by polyphosphate derivatives, mainly adenosine triphosphate. The activating group should not contain a negative charge close to the central atom, since this would repel the electrons. In the cell, the negative charges of the phosphoryl or pyrophosphoryl groups are probably removed by the condensing enzymes.

We found in our laboratory that many of these biological condensations can be imitated by use of a simple metaphosphate ester (MPE). With this agent we achieved the formation of polypeptides from peptides and amino acids (Schramm and Wissman, 1958), polyglycosides from simple sugars, nucleosides from sugars and bases, and finally the condensation of nucleotides to polynucleotides (Schramm et al., 1961).

Starting from sugars and heterocyclic bases, the nucleic acids are formed in three subsequent steps of condensation: (1) condensation between sugars and bases leading to nucleosides; (2) condensation between nucleosides and phosphoric acid leading to nucleotides; and (3) condensation between nucleotides leading to long chains. All three types of condensation can be achieved with MPE.

According to this procedure, nucleic acids can originate, if sugars (especially pentoses), purines, or pyrimidines and MPE are present. Oró (1963) has demonstrated that the starting material for the nucleic acid can be formed during the early history of the Earth. Pentoses are formed selectively from formaldehyde in the presence of alkaline earth hydroxides (Mayer and Jäschke, 1960; Pfeil and Ruckert, 1961). Deoxyribose can easily be obtained from triose and acetaldehyde (Oró, 1963).

Above 300°C orthophosphates are not stable. Therefore, large deposits of condensed phosphates presumably existed in water-free regions, after the Earth was cooled. These condensed phosphates might have been esterified by reaction with organic compounds. In the presence of metaphosphate esters the formation of polypeptides, polyglycosides, and polynucleotides can occur simultaneously. Hexoses yield relatively stable polymers, whereas ribose gives unstable polymers due to its furanosidic structure, but ribose reacts very easily with purines to nucleosides. These nucleosides can be transformed to polynucleotides in a one-step reaction by heating them with metaphosphate esters. Many interactions are possible, with the polypeptides, and polyglycosides, formed simultaneously. Thus the conditions are favorable for the origin of complicated prebiological systems. The water-free region in which the condensations occur may be inside the coacervates, as was proposed by Oparin (1961), or in other aggregates protected by a waterproof membrane.

III. The Synthesis of Nucleosides with Metaphosphate Esters

In the last years we have studied some of these condensing reactions in more detail. The simplest way to prepare metaphosphate esters is the reaction of P_4O_{10} with diethyl ether. By breakage of two P—O—P linkages a mixture of tetrametaphosphate and isotetrametaphosphate ester is obtained. The structure of these compounds was already described correctly by Rätz and Thilo (1951) and confirmed recently by Pollmann and Schramm (1964) and by Weill *et al.* (1963). It has been shown by Pollmann and Schramm (1964) that the ester has to be prepared under mild conditions; otherwise, the cyclic products are transformed to linear polyphosphate esters which are less reactive. Furthermore, polyphosphates and other hydroxyl compounds must be removed from the reaction mixture, otherwise they destroy the cyclic meta-phosphate ester.

The reaction of the MPE with various NH and hydroxyl containing compounds can easily be followed by titration in nonaqueous solution.

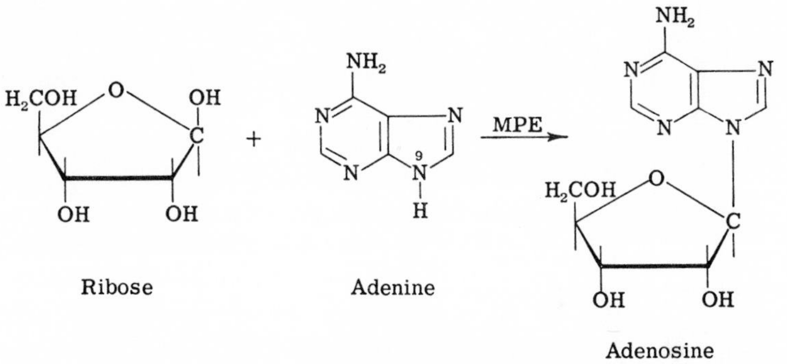

FIG. 1. Synthesis of adenosine.

Experiments with sugars have shown that the acetalic hydroxyl on C-1 is the most reactive group. The next reactive group is the primary hydroxyl in C-5 in pentoses or C-6 in hexoses. The other secondary hydroxyl groups react very slowly or not at all. Thus a rather specific activation of sugars is possible, leading to different types of reactions. If we combine activated riboses with one another, we obtain polyribosides under elimination of the phosphate ester residues. By addition of an excess of purines, this self-condensation of sugars can be avoided. The NH group is more reactive than a hydroxyl group. In particular, the condensation of ribose and deoxyribose with adenine was studied (Lünzmann and Schramm, 1964) (Fig. 1). Adenine reacts with two moles of MPE probably in position 9 and in the amino group at C-6. The activated nitrogen reacts with the activated hydroxyl group of the ribose probably in a concerted reaction. The condensing reaction depends on the proton concentration (Fig. 2). At an apparent pH of 7 in the dimethylformamide solution the reaction is very slow; it becomes much faster at pH 1.5. The kinetics are complicated, since the reaction is reversed after a certain period. The reversion can be avoided by the addition of a buffer. From ribose and adenine only the natural β-glycosidic adenosine was obtained. This is due to the directing influence of the hydroxyl group at C-2. With deoxyribose, in which this hydroxyl group is missing, a mixture of α- and β-nucleosides was formed. This was also observed by Carbon (1963). Probably the free amino group at C-6 reacts also with the sugar, but this Schiff base is hydrolyzed during the isolation of the product. Therefore it is not necessary

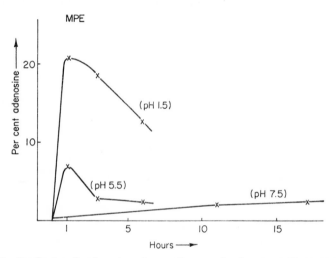

FIG. 2. Synthesis of adenosine from ribose and adenine with metaphosphate esters (MPE) at different proton concentrations. The pH values given indicate apparent pH in dimethylformamide. The yield is given as per cent ribose transformed to adenosine.

to protect this amino group. Although the yields of these reactions are not very high (20–40% of the sugar is transformed to nucleoside), this method is superior to the conventional ones in which substituted sugars and substituted bases are used.

IV. The Synthesis of Polynucleotides with Metaphosphate Esters

In the absence of a solvent and the presence of an excess of MPE, nucleosides are phosphorylated and condensed. Clearer results are obtained if nucleotides are used as starting material. By titration in non-aqueous solution it was demonstrated that the phosphate group in position 2′ or 3′ and the free hydroxyl group in position 5′ of the nucleotides react with MPE. Subsequently, both activating residues are eliminated during condensation. This condensation depends less on proton concentration than the formation of the nucleosides. It proceeds also if tertiary bases are present. This is important, because some nucleotides, such as deoxyadenylic acid or deoxyguanylic acid, are unstable in an acidic medium.

In order to obtain polynucleotides of high molecular weight, the concentration of nucleotides must be as high as possible; dilution by a solvent therefore should be avoided. On the other hand, a homogeneous phase is necessary, at least at the end of the reaction. The addition of a small amount of phosphoric acid trisdimethylamide $= OP[N(CH_3)_2]_3$ reduces the viscosity of MPE and promotes the dissolution of the nucleotides, whereas other solvents are mostly inhibitory. Sometimes it is difficult to dissolve the nucleotides in MPE directly. In this case an aqueous solution of the nucleotides was freeze-dried under a good vacuum. The voluminous residue dissolves easily in MPE. In other experiments a homogeneous solution was obtained by ultrasonic vibration under vigorous cooling.

The structural analysis of the polynucleotides, obtained with MPE, is not yet completed. An inhomogeneous mixture was obtained with a broad distribution of molecular weights. The smaller oligonucleotides can be separated by column chromatography on Sephadex or DEAE-Cellulose. In other experiments the smaller molecules and the hydrolyzed metaphosphate ester were removed by dialysis, and the remaining polynucleotides of higher molecular weight were characterized by sedimentation and diffusion measurements. This nondialyzable fraction comprises about 10% of the starting material. It contains material with sedimentation constant between 1.4 and 2.4S, corresponding to an average molecular weight of about 10,000. Top fractions having a higher molecular weight can be isolated.

In the natural polynucleotides the phosphate links the C-3' position with the C-5' position. In the polymerization of the deoxynucleotides, pyrophosphate linkages were formed instead of the natural 3'-5' phosphate linkages. Further studies are necessary to find out whether this undesirable reaction can be avoided.

The commercially available ribonucleotides are mainly mixtures of 2' and 3' nucleoside phosphates. The free hydroxyl groups, adjacent to the phosphate group, split the pyrophosphate linkages, forming 2'-3' phosphates. Therefore pyrophosphate linkages are not found in the synthetic polyuridylic acid. On the other hand, these free hydroxyl groups can lead to unwanted 2'-2' and 3'-3' phosphate linkages and become branching points. In the polymer obtained from 2'(3')-uridylic acid, the amount of phosphate linkages at the 5' position can be determined by degradation with snake venom phosphodiesterase which is specific for phosphate groups in the 5'-position. Figure 3 shows the fractionation of polyuridylic acid (poly-U) on a Sephadex G 25 column before and after treatment with snake venom. It is obvious that a considerable number of linkages exist that are resistant to snake venom and are not located at the 5'-position.

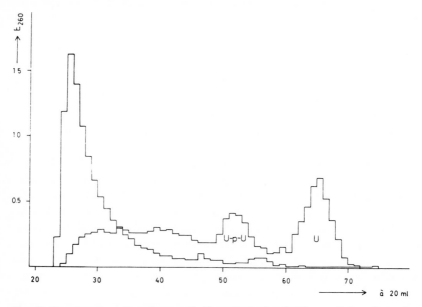

Fig. 3. Fractionation of synthetic poly-U on Sephadex G 25. a = Before, b = after degradation with snake venom phosphodiesterase.

The proportion of phosphate groups in the 3'–position can be measured by degradation with ribonuclease, which splits only polynucleotides with a free hydroxyl group in 2' and a phosphate bridge in 3'. From the commercial mixture of 3'(2')-uridylic acid a polymer was obtained which ribonuclease degraded only slightly. Polymers from the purified 3'-uridylic acid gave better results. This resistance may be due to the fact that the phosphate groups migrate from 3' to 2' or that the free hydroxy group in 2' is substituted. Further experiments are needed to clarify this point.

The polymerization of nucleotides with MPE was studied recently by Kochetkov *et al.* (1964). The molecular weight was estimated to be

10,000, although no exact measurements were made. From enzymatic and alkaline hydrolysis the authors concluded that most linkages are un-natural. These results differ from those obtained in our laboratory. One reason for this may be that the starting material used by the Russian authors contained a large amount of 2′ nucleotides that are resistant to ribonuclease.

Matthaei (personal communication) compared the coding activity of our synthetic poly-U with that of poly-U prepared by phosphorylase. The incorporation of phenylalanine was determined in a cell-free system of *Escherichia coli*. Since smaller polynucleotides are inactive or even inhibitory, a fractionation of the preparations was necessary. Fractions of the synthetic poly-U and the enzymatic poly-U with the same molecular weight had approximately the same coding activity. Therefore the structure of the synthetic product is apparently not too different from that of the natural product. Further experiments will have to show whether the specificity of the polymerization can be improved.

In conclusion, the foregoing experiments demonstrate that poly-nucleotides can be formed from sugars and heterocyclic bases by means of MPE. The products have various molecular weights and structures. The nucleotides are distributed randomly and have no definite sequence.

The problem now is how a self-reproducing system can have orig-inated from such a mixture of polynucleotides. As mentioned before, self-reproduction begins when one polynucleotide is used as matrix to form a complementary polynucleotide, which in its turn catalyzes the formation of the original polynucleotide chain. Therefore we investi-gated whether a polynucleotide can function as a template in a non-enzymatic system.

The polymerization of uridylic acid was not catalyzed when poly-U was added, but did so by addition of complementary poly-A (poly-adenylic acid). The initial polymerization rate increased tenfold. When 20–30% of the uridylic acid was polymerized, the reaction slowed down. Obviously the template mechanism was not perfect. The reason may be that the newly formed poly-U did not separate easily from the poly-A template. Of course more experiments are necessary to support the working hypothesis that in a population of growing polynucleotide chains certain polynucleotides can catalyze the formation of comple-mentary chains and these in turn can accelerate the formation of the original chains.

If this mechanism works as presumed, the most suitable templates would be selected and would then be substituted for branched and other chains less suitable. I wonder, however, whether a definite sequence of nucleotides can be selected by this mechanism and whether a higher amount of information accumulates in the nucleotide chains.

To get more insight into this complicated selection process, we have to reconsider how the DNA is multiplied in the living cell. The genetically active DNA has a double function, first it contains the information for its own multiplication, and second, the information for the construction of polypeptide chains serving as catalysts for various synthetic processes, including the polymerization of nucleotides to form DNA. The very simplified scheme in Fig. 4 illustrates this correlation. The matrix M_0 catalyzes the formation of the matrix M_C and vice versa. One or both of these matrices controls the formation of polypeptides which in their turn control the synthesis of the matrices. This would be the

FIG. 4. Scheme of a self-reproducing system. M_0: original matrix; M_C: complementary matrix.

simplest form of a prebiological self-organizing system: each catalyst controls the formation of the other and thereby its own formation. Supposing the sequence of the nucleotides determined the sequence of amino acids in the polypeptide catalyst, a specific sequence of nucleotides would then be selected, producing the most effective peptide.

Any alteration in this self-regulating circuit improving the effect and number of catalysts will favor the multiplication of this system. But evolution on the molecular basis is only possible if the templates storing the information have a similar ratio of stability to mutability as the genetic material of the living organism. This is warranted, if we assume that the matrices M_0 and M_C have a similar chemical structure as the genetic material and are closely related to polynucleotides. More experiments have to be done to verify the self-regulating system shown in Fig. 4. It is not clear how under primordial conditions a polynucleotide chain can control the formation of polypeptide chains. This may be achieved by aminoacyl polynucleotides, similar to aminoacyl transfer RNA. Such mixed polymers can easily be formed in the water-free region described above. Furthermore, very little is known concerning how polypeptides can catalyze the formation of polynucleotides.

Of course I am aware that this molecular model of self-reproduction is still very incomplete, but it may stimulate new experiments and new measurements, thus providing a more reliable basis for further studies on the origin of life.

Revised Manuscript Received March 20, 1964

REFERENCES

Carbon, J. A. (1963). *Chem. Ind.* (*London*) p. 529.
Kochetkov, N. K., Budowsky, E. I., Domkin, V. D., and Khromov-Borissov, N. N. (1964). *Biochim. Biophys. Acta* **80**, 145.
Lünzmann, G., and Schramm, G. (1963). Unpublished results.
Mayer, R., and Jäschke, L. (1960). *Ann. Chem.* **635**, 145.
Oparin, A. I. (1961). "Life, Its Nature, Origin, and Development." Oliver and Boyd, Edinburgh and London.
Oró, J. (1963). *Lunar and Planetary Exploration Colloq., Downey,* Calif. Vol. III, p. 9.
Pfeil, E., and Ruckert, H. (1961). *Ann. Chem.* **641**, 121.
Pollmann, W., and Schramm, G. (1964). *Biochim, Biophys. Acta* **80**, 1.
Rätz, R., and Thilo, E. (1951). *Ann. Chem.* **572**, 173.
Schramm, G., and Wissmann, H. (1958). *Chem. Ber.* **91**, 1073.
Schramm, G., Grötsch, H., and Pollmann, W. (1961). *Angew. Chem.* **73**, 610.
Weill, G., Klein, M., and Calvin, M. (1963). *Nature* **200**, 1005.

DISCUSSION

Dr. Fox: As I recall the paper by G. Schramm and H. Wissmann [(1958), *Chem. Ber.* **91**, 1073] no formation of polypeptides from amino acids by MPE is described. That paper does describe polymerization of DL-alanylglycylglycine and formation of peptide bonds between amino acid *derivatives*. Since none of these are amino acids, the 1958 reference given does not support the statement in Dr. Schramm's paper; perhaps his statement had some other meaning. In a prebiological context, the difference between amino acids and their derivatives can be crucial since the geosynthesis of free amino acids has been explained.

Dr. Schramm: The same method can be applied to amino acids. From a mixture of tyrosine, alanine, and glutaminic acid a polypeptide with an average molecular weight of 7300 can be obtained in a yield of about 70%. ($s_{20} = 1,2$ S, $D_{20} = 12.0.10^{-7} cm^2/sec$).

Dr. Dobzhansky: Dr. Schramm's introduction gives me an opening for making a few remarks on my own. Natural selection is sometimes descibed as a mechanism capable of realizing the highest degree of improbability, as Dr. Schramm has quite correctly pointed out. I would like, however, to express the belief that the words "natural selection" must be used carefully. Dr. Schramm has so used them. In reading some other literature on the origin of life, I am afraid that not all authors have used the term carefully.

Natural selection is differential reproduction, organism perpetuation. In order to have natural selection, you have to have self-reproduction or self-replication and at least two distinct self-replicating units or entities.

Now, I realize that when you speak of origin of life, you wish to discuss the probable embryonic stages, so to speak, of natural selection. What these embryonic stages will be is for you to decide.

I would like to plead with you, simply, please realize you cannot use the words "natural selection" loosely. Prebiological natural selection is a contradiction of terms.

Dr. Mora: I was very impressed by Dr. Schramm's polymerization work. He has shown me some polyglucose which was white and had high molecular weight. Apparently the advantage of metaphosphate in a water-free medium is that this allows lower temperatures to be used; therefore there should be less branching in the polymers, as compared with our melt polymerization method using phosphorous acid [Mora, P. T., and Wood, J. W. (1958), *J. Am. Chem. Soc.* **80**, 685]. However, both are fundamentally similar acid-catalyzed polycondensation methods, in which the water of condensation is eliminated by some means.

Dr. Schramm: We have prepared a polyglucose by use of MPE in dimethylformamide. Under mild conditions we got a rather specific polymerization in which we have mainly $1 \to 6$ glycosidic linkages. This was found by Dr. Schlumberger in my laboratory by oxidation with periodate. Some of the glucose units did not react with periodate, since they were substituted by pyrophosphate or polyphosphate groups.

Dr. Mora: Turning to your ribose and the polymerization leading to poly-A, it is interesting that it stimulates amino acid incorporation in spite of the fact that you would expect branching.

Dr. Schramm: It is not very probable that branching occurs during polymerization of the ribonucleotides. It is known that substitution of the hydroxyl group in 3′ is a steric hindrance for further phosphorylation in 2′. Of course it is not possible that our syntheses are absolutely specific. In this respect we cannot compete with the enzymes. But at least we can achieve a certain degree of specificity in our nonenzymatic polymerization.

I should mention that the alkaline hydrolysis of our polyribonucleotides does not lead to nucleoside diphosphates in a significant amount. Therefore, I think we have not too much branching.

Dr. Mora: You are well aware of work that shows that nucleotides stack. Probably when you have complementary nucleotides in addition, you have established portions which are oriented by the hydrogen bonds.

DR. SCHRAMM: The template function of poly-A can be explained by the assumption that on the surface of the template the concentration of uridylic acid is increased locally. An increase in concentration would, of course, accelerate the polymerization.

DR. MORA: I would like to say something concerning your calculations on probability, because you are touching upon an argument that Horowitz [Horowitz, N. H., (1945), *Proc. Natl. Acad. Sci. U.S.* 31, 153] and Oparin [see for example, Oparin, A. I. (1961), "Life, Its Nature, Origin, and Development," Oliver and Boyd, Edinburgh and London] presented. They propose that some type of selection operates on the molecular level before the appearance of a living unit and then this brings about accumulation of molecules or aggregates which approach more and more, and finally reach, the property of the living, which has the ability to reproduce persistently and then with sufficient mutability to evolve through selectivity and adaptability.

The trouble is that this type of argument requires that molecules have a high capacity of self-copy and it also tacitly endows molecules with the ability of really natural selection and evolution similar to that which operates in the biological domain.

Of course, there is chemical selectivity (affinity, specific reactivity, complementariness, etc.) and, incidentally, much of this is important in many biochemical details we study nowadays (enzyme-substrate, antigen-antibody interaction, etc.). There is also a continuous flux of atoms and molecules building up and down in complexity depending on the physical and chemical environment and on the property of the molecules (free energy, etc.). Some of the more complex molecules (aggregates) are more stable under certain conditions than the less complex molecules from which they are formed. Much of the synthesis and polymerization work presented here is this type of chemistry. Some of the molecules (polymers) also have great affinity to associate with similar molecules (cf. crystallization). The question is, will this lead through selection to a continuously evolving hierarchy of molecules' with greater and greater ability of more and more accurate self-reproducibility until the self-reproducibility reaches a frequency and accuracy which will persistently overcompensate the combined randomization effects?

To allow this to happen, one requirement is that more than half of certain kinds of molecules (polymers) must copy themselves quite faithfully before they break down. This is difficult to account for if we use the known theories of physics and chemistry. According to current quantum mechanics, the probability of self-reproducing states is zero [Wigner, E. P. (1961), *in* "The Logic of Personal Knowledge, Collection of Essays presented to Michael Polany," Routledge and Kegan Paul, London]. An even further requirement is that with increasing complexity and organization, self-reproducibility of molecules should be more and more probable. Obviously, this cannot be reconciled with thermodynamic principles. A third requirement is that these processes should go on persistently.

Selection and evolution can occur only if there is a persistent reproduction first which overcompensates the randomization effects, and furthermore if there is some differential in the reproduction rate in more than one persistently self-reproducing species. Therefore a further requirement is that there should be occasional changes ("mutations") in the reproducing molecules to allow selection by preferential rates of reproduction, "adjusted" to a constantly changing environment. Of course, the rate of "beneficial mutations" should be greater than that of the "damaging mutations."

All of the foregoing is assumed by Horowitz and Oparin to happen to molecules. I am afraid they do assume that molecules possess a highly accurate and persistent self-copy ability (that is, persistent self-reproducibility) sufficient to overcome the combined effects of randomization; then they possess capacity for a moderate mutability rate, and thus the capacity for natural selection. Then they propose that this type of behavior of molecules may have accounted for the "evolution" of the first persistently self-reproducible system with the capacity for natural selection. I don't follow their logic.

Dr. Schramm: I agree with you, Dr. Mora, that the term evolution may only be used if the carrier of the genetic information is very similar to that of the living organism. This is another reason to believe that the origin of nucleic acids is really the central problem in the understanding of the origin of life.

Dr. Oparin: I would like to make some remarks concerning the introductory part of the very important and significant paper of Dr. Schramm.

I am afraid that what I am going to say will not be agreed with, not only by Dr. Schramm but also by Dr. Dobzhansky. The preservation of the code in the transmission of the information through nucleic acid is obviously playing a very important role in the preservation of life. But that should not be made into an absolute, and we should not see in this the entire basis of life. That can be explained by the following analogy. Imagine that the Earth is being visited by some rational being for example, an enlightened Martian making acquaintance with our life. He might come to the conclusion that the essence of life is included in the libraries. There are preserved the ideas of people and perpetuated the ideas which are so important in the progress of human activity. But our whole life, with its pleasures and sadness is merely an incidental and secondary addition, addendum. You would hardly agree with that Martian.

DR. DOBZHANSKY: Well, I agree with Dr. Oparin. Certainly such a Martian would be a very naive fellow. I may perhaps say that self-replication, self-reproducibility, and mutability are in a certain sense contrary things. Mutability is, in a way, the denial of self-replication. Self-replication, if it were 100% accurate, would have no mutability.

DR. SCHRAMM: I would agree, at least partially, with this naive Martian. It is most fascinating that a human being can recognize what is going on in his genes and that he can deposit this knowledge in books, libraries, and so on. It seems to me that the singularity of the human brain is based on a very complicated feed-back and reflection mechanism by which molecules can become self-conscious.

DR. FOX: In September, Dr. Nirenberg reported in New York that he found coding properties in polynucleotides as synthesized by Khorana's method. He referred to this as, quite properly, chemically synthesized polynucleotides, to distinguish it from the Ochoa type of polymer. I think Dr. Schramm is to be congratulated for providing evidence for an additional kind of at least chemically synthesized polynucleotides.

In the context with which we are concerned, the question arises as to whether this kind of chemically synthesized polynucleotide is pre-biological.

One of the questions pertains to this very properly, and that is the possible origin of the kind of polyphosphoric derivatives which you employed in your synthesis. I wonder if you would tell us something about the mode of preparation of the material which you used for this purpose, and discuss the possible natural origin.

DR. SCHRAMM: It is very important that you get these cyclic phosphate esters. If you treat P_4O_{10} too long with ether or at too high a temperature, you get an open chain which is not very reactive, and you get the same kind of result if you have some polyphosphate in the pentoxide. It also opens the ring very fast. I think now there is no difficulty. We know what we should avoid and what we should do.

DR. FOX: I am glad you addressed yourself to that last question, but that is not the one I asked. The question is how you have demonstrated, if you have, or how you would postulate that the origin of your particular esters of polyphosphoric acid would emerge in a prebiological situation. Don't you use diethyl ether?

DR. SCHRAMM: Yes. But instead of ether other organic compounds can be used which contain alkyl groups bound to oxygen.

The production of polyphosphoric acid itself can be expected from some carbonaceous matter and phosphate. If you had a temperature above 300°C you do not have orthophosphate, you have polyphosphate. After the cooling of the Earth, you have large deposits of condensed phosphate or polyphosphate, which are similar to pentoxide and can easily be esterified.

DR. ORÓ: Professor Schramm has a set of instructions which I think he will be pleased to give to anyone that wishes to make ethyl polyphosphate. It is not difficult to prepare this ethyl polyphosphate ester if anhydrous conditions and a solvent like chloroform are used in addition to the diethyl ether and P_4O_{10}. In the absence of chloroform as in the original method published by Langheld in 1910, it becomes more difficult to obtain a uniform product, yet the chemical nature of the product appears to be identical to that prepared by the addition of chloroform. Paper chromatographic analysis carried out in my laboratory by Mr. Nooner have revealed the presence of two components in this polyphosphate ester which qualitatively and quantitatively appear to correspond with the two cyclic components postulated some time ago by Thilo and Woggon on the basis of alcoholysis and hydrolysis studies. Therefore, with the additional results presented by Professor Schramm the nature of this compound appears to be well understood.

With regard to the ability of this polyphosphate ester to bring about polycondensation reactions at about 60°C, I would like to say that the first time that Mr. Nooner used it for the synthesis of polypeptides, positive results were obtained. So far a number of polypeptides (leucine, valine, serine, etc.) have been obtained in yields of up to 60%. There seems to be no question that homo- and heteropolypeptides can be prepared with this compound.

DR. MORA: I wanted to make clear a limitation in the polynucleotide-directed polymerization reactions in cell-free extracts. Nirenberg took an oligo-dT_{13-14} as synthesized by Khorana [cf. Khorana, H. G., and Vizsolyi, J. R. (1961), J. Am. Chem. Soc. 83, 675]. Then he used this oligo-dT_{13-14} in the presence of the DNA-dependent RNA polymerase of M. Chamberlain and P. Berg [(1963), Proc. Natl. Acad. Sci. U.S. 48, 81] and ATP to make the complementary poly-A, which might go up to as high as 100 Å units in length. Of course, he needed this

Chamberlain-Berg enzyme, and the polymerization ceased in less than an hour [Leder, P., Clark, B. F. C., Ely, W. S., Pestka, S., and Nirenberg, M. W. (1963), *Proc. Natl. Acad. Sci. U. S.* **50**, 1135].

Then Nirenberg went on from poly-A in his incorporating system, which is an *Escherichia coli* extract and has ribosomes and all kinds of enzymes, and the poly-A then directed the incorporation of lysine into polylysine. This process also ceased in less than an hour.

Your case (Dr. Schramm), of course, was similar to the second step, when Matthaei followed through with the well-known poly-U-directed polyphenylalanine synthesis in the ribosomal extract [Nirenberg, M. W., and Matthaei, J. H. (1961), *Proc. Natl. Acad. Sci. U.S.* **47**, 1588]. This process also ceases within an hour.

DR. BUCHANAN: Have you analyzed for the chain length of your polyphenylalanine that was produced in the experiments in which you say the enzymatic translating machinery skipped over a mistake? It could have been possible that the polymerization went so far as the mistake that your product sloughed off and you started again. Possibly, then a mistake in the reading was not skipped over by the enzyme.

DR. SCHRAMM: I have to stress the point that all these biological experiments were done by Matthei and not by myself.

DR. BERNAL[1]: I feel Professor Schramm's contribution on the importance of the multiplying molecule is central to the discussion of the origin of life. The long, effective lifetime of multiplying molecules is, I agree, an absolute necessity, not only for evolution but for the existence of anything that might be called life. What we have to seek for, then, is the mechanism for such multiplication, and in general for a simpler one than that which we actually find in biological systems.

[1] *In absentia*

Thermal Condensation of Cytidylic Acid in the Presence of Polyphosphoric Acid

A. W. Schwartz, E. Bradley, and S. W. Fox

Institute for Space Biosciences and Department of Chemistry,
Florida State University, Tallahassee, Florida

The value of polyphosphoric acid in condensation reactions has long been appreciated. Of particular interest to prebiological theory has been its use in the polymerization of arginine by Schramm *et al* (1962) and in the polymerization of amino acids by Harada and Fox (Fox and Harada, 1961; Fox, 1963). In the latter case, the thermal polymerization of all of the common amino acids, which is usually effected at 160–170°C, is found to proceed at temperatures as low as 65°C in the presence of polyphosphoric acid (PPA). In the realm of nucleic acids, too, polyphosphate has found application. Fox and Harada (1961) reported on the synthesis of uracil from malic acid and urea in the presence of polyphosphoric acid. Recently Schramm and his co-workers (1962) have reported on the polymerization of mononucleotides catalyzed by ethyl metaphosphate, which can be considered a kind of polyphosphate derivative.

We have been studying for some years the effect of free polyphosphoric acid on mixtures of purines, pyrimidines, and ribose, and also on nucleosides. Dr. Schramm's work focused our attention on the mononucleotides, and suggested that the extensive degradation which has been observed in our earlier work might be avoided by reducing the acidity of the reaction mixture under conditions that might be entertained as geological. Consequently, our earlier studies on mononucleotides were carried out in the presence of several bases, but most commonly, urea. With shorter reaction times, urea was subsequently shown not to be necessary. The present procedure, which is shown in Fig. 1, consists of simply mixing the mononucleotides with the polyphosphoric acid, with care to limit water uptake from the air, and heating the mixture at 65°C for 1 or 2 hours. Several different preparations of polyphosphoric acid have been used in these studies; some were obtained commercially and others were

317

synthesized from phosphorus pentoxide and/or phosphoric acid. The preparations to be reported here have been made in all cases with a Victor Chemical Works polyphosphoric acid, of 82–84% phosphorus pentoxide content.

The reaction product is dissolved, with cooling, in aqueous ammonia solution, the pH being kept near neutrality. After 3 days of dialysis against distilled water, the solution is lyophilized to yield a pure white powder which, however, seems to contain a large proportion of poly-phosphates. This material must then be fractionated to obtain the desired

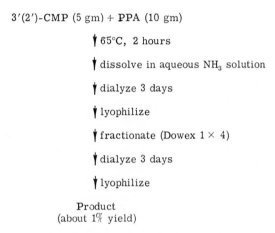

3'(2')-CMP (5 gm) + PPA (10 gm)

↓ 65°C, 2 hours

↓ dissolve in aqueous NH₃ solution

↓ dialyze 3 days

↓ lyophilize

↓ fractionate (Dowex 1 × 4)

↓ dialyze 3 days

↓ lyophilize

Product
(about 1% yield)

FIG. 1. Preparation of cytidylic acid polymer.

product. For this purpose, Dowex-1 has been used, the product being eluted in 4 N formic acid plus 0.5 N ammonium formate. Polyphosphates may then be stripped from the column with 4 N HCL. The formate fraction is dialyzed against distilled water for an additional 3 days and lyophilized to yield the final product. Typically, yields are of the order of 1%, although the best conditions for this preparation are still under study.

Table I shows a few of the reaction mixtures which have yielded product. Thus far, 2'(3')-cytidylic acid has been the only nucleotide which we have been able to self-condense, although cytidylic-adenylic mixtures have given products which encourage further investigation, and there is some indication that uridylic acid may be co-condensed with cytidylic acid. In the case of the cytidylic-adenylic materials, the content of adenine was determined directly by use of a colorimetric method developed by Davis and Morris (1963). In the case of the cytidylic-uridylic product, the composition was estimated by comparison of the ultraviolet absorption spectrum with spectra of standard mixtures of cytidylic and uridylic acids. Cytidylic acid content, calculated by difference, is shown here for convenience. (It should be mentioned that we have recently discovered three trace contaminants present in our cytidylic acid starting material. One of these is probably adenylic acid. Another may be cytidine, and the third is an as yet unknown

TABLE I

COMPOSITION OF REACTION MIXTURES[a]

Product	Rectants[b]	Time (hr)	Yield (%)	P (%)	CMP[c] (%)
1-53/2	CMP (5 gm) + PPA (20 gm) + urea (4 gm)	2	0.6	9.1	—
2-4/2	CMP (5 gm) + PPA (20 gm) + urea (4 gm)	2	0.5	9.6	—
2-75/2	CMP (5 gm) + PPA (10 gm)	1	1.7	9.8	—
2-91/A	CMP (5 gm) + PPA (10 gm)	1	0.8	9.3	—
2-73/A	CMP (0.5 gm) + AMP (0.5 gm) + PPA (2 gm)	1	0.6	9.9	75
2-73/B	CMP (0.7 gm) + AMP (0.3 gm) + PPA (2 gm)	1	0.8	10.5	80
2-76/A	CMP (1 gm) + AMP (1 gm) + PPA (4 gm)	1	1.0	10.4	60
2-76/B	CMP (1 gm) + AMP (1 gm) + PPA (4 gm)	1	1.5	10.4	60
2-89/2	CMP (1 gm) + UMP (1 gm) + PPA (4 gm)	1	0.2	7.6	70–80

[a] Temperature in all experiments was 65°C.
[b] All nucleotides are 3'(2').
[c] Estimated error ± 20%.

ultraviolet-absorbing material. Control experiments, however, show that none of these trace contaminants survives the purification procedure.)

The absorption spectrum of each of these materials is free from anomalies. Figure 2 shows the spectra of one of the cytidylic acid products, 2-75/2, in acid and basic solution. Of particular interest here is the fact that the magnitude of the shift of the absorption maximum between acid and basic solution is at least as great as is obtained with free cytidylic acid, indicating that the amino group of cytosine has not taken part in the condensation (as, for example, in the formation of phosphoamide ester linkages).

The increase in extinction coefficient at the absorption maximum in basic solution, upon incubation at 37°C for 48 hours, is referred to as a hyperchromic shift, and is generally reported as alkaline hyperchromicity in terms of percentage increase. Michelson (1959) has shown that such a shift is due to the cleavage of bonds between linked nucleotides, and that the magnitude of the effect increases with increasing chain length of oligonucleotides.

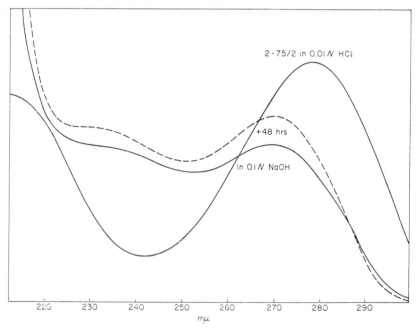

FIG. 2. Ultraviolet absorption spectrum of a polymer of cytidylic acid (2-75/2) in 0.01 N HCl, and in 0.1 N NaOH before and after 48 hours incubation at 37°C.

In Table II are shown some optical properties of four cytidylic acid products, and for comparison, a series of oligonucleotides of cytidylic acid synthesized by Michelson (1959). One may note that the alkaline hyperchromicities shown here suggest a chain length of at least four to ten residues for these products. However the results of some preliminary enzyme experiments to be described complicate this interpretation.

Figure 3 illustrates the type of experiment which is being used as a first approach to characterizing these materials. In this case the material is first incubated with bacterial alkaline phosphatase to hydrolyze

TABLE II
OPTICAL PROPERTIES OF MATERIALS

| Material | In 0.01 N HCl | | In 0.1 N NaOH | | Alkaline hyperchromicity (%) |
	λ_{max} (mμ)	λ_{min} (mμ)	λ_{max} (mμ)	λ_{min} (mμ)	
3'(2')-CMP	279	240	272	250	0
Dicytidylic acid[a]	278	240	270	250	8.7
Tricytidylic acid[a]	278	241	270	251	13.9
Tetracytidylic acid[a]	278	241	270	251	15.3
Polycytidylic (9.8)[a]	278	241	270	251	15.9
1-53/2	278	240	270	252	(24)[b]
2-4/2	278	242	269	251	16
2-75/2	278	242	269	252	16
2-91/A	278	242	268	252	16

[a] Data from Michelson (1959).
[b] Single determination.

phosphomonoester groups. The determination of the maximum liberation of inorganic phosphate in the presence of this enzyme is then a measure of the number of end groups per molecule. Controls are also maintained for the phosphate content of the enzyme preparation, and

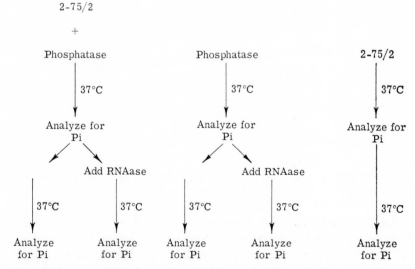

FIG. 3. Enzymatic degradation of a cytidylic acid polymer (2-75/2) with bacterial alkaline phosphatase and pancreatic ribonuclease.

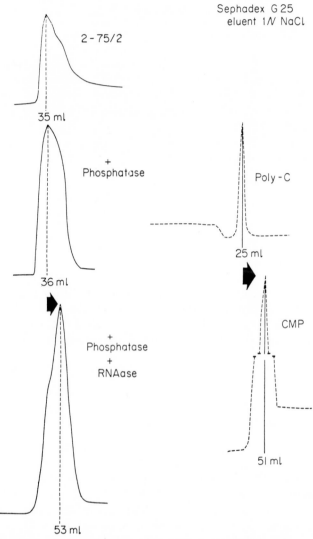

Fɪɢ. 4. Effect of ribonuclease on the molecular size of a polymer of cytidylic acid (2-75/2).

for spontaneous breakdown of the substrate, which is generally negligible. When hydrolysis of end groups has gone to completion, the experimental and enzyme blank solutions are divided into halves, and pancreatic ribonuclease plus additional phosphatase, if necessary, is added to one tube of each set. In this manner, controls are maintained not only on enzymatic contamination and product breakdown, but on background phosphatase activity during the ribonuclease digestion as well. Liberation of additional inorganic phosphate after introducing ribonuclease can only result from the production of new end groups, which are then available for attack by the already present phosphatase. By means of such experiments, preliminary evidence for limited ribonuclease activity, and thus for the presence of 3′ phosphodiester linkages in some of these products has been obtained.

The suggestion that the liberation of additional phosphate by the ribonuclease does indeed correspond to an enzymatic degradation of

TABLE III
RESULTS OF ENZYME EXPERIMENTS

Material	Experiments	Per cent of total P liberated by phosphatase	Per cent of total P exposed by RNAase
1-53/2	1	36	
2-4/2	3	35–36	21–24
2-75/2	2	36–40	26–29
Theoretical			
Dicytidylic acid		50.0	25.0
Tricytidylic acid		33.3	33.3
Tetracytidylic acid		25.0	37.5

the material is further supported by the experiment illustrated in Fig. 4. The peaks show elution volumes obtained in gel filtration on Sephadex G 25 in 1 N NaCl. The elution volume for a polymer which is totally excluded from the gel grains (in this case enzymatically synthesized polycytidylic acid) is 25 ml. The elution volume for maximum retention of small molecules, here determined with 2′(3′)-cytidine monophosphate [2′(3′)-CMP] is 51 ml. The curve labeled 2-75/2 shows the normal elution pattern of that substance, with an elution volume of 35 ml. Incubation of 2-75/2 with bacterial alkaline phosphatase under the conditions used in the enzyme experiments results in no decrease in the molecular size of the material. However, addition of pancreatic ribonuclease shifts the elution volume to 53 ml, the maximum volume obtained for small molecules. The fact that the peak is still somewhat broad and shows a slight shoulder at approximately 35 ml suggests that degradation by ribonuclease has not been complete. To return now to the experiments already described, the results are tabulated in Table III.

Here the results are expressed as per cent of the total phosphate liberated by the phosphatase alone (in other words the per cent of the phosphates which are terminal), and as the per cent of the total phosphate exposed by ribonuclease. Since the cytidylic acid used to synthesize these materials is a mixture of 2′ and 3′ cytidylic acids, one may assume that there would be approximately as many 2′ linkages as 3′ linkages formed in the condensation. If ribonuclease is specific for the 3′ linkages, then it may be estimated that twice the amount of phosphate liberated in the ribonuclease experiments, or roughly 40–60%

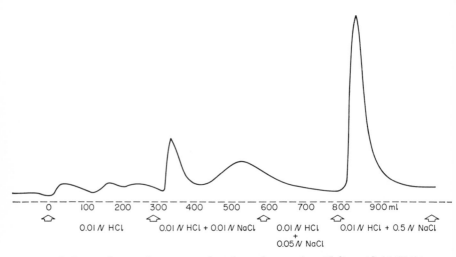

FIG. 5. Ion exchange chromatography of a polymer of cytidylic acid (2-75/2) on Dowex 1 × 4 (200–400 mesh). Elution with 0.01 N HCl, 0.01 N HCl + 0.01 N NaCl, 0.01 N HCl + 0.05 N NaCl, and 0.01 N HCl + 0.5 N NaCl.

of the total is involved in phosphodiester linkages. The theoretical values shown here, incidentally, have been calculated for similarly mixed 2′(3′) materials. Comparison of the data thus far obtained with these theoretical values suggests that we are dealing with mixtures of predominantly di- and trinucleotides, as such mixtures would be expected to show approximately the enzyme results which have been obtained. At this time, however, these products seem to be somewhat more complicated than simple mixtures of di- and trinucleotides, as has already been indicated by the hyperchromicity data.

Figure 5 shows the elution pattern given by 2-75/2 on Dowex-1 chloride. The largest fraction of this material is not eluted until well beyond conditions which would be expected to elute di- and tricytidylic acids. The results of paper electrophoresis also suggest products other than simple di- and trinucleotides, since the electrophoretic mobility of 2-75/2 is slightly greater than that of enzymatically synthesized polycytidylic acid, rather than less, as would be true for oligocytidylic acids.

All of these observations suggest molecules which, although containing significant regions of phosphodiester linkages, are still somewhat more complex than simple oligo- or poly-nucleotides. The possibility of chain branching, for example, must be investigated.

Further characterization of these materials is being undertaken.

ACKNOWLEDGMENTS

This study is contribution number 27 of the Institute for Space Biosciences. It was aided by grant NsG-173-62 of the National Aeronautics and Space Administration.

Revised Manuscript received March 21, 1964.

REFERENCES

Davis, J. B., and Morris, B. N. (1963). *Anal. Biochem.* **5**, 64.
Fox, S. W. (1963). *Symp. Protein Nutrition Metabolism. Univ. Illinois College Agr. Special Publ.* **4**, 141.
Fox, S. W., and Harada, K. (1961). *Science* **133**, 1923.
Michelson, A. M. (1959). *J. Chem. Soc.* p. 3655.
Schramm, G., Groetsch, H., and Pollmann, W. (1962). *Angew. Chem.* **74**, 53.

DISCUSSION

DR. SCHRAMM: We have just about the same difficulties. We are using products which are dialyzed and at the moment we don't care too much about the smaller molecules, the di- and trinucleotides, but, of course, this is hard work to separate them all with cellulose.

Do you get much black stuff in this acidic solution?

MR. SCHWARTZ: Possibly I didn't emphasize enough that this polymerization is not done in aqueous solution. The only solvent is the polyphosphoric acid. There is charring with some of the nucleotides we have tried. With cytidylic acid, however, there is practically no discoloration at all. The material that is isolated is white.

DR. SCHRAMM: The polyphosphate used in these experiments is a negatively charged material. I think if you remove these charges by esterification you will have a better catalyst. Recently we did some condensing experiments with polyphosphoric acid, prepared by mixing P_4O_{10} with phosphoric acid. The yield of poly-U after dialysis was very small, indicating that the polymerization does not proceed as successfully as with the metaphosphate ester.

MR. SCHWARTZ: This is the problem at the moment. Certainly, average molecular weight cannot be higher than, say four or five thousand. However, we were using minimal conditions in this work because we got right away a clean product which permitted us to begin structural characterization. We could expect to get more polymerization under more extreme conditions at higher temperatures. These conditions will be studied.

DR. FOX: Some of the experimental concentration has been on these reactions with urea as well as on polyphosphoric acid itself, because polyphosphoric acid and urea strike us as kinds of material which we can rationalize as existing in the primitive terrestrial environment rather easily, the urea ameliorating the acidic nature of PPA.

Part IV

MODELS OF PRECELLULAR ORGANIZATION

INTRODUCTORY REMARKS

H. Burr Steinbach

Department of Zoölogy, University of Chicago, Chicago, Illinois

In this conference we have now heard much interesting discussion of the formation of organic molecules and their aggregation into polymers under conditions that might have existed in prebiotic worlds. There has also been a proper and stimulating consideration of the requirements evident in the activities and structures of present-day living forms. These discussions have been provocative indeed. If they are considered against the historical background offered by such scholars as Max Verworn in his "General Physiology," [Macmillan, New York (1899)][1] it is clear that it is now possible, for the first time, to discuss in exact detail some of the chemical mechanisms and physical conditions that might well have led to the creation of the organic stuffs prior to the emergence of formed living things on the planet Earth.

In the following sessions, more attention will be directed to the orientation and interaction of polymers that might have been so formed. This orientation and interaction, so essential in providing the structures now being demonstrated in modern living cells, may be presumed to have been a late step toward a biotic world following the formation of the organic building units.

Coacervates have been mentioned several times and we will hear more of them. The tendency of mixtures or organic and inorganic materials to form structures with phase boundaries and inclusions within those boundaries has been known for many years and deserves closer attention with modern skills and theoretical insights. Reports will be made shortly on this subject.

Much of the work in the past, on the formation of discrete, microscopically visible bodies from mixtures of chemicals has been done under

---

[1] The English translation by F. S. Lee of the "Allgemeine Physiologie" first appeared in 1894. This book provides references to much of the old literature on origin of life and on formation of cell models.

the rubric of forming "cell models," a term that probably should not be used. Starting with the oil droplets of Rhumbler and Bütschli and going up to the present time, the literature offers a wide and artistically fascinating series of descriptions and pictures that show, if nothing else, that almost any structure seen in living cells can be mimicked by some combination of physical and chemical circumstances. Perhaps the most complex and bizarre of these older "cell models" are those reported by A. L. Herrara [especially see *Arch. Plasmol. Gen.* 1, 55 (1912), for a summary with illustrations of the work of this school]. Crile, in the 1930's studied and reported on his "autosynthetic cells," their structure, locomotion, division, and metabolism [see Crile, G. Telkes, M., and Rowland, A. F., *Protoplasma* 15, 337 (1932); cf. "The Nature of Living Things," by the same authors, *Arch. Surg.* 23, (1931)]. More recently, of course, there is considerable attention being paid, in a precise fashion, to the behavior of monolayers and mixed layers, either as sheets spread in troughs or as boundary layers investing globules. Most of this work is directed at an attempt to simulate the selective properties of excitable cell membranes.

An historical background is not needed, however, to justify an examination of the ways in which polymers and other compounds, formed under possible prebiotic conditions, can interact to form structures that can then do things that the single isolated units cannot do. Gradients of all sorts may be set up and we need to know how this is done. We need to know not only what substances oriented into structures can do, but what their information content is, relative to the information content of the linear polymers that enter into the formation of the more complex units. It is the organization of materials into two- and three-dimensional structures that provides the machinery of life.

THE PATHWAYS OF THE PRIMARY DEVELOPMENT OF METABOLISM AND ARTIFICIAL MODELING OF THIS DEVELOPMENT IN COACERVATE DROPS

A. I. Oparin

A. N. Bach Institute of Biochemistry, Academy of Sciences of USSR, Moscow, USSR

For the time being, the thesis that in a certain period of the existence of the Earth "the primeval nutritive soup," i.e., aqueous solution of diverse organic substances and of their more or less high molecular weight polymers, has been formed abiogenically on the Earth's surface can be regarded as scientifically grounded in principle.

I would like to try to take a step farther and to outline experimental approaches to the solution of the problem of the pathways of the development of primary living beings in this "soup."

Life is characterized by the fact that it is not simply dispersed in space but is represented by individual systems—organisms separated from the external world. The appearance of these beings could have taken place only on the basis of a long-term evolution, of gradual perfection of some much simpler initial systems which separated from the primeval homogenous soup.

In this soup, as well as in a simple aqueous solution of organic substances and mineral salts, chemical conversions have not been of some specifically organized character but have proceeded independent of each other in all directions possible, chaotically intercrossing. Unlike this, individual chemical reactions in living beings are strictly coordinated and proceed in a certain sequence, which as a whole forms a network of biological metabolism directed toward the perpetual self-preservation, growth, and self-reproduction of the entire system under the given environmental conditions.

The task is just to obtain on an experimental basis possible pathways for the development of such initial systems which could interact with their environment as open systems do, and in which chemical conversions

331

would become ever more organized, approaching in the process of their evolution the biological order of metabolism.

A viewpoint advanced in the scientific literature at present, is that individual polynucleotide molecules with a random arrangement of monomeric residuals that had primarily arisen in the nutritive soup might be such initial systems. These molecules would have possessed the complement fixation capacity, which is intrinsic to polynucleotides. Therefore, according to Schramm, even under abiogenic conditions the possibility would be created of an ever more rapid synthesis of polynucleotide molecules which would undergo evolution the whole time, improving their secondary structure and thus approaching in this respect present nucleic acids.

However, it is hardly possible to conceive, all the more to reproduce experimentally, metabolism on the basis of such an evolution "at the molecular level."

When polymerization of mononucleotides is carried out in their pure solutions, it results only in the production of peculiar aggregations of polynucleotides, which under natural conditions would create only deposits of these substances resembling those of ozocerite or some other organic mixture of homologs. But if this polymerization occurs in the presence of other polymers, for example, polypeptides (which seems to have taken place in the case of the primeval soup), the polynucleotides arising would necessarily produce polymolecular complexes with these polymers. These complexes, once separated from the surrounding solution, seem to be initial systems that interact with their environment in the process of evolution and give rise to primary living beings endowed with metabolism.

Polymerization of nucleotides (e.g., polyadenine synthesis) from adenosine diphosphate (ADP) has been carried out in our laboratory, using well known methods involving bacterial polynucleotide phosphorylase as a catalyst. When this synthesis proceeds in the presence of or in parallel with the production of some other polymer (e.g., of a polypeptide), the solution gradually becomes opaque. This is related to the fact that, having reached a certain size, polymer particles combine into multimolecular aggregations separating from the solution as coacervate drops visible under a microscope.

Figure 1 presents a photomicrograph of these drops formed in polyadenine synthesis in the presence of histone.

It is of interest that, as a result of the formation of drops, the equilibrium of the polymerization reaction sharply shifts toward synthesis, as can be seen from comparison of the curves represented in Fig. 2.

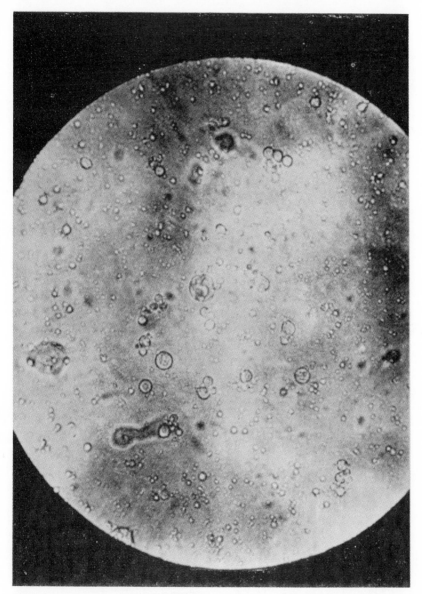

FIG. 1. Coacervate drops, formed in polyadenine synthesis in the presence of histone.

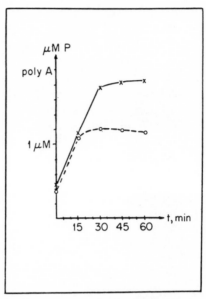

FIG. 2. Synthesis of polyadenine in solution (-O-O- line) and in coacervate drops (X-X-X line).

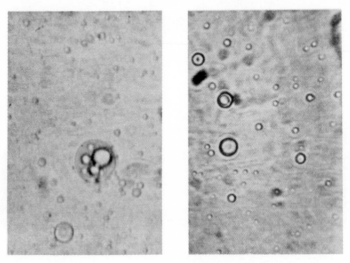

FIG. 3. Coacervate drops containing polypeptides and polynucleotides. *Left:* RNA + polylysine. *Right:* poly-A + polylysine.

In our experiment, histone may be replaced by other nonspecific polypeptides. For example, Fig. 3 shows a photograph of the drops formed of polyadenine and polylysine.

Under the conditions of the primeval soup, there certainly could have arisen other multimolecular products as well (for example, Goldacre vesicles or Fox's microspheres). Investigation of these initial systems representing the origin of life is also of interest. In our experiments, however, we used coacervate drops since they seemed to be the most suitable models for the reproduction, under working conditions, of possible pathways that could have been followed by primary develop-

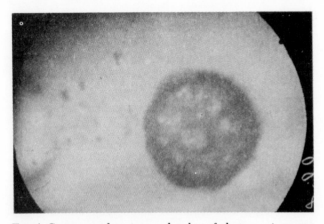

FIG. 4. Coacervate drop in gas chamber of electron microscope.

ment of metabolism. A very high concentration of polymers occurs upon the formation of coacervate drops.

Despite their liquid consistency, the drops possess a certain internal structure and show a marked interphase with the external medium.

Figure 4 shows electron microscopic photographs of the drops consisting of serum albumin, gum arabic, and ribonucleic acid (RNA); the photos were taken in a gas microchamber (without preliminary drying of drops). Figure 5 shows a drop with inclusion of the ribonuclease with partially hydrolyzed RNA of the drop during 20 minutes incubation. Here the heterogeneity of the drop is especially marked.

Coacervate drops are able selectively to adsorb and accumulate diverse substances from the surrounding solution. An example can be seen when methylene blue from the external solution has concentrated in the drop. Concentration of other substances, e.g., of amino acids, in the drops proceeds very selectively, depending upon the composition of the drops.

When substances entering a drop undergo more rapid chemical conversions than in the external medium, the drops acquire properties of open systems whose very existence is related to their interaction with the environment. This is most readily achieved when catalysts easily adsorbed by the drops are introduced.

To obtain our coacervate models, we employed proteins, nucleic acids, and other polymers isolated from recent organisms, utilizing enzyme preparations as catalysts. We are well aware that this is a con-

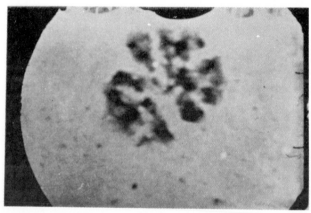

Fig. 5. Coacervate drop in gas chamber of electron microscope after 20 minutes incubation with RNAase.

ditional procedure since certainly none of the above-mentioned well-organized substances existed in the primeval soup of the Earth's hydrosphere. But, as it has just been demonstrated, coacervate drops can be formed also of nonspecific polymers, while the enzymes can be replaced later on by less perfect organic and inorganic catalysts. However, at this initial stage of investigation, the utilization of natural polymers and enzymes gave valuable advantages.

When potato phosphorylase is introduced into a coacervate drop formed of gum arabic and histone at pH 6.0–6.2, glucose 1-phosphate is dissolved in the surrounding liquid, while starch is being accumulated within the drops. This is easily revealed by iodine test, but when β-amylase is also introduced into the drop, starch begins to disintegrate to maltose, which may be found in the external medium. Thus, the whole process can be schematically represented as a flow of substances through the coacervate drop which is depicted in Fig. 6 by the rectangle. Depending upon the rate ratio of the processes 1 and 2, the amount of polymer (starch) produced within the drop at the expense of the substances of the external medium can augment and the drop will either grow, or diminish and undergo destruction.

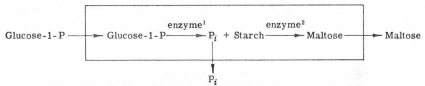

FIG. 6. Synthesis and hydrolysis of starch in the coacervate drop.

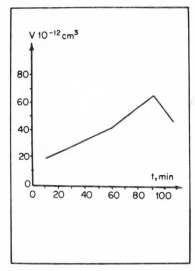

FIG. 7. Increase in the volume of a coacervate drop upon the starch synthesis in it. Data obtained at the Chair of Biochemistry, State University of Moscow.

Figure 7 shows a curve of the consecutive increase in the volume of the drop on account of the starch synthesized within it.

Both enzymatic disintegration and enzymatic synthesis of polynucleotides involved in the coacervate drop can be induced in a similar way. Such synthesis is schematically represented in Fig. 8. Here bacterial polynucleotide phosphorylase was introduced into a coacervate drop formed of RNA and histone, while ADP was dissolved in the external medium. Under these conditions (at pH 9.5) accumulation of the polynucleotide took place at the expense of ADP entering from the external medium while inorganic phosphate went out of the drop.

Thus, we possess models of open multimolecular systems, which as a result of acceleration of the processes going on within them may grow on account of the surrounding solution or, on the contrary, can undergo disintegration. The growth of our models, however, could be achieved only in the presence of energy-rich phosphate compounds in the external medium. Such compounds can be assumed to have been present in the

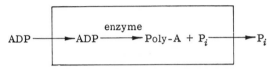

FIG. 8. Scheme of polyadenine synthesis by polynucleotide phosphorylase in the coacervate drop.

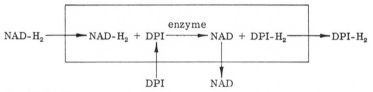

FIG. 9. Scheme of NAD-H$_2$ dehydrogenase action in the coacervate drop.

primeval soup, but in minimal amounts that would have been exhausted in the very first stage of evolution of the initial systems. Later on, these systems could have been able to exist and to grow further only in cases where premises had been created within them for the production of macroergic compounds from ordinary substances in the surrounding medium.

The data of comparative biochemistry show that the metabolism of any present organism is underlaid, apart from the reactions of polymerization, by those of anaerobic oxidative-reductive reactions and conjugated phosphorylation.

While introducing appropriate catalysts into coacervate drops, we succeeded in obtaining models of systems which involved oxidative-reductive reactions according to the scheme shown in Fig. 9. Here NAD—H$_2$ enters the drop from the external medium, where it transfers its hydrogen to the dye with the assistance of bacterial oxidoreductase. Reaction products are emitted into the surrounding medium.

Figure 10 represents a scheme of a more complicated oxidative-reductive model working with the participation of light and with chlorophyll included in the drops. Ascorbic acid entering the drop transfers its hydrogen to chlorophyll, which proceeds only with the participation of a quantum of light. Chlorophyll then passes hydrogen

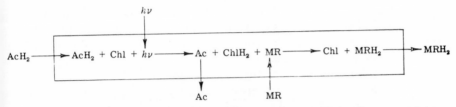

FIG. 10. Scheme of ascorbic acid oxidation in the coacervate drop, containing chlorophyll.

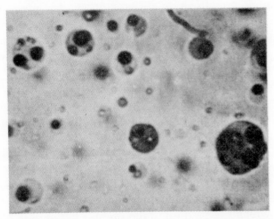

FIG. 11. Coacervate drops to which chlorophyll was added.

to the dye entering from the external solution, while chlorophyll itself undergoes regeneration to its initial state. Corresponding reaction products dehydroascorbic acid and reduced dye) go into the external medium.

Experiments on the modeling of conjugated anaerobic phosphorylation in coacervate drops gave positive results, but they cannot be regarded as accomplished, so I shall not present them here.

This is the end of the experimental part of my paper, but I would like to draw some conclusions on the pathways of the further evolution of open multimolecular systems resembling our coacervate models. Certainly for the time being these conclusions are of a hypothetical nature, but they may be of interest for further experiments in the same direction.

It is evident that systems similar to our coacervate models—to involve oxidative-reductive reactions, conjugated phosphorylation, and polymerization, besides existing for a long time, could also become larger, grow in solutions of substances whose presence and even abundance can be conceived for the primeval soup of the Earth.

Reduplication of polynucleotides in the course of their synthesis at the expense of the minomers of the medium contributed to the preservation of the constancy of the composition of the growing drops. This reduplication was based on the complement fixation capacity of polynucleotides. But the point is that such drops have been all the time selectively adsorbing the same organic and inorganic catalysts from the external medium and have been preserving invariably increased concentrations of these promoters, and therefore, the constancy of the ratio of the reaction rates within the drops. A shift in this ratio resulted either in acceleration of growth or in disintegration of a given system. This was the prerequisite for the natural selection of such systems.

Single drops would scarcely grow the whole time as entities. Under conditions of the primary hydrosphere of the Earth, they would necessarily break into fragments under the effect of external mechanical forces (e.g., waves or tide), as emulsion drops break upon shaking.

Such systems, interacting with the external medium, growing, and increasing in number, ever improved due to the action of natural selection—the organization of their metabolism.

For a primary combination of a small number of reactions, the action of relatively simple catalysts, inorganic salts, and organic compounds, as well as of their more or less catalytically active complexes, was sufficient. Natural selection contributed to the preservation of most successful complexes which survived up to the present in the form of coenzymes. The number of these specific catalysts is very small but they are universal promoters found in all living beings, so that they had to be formed at a very early stage in the origin and development of life.

The required constancy of coenzyme concentration in the development systems could have been maintained not only by synthesis but also by their constant entry from the external medium, as has been the case with the simplest inorganic and organic catalysts. The study of the vitamins gives several examples of such a phenomenon found even in recent organisms.

However, with the later complication of metabolism, coenzymes turned out to be insufficient, and the progressive evolution of biological systems proceeded toward the appearance of a whole set of new, much more effective catalysts—the enzymes, i.e., proteins with a certain arrangement of amino acid residues in their polypeptide chain. Primary protein-like polymers with their random arrangement of amino acid residues seemed to be either completely lacking in catalytic activity or were very poor catalysts. Of the great number of variants arising upon nonspecific polymerization only those were preserved in the course of natural selection whose participation in the metabolism of a given system contributed to its longevity, growth, and reproduction.

This is how the gradual perfection of both the living system as a whole and of its individual mechanisms proceeded. Proteins-enzymes and the nucleic acids related to their synthesis, adapted themselves ever better to performance of their biological functions, the selection of these compounds being a function of the strictly definite arrangement of monomers in their polynucleotide chains—which was an indispensable condition for the constancy of enzyme synthesis in growing and reproducing systems.

Manuscript received October 29, 1963.

DISCUSSION

DR. VALLENTYNE: I might make one comment that is a carry-over to nature. Gordon Riley at Yale has discovered the appearance during winter and early spring of particulate material that turns up in sea water. The transformation from dissolved to particulate is obviously not biological since it can happen by simply bubbling air or nitrogen through sea water that has been filtered to remove all particulate material.

DR. OPARIN: I would appreciate a literature reference to this work.

DR. VALLENTYNE: Riley, G. A. (1963). *Limnology and Oceanography* 8, 372–381.

DR. ORÓ: May I ask Dr. Vallentyne, what sea water it was? And secondly, with regard to the nature of the organic matter, does it contain hydrocarbons or not?

DR. VALLENTYNE: It was Long Island Sound.

DR. ORÓ: There are a number of cases in which similar observations have been made. Dr. Weeks in "The Origin of Petroleum" symposium held at the University of Texas this past October reported that in the southern coast of Australia (or New Zealand), there are times of the year when the appearance on the beach of petroleum coming from the sea can be observed. I inquired about the formation of this petroleum. The answer was that it was derived from petroleum formations underneath the sea someplace removed from the coast, and that some geological movement did force its escape into the ocean, and eventually it was deposited on the seashore in the form of oil droplets and particulate matter. Therefore, I would like to ask, did you mean that the origin of the organic matter was nonbiological?

DR. VALLENTYNE: That was what I meant to imply.

DR. STEINBACH: I think that you will find many products which may well resemble the coacervates and which, in all probability, are degradation products of organisms. But I don't think this is an unusual finding. As one who has been in Long Island Sound, I wouldn't be surprised at anything that was found there.

DR. VALLENTYNE: I should say two things about this. They usually follow plankton bursts and they do take nitrogen out of the water.

DR. STEINBACH: Could I ask a question of both Dr. Oparin and Dr. Dobzhansky? Thinking now of Darwinian natural selection, at which point is there a difference between the sort of selection of the molecular species themselves as compared with the selection of a total system which might be taking up these molecular units? You have the formation of a coacervate, which could arise with practically no information content, we could say, that will mostly involve certain things which may react much more rapidly. Is this more nearly a biologically selected system or not?

DR. OPARIN: Any new evolutionary regularity would be expected to arise during the new forms of organization. One should not think that life arose first and biological regularities afterward. The origin of life, the emergence of life, the origin of these regularities went parallel. This can well be observed in another transitional stage of the existence of matter, origin of man and formation of social forms of evolution.

We cannot say that up to a certain year this human form did not exist and after that year it started to exist, and this, in spite of the fact that the present human relations are reasonably well known.

The same was taking place in the former case, the origin of life.

The natural selection in its perfect biological shape has become formed in the later stages of development.

What, then, did we observe in this hypothetical system, models of which I intended to show in the coacervate droplets? Imagine that you have numerous systems like the models shown. These systems interact with environment, according to the scheme of open systems.

Substances carry energy into these systems, and other substances leave them, carrying the products of decomposition and breakdown. This is what I intended to show with the system of the breakdown of starch.

In this light, it can be shown that if you speed up the process 1, that is to say, take substances going into the drop, the drop increases in size faster; if, on the other hand, you speed up the process 2, the drop breaks down more rapidly into component parts.

It is, of course, a crude analogy, but it can show you that the drop in the first case is preserved and in the second place disappears. Thus the internal organization of the droplets determines whether this droplet will continue to exist or not. Some forms of organization are preserved and others are broken down in these environmental conditions.

These are the beginnings of the elements of selection. This is certainly remote from Darwinian selection, but this is a starting point on the basis of which Darwinian selection is arising. It is only when you have not a single reaction but a combination of three different reactions—the reaction of polymerization, the oxidation-reduction, and the third, phosphorylation.

Then the fate of the individual droplet is determined by the relationship of these three reactions. These relationships speed different reactions. This is what is at the basis of more complex systems; it depends on the relationship of the speeds of these three reactions.

The final record depends on the same thing on which depends the metabolism of the living organism, because the speed of metabolism in the sense of Hinshelwood is precisely dependent on the relative speeds of these reactions. These relative velocities, speeds, I think are better determined by the entire sum of organization of the given system—chemical composition, catalyst, structural conditions, etc.

Any change would lead either to increasing stability of the system or to decreasing stability and breakdown, on the contrary.

Here we then have, in the full sense of the word, the biological metabolism applied to the chemical processes which are taking place.

DR. MORA: I believe that the use of selectivity in trying to account for the appearance of the first persistently self-reproducing unit in a biological system is an unwarranted extension of Darwin's use of the word "selection" in a valid, but different operational meaning.

DR. OPARIN: It may be a semantic problem. It may be that, to start with, you have simply a selection, then you have natural selection, and then you have a Darwinian natural selection. It is possible that it is desirable to advance separate terminology for these things. If the term "selection"—"natural selection"—should mean Darwinian selection—Darwinian natural selection—then a new term is necessary, and for myself, I say it is.

DR. FOX: I would be inclined to second the last statement, if one recognizes that the original situation required not a use of gelatin, as in coacervate droplets, but of polymers formed from simpler units in ways we are discussing here.

I think that we can find both in nature and in the laboratory (the laboratory being in this relationship more significant), many polymers which have morphological properties.

Under the title of precellular organization, I think our attention and interest should be directed at identifying those processes which led to the formation from simpler units of polymers which had, prior to life, morphogenic properties, and that there could then be a "competition" or "selection" from among those of *at least one line which fed into a self-reproducing line* of units of which we are the descendants.

In this case, it seems to me that there is a kind of prebiological selection, and in this context, I think it may be a matter of semantics or definition, as to where one wishes to place his finger on the start of Darwinian evolution.

DR. BUCHANAN: Is there any way of knowing how much of the reactions occurs at the surface of the droplet as compared with the inner part of the droplet?

DR. OPARIN: This is being studied and preliminary data indicate that different reactions occur in different places. The starch synthesis is taking place inside the droplets; as for the nucleotides, the polynucleotides, that is an open question.

DR. GAFFRON: One of the reactions was, I think, the Krasnovsky reaction, with chlorophyll and ascorbate in the coacervate. If so, is anything known as to an advantage in terms of the reaction rate? Do the reactions with the coacervate droplets go faster than they would in more homogeneous substances?

DR. OPARIN: If you recalculate the speeds for the volume of the droplet, then you get a result several dozen times faster, possibly hundreds of times.

DR. PONNAMPERUMA: In the coacervates described, there was polylysine in one case and histone in another. Does this mean that basic protein favors the formation of the coacervate?

DR. OPARIN: The use of histone protein is to obtain in coacervates the alkaline milieu of pH 9.5. This is needed to make the polynucleotide.

If, on the other hand, it is a synthesis of starch which is intended, then other components are being used. However, histone plays some interesting roles in the process of coacervation. It gives a superior coacervate nucleotide.

DR. GROSSENBACHER: It would appear that this kind of coacervate drop might be an ideal basis for structure of organelles within a cell. How do we get from organelles to a cell? The cell contains many organelles.

DR. OPARIN: A billion years are needed in order to realize that.

DR. FOX: Bungenberg de Jong showed a long time ago that one could obtain coacervate droplets which had smaller droplets and other structures within them.

DR. GROSSENBACHER: Would you look for the coacervate droplets getting big enough to become cells and contain other coacervate droplets?

DR. OPARIN: The living cells are probably more complex. In general, according to Bungenberg de Jong, the protoplasm does have the coacervate structure. But this is an oversimplification because the surface structure of the cell, of the lipoid envelopes, lipoid surface, are not identical with simple coacervate drops.

The American investigator, Hans Ris, of Wisconsin, visited the Soviet Union and has advanced an idea similar to what was expounded several years ago in Russia by Mereshkowsky, namely, that a cell represents a symbiotic structure. They said that for the time being the idea was rather too audacious. But it is possible you could develop it in the direction of representing the formation of cells as a gradual association, aggregation of symbionts.

Ris has shown some quite interesting electron microscopic photographs illustrating this idea.

DR. BLOIS: Has Professor Oparin evaluated the effect of ultraviolet light on these particles with respect to their undergoing photolysis?

DR. OPARIN: No special experiment has been done. However, by analogy with the influence of visible light, ultraviolet, you would think, should have an even stronger effect.

DR. FOX: Professor Oparin has referred to prebiological selection as a route by which stability comparable with that in cells, as we know them, might have arisen in natural coacervate droplets. All the coacervate droplets with which I am acquainted do not have that level of stability that we impute to natural cells in general. For example, they tend to break down by whirling in an ordinary clinical centrifuge.

I emphasize at this point that, while not rejecting Professor Oparin's suggestion of this kind of approach toward a more stable unit than a coacervate droplet, there is an alternative and this alternative is the kind of unit which Dr. Young and I each intend to discuss and to present some data for.

DR. OPARIN: I would like to add that in experiments of this sort, several systems, several methods were utilized, including Dr. Fox's proteinoids, which Dr. Fox has kindly supplied. Some interesting results were obtained, but the material was scarce and I hope that I may get a little more.

DR. FOX: Surely.

MORPHOLOGY AND CHEMISTRY OF MICROSPHERES FROM PROTEINOID

RICHARD S. YOUNG

Exobiology Division, National Aeronautics and Space Administration,
Ames Research Center, Moffett Field, California

How the chemical pathways leading to the origin of the "living" system may have evolved is now being demonstrated in the laboratory. It is becoming more and more obvious that a primitive nonoxidizing atmosphere, composed of various proportions of methane, ammonia, and water, subjected to one of many forms of energy (UV, heat, electrical discharge, ionizing radiations, etc.) gives rise to a variety of organic compounds. Many of these compounds (e.g., amino acids, purines, pyrimidines) have great biological significance in that they are the fundamental building blocks of the component parts of living cells (e.g., cell walls, protoplasm, and nucleic material). Recent reports (Fox and Harada, 1960; Harada and Fox, 1960; Oró, 1963; Ponnamperuma et al., 1963) indicate that when these building blocks are subjected to a suitable energy source, a building up of still more complex molecules takes place and protein-like molecules are formed, as well as components of the nucleic acid molecule.

It seems clear, then, that at some point during chemical evolution on a primitive planet, the necessary ingredients for the synthesis of a living unit were available, perhaps in the oceans. The early pathways for the synthesis of many biologically important molecules remain to be demonstrated, but it seems likely that these experiments will soon be done.

Between the time of the primitive ocean with its dilute solution of chemical building blocks and the arrival of the first cell capable of self-replication, metabolism, and mutation, there is a large gap in our knowledge, and I would like to describe some possible contributions toward filling that gap.

Many scientists today feel that a molecule of nucleic acid or nucleoprotein was the "beginning" of life. The nucleic acids serve as templates

347

for cellular syntheses, and there is evidence by Kornberg (1960) and others that under certain special conditions one of the nucleic acids (DNA) can be made to replicate outside the cell. However, most of the complex components of the cell must be present in the medium in adequate concentrations before this replication will occur, and it hardly seems likely that this would have been the composition of the early ocean, even considering the probability of the first nucleic acid molecule being considerably simpler than now. It seems much more likely for the first replicating system to have had a specialized environment in which it was able to assemble the required materials and keep out those which were deleterious to this function. This is accomplished by cells today by means of a cell membrane, which is a selectively permeable barrier composed of protein and lipid. It permits the cell to create its own internal environment necessary for its metabolic and reproductive activities. It is difficult to imagine a living unit, no matter how primitive or simple, without some such capability.

Thus we must conceive of the primitive sea in which specialized units (perhaps of protein and/or lipid) provide a selected medium for the reproductive template to accumulate the molecules needed for replication and exclude others.

There is some experimental evidence to suggest how all this may have taken place. Oparin (1957), following Bungenberg de Jong, has shown that the simple mixing of solutions of different proteins and other substances of high molecular weight produces coacervate droplets. When coacervates of proteins are formed, there are molecular migrations and formation of a surface layer with altered structure and mechanical properties. Some coacervates may have an internal structure quite different from that of simple liquid droplets. According to Oparin, these coacervates have a marked power of adsorption of various organic substances from the surrounding medium, and this adsorption is selective. He feels that coacervates are the most likely form of organization of multimolecular systems to have formed a basis for further evolution. The coacervate is appealing as a primitive unit in that it does offer a somewhat selective barrier in which to house a molecular system capable of replication. However, coacervates leave much to be desired in that they are quite unstable structurally and leave unexplained the origin of the high molecular weight molecules (including protein) needed to form them.

Other interesting possibilities as cell precursors are the microspheres of Fox et al. (1959). These structures are produced by solution and then condensation of the "proteinoid" described by Fox and Harada.

They offer certain advantages over the coacervate in that structurally they are much more stable, they are derived from material synthesized under primitive conditions, and thus are easier to imagine in a primitive sequence of events than the coacervate. Actually, it is difficult to imagine that this phenomenon of microsphere formation, so easily demonstrable

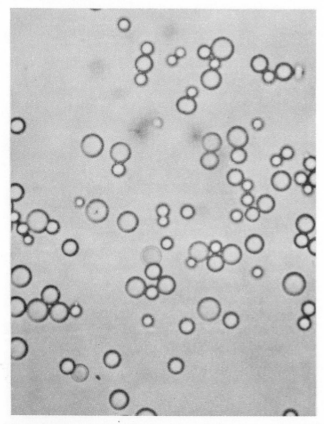

FIG. 1. Microspheres made by cooling a solution of proteinoid from 25°C to 0°C. Note "budding." (× 900.)

in the laboratory, did not occur in nature if there were a suitable accumulation of building blocks. Whether this had anything to do with the origin of the cell is purely speculative at this stage, but it is certainly suggestive.

Fox (1960) theorizes that protein could have first been formed on the surface of the Earth near areas of geothermal activity where accumulations of amino acids could have been heated, polymerized, and ultimately washed into the oceans. He (1960) has shown that this polymerization can be accomplished at temperatures as low as 70°C in the presence of polyphosphoric acid. We have recently shown that this polymerization can be conducted at 25°C in the presence of the ethyl ester of polyphosphoric acid. Although ethyl metaphosphate may not

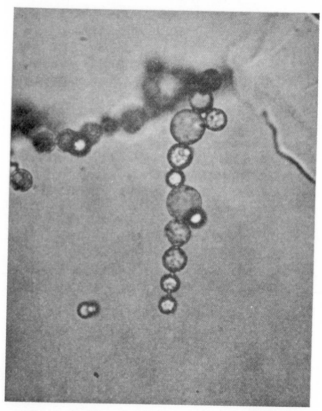

Fig. 2. "Budding chain" of microspheres. (× 900.)

have been present in great abundance on the primitive Earth, some other polyphosphate may have served the same purpose in a primitive environment. Fox has shown that when proteinoid is dissolved in water by heating to boiling and allowed to cool, a large number of uniform microspheres are formed. We have now made microspheres from proteinoid simply by the slow cooling (from 25°C to 0°C) of a saturated solution of proteinoid; heating is not necessary. Figure 1 shows microspheres made by this method. Some can be seen in various stages of a "budding" process. This phenomenon of "budding" can be induced in several ways, such as by altering the pH of the medium. Figure 2 shows a "budding chain" of microspheres made by cooling a solution of proteinoid. Such structures are not due to a coalescence of individual

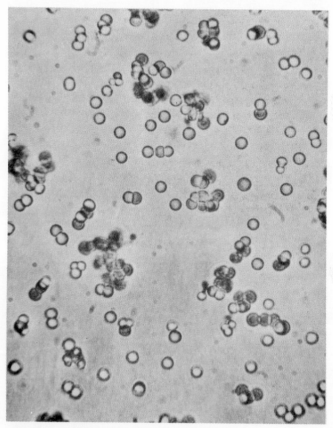

FIG. 3. Microspheres made by boiling proteinoid in water and allowing it to cool. ($\times$ 900.) Courtesy of S. W. Fox and K. Harada.

microspheres, although clumping of microspheres does occur under some conditions. Figure 3 shows a typical population of microspheres made by boiling a proteinoid in water and allowing it to cool. Here again "budding" can be seen. Actually this is a fission process rather than a coalescence, as can be shown by means of time-lapse photography. Figure 4 shows chains of microspheres made by forming microspheres

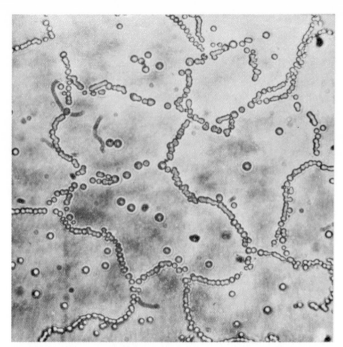

Fig. 4. Microsphere chains made by extending slight pressure on forming microspheres. (× 900.) Courtesy of S. W. Fox and S. Yuyama.

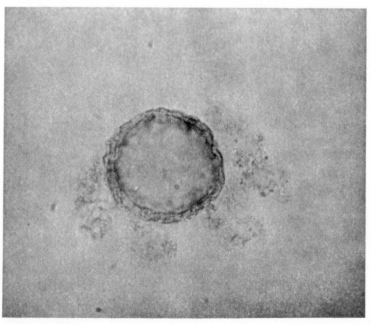

Fig. 5. Microsphere made from proteinoid plus 1% (by weight) histone. (× 900.)

under slight pressure on a microscope slide. The addition of small amounts (1% by weight) of a basic protein, such as histone, to the acidic proteinoid has a marked effect on the morphology of microspheres. Figure 5 shows one large (25 μ) "blastula-like" microsphere made from

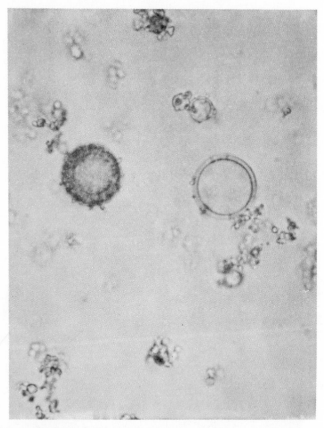

Fig. 6. Microspheres made from proteinoid plus histone, in $CaCl_2$, showing "double membranes." ($\times$ 900.)

such a mixture. Figure 6 shows two other types of microspheres made with proteinoid plus histone. One shows a "double membrane," the other a very dense-walled hollow structure. These are made in a $CaCl_2$ histone solution, which typically alters the size and structure of the microsphere walls. Figure 7 shows a dense, very reticulate matrix of proteinoid with histone added. Figure 8 shows a 5-μ-thick paraffin-embedded section of a typical microsphere, which in this case is a very thick-walled structure.

It is quite obvious that there is a tremendous diversity of size and morphology in these microspheres, and that structure is dependent upon environmental variations. For example, changes in the salt concentration

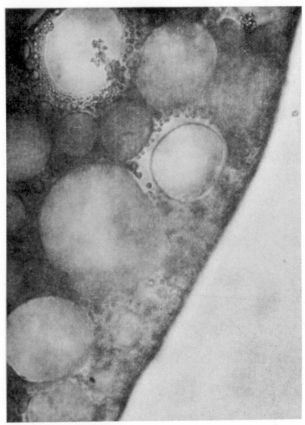

Fig. 7. Reticulate mass of proteinoid. (× 600.)

or ionic species give corresponding variations in the resultant microspheres. The pH of the medium, the temperature and pressures used, as well as the treatment of microspheres after formation, all have an effect on microsphere morphology. The microsphere is a remarkably stable structure in that it can be centrifuged at high speeds, lyophilized, heated, etc., without destroying its integrity. On the other hand, simple shaking of a suspension of microspheres results in fragmentation and increases in number of spheres, which under certain circumstances could be mistaken for division.

In addition to such interesting morphological properties, there are several suggestive points in the chemistry of microspheres. We (Ponnamperuma *et al.*, 1964) have shown that guanine is synthesized during a typical proteinoid synthesis from amino acids, and we recently have shown that fatty acids are also formed during such a synthesis. All of

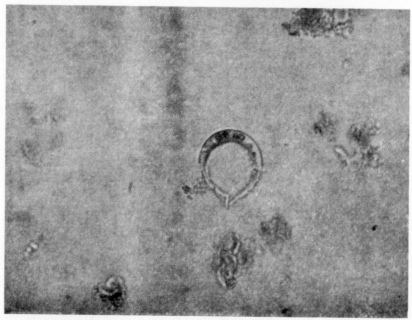

Fig. 8. Section (5μ) of paraffin-embedded section of typical microsphere (× 600.)

these factors, and others, make the microsphere an extremely appealing object of study, from the point of view of possible pathways for cellular origins.

A major stumbling block in our knowledge of the origin of life is the enormous gap between chemical evolution and the first self-replicating metabolizing unit which we might call a cell. We can now see how the individual molecules required for a living system could have been synthesized on the primitive planet. We can also see how a protective structure could have been synthesized at the same time, providing the very specialized environment most likely required for metabolism and replication. Although we may never duplicate the exact sequence of events leading to life as we know it, we should be able to understand and demonstrate possible pathways for chemical and biological evolution, which are consistent with our knowledge of the universe during the time span involved. The microsphere (or coacervate) may or may not represent such a pathway, but our present knowledge does not exclude the possibility, and studies with synthetic cell models are surely as valid an approach to the origin of life question as is the dissection of "modern" cells, which may be as far removed (in an evolutionary sense) from the "first cell" as were the products of chemical evolution on the primitive Earth. In fact, since evolution is in a sense a logarithmic process, the "modern cell" is most likely a distant relative indeed of the primitive precursor unless, of course, the primitive cell has survived unchanged since its formation. In either case, the use of the microsphere as a cell (or pre-cell) model is proving to be an unusually suggestive and productive approach to an understanding of pathways for the origin of cellular life.

Manuscript received October 29, 1964.

REFERENCES

Fox, S. W. (1960). *Science* **132**, 200.
Fox, S. W., and Harada, K. (1960). *J. Am. Chem. Soc.* **82**, 3745.
Fox, S. W., Harada, K., and Kendrick, J. (1959). *Science* **129**, 1221.
Harada, K., and Fox, S. W. (1960). *Arch. Biochem. Biophys.* **86**, 274.
Kornberg, A. (1960). *Science* **131**, 1503.
Oparin, A. I. (1957). "The Origin of Life on the Earth." Academic Press, New York.
Oró, J. (1963). *Nature* **197**, 862.
Ponnamperuma, C., Lemmon, R. M., Mariner, R., and Calvin, M. (1963). *Proc. Natl. Acad. Sci. U.S.* **49**, 737.
Ponnamperuma, C., Young, R. S., Munoz, E., McCaw, B. (1964). *Science* **143**, 1449.

DISCUSSION

Dr. Steinbach: I might say that interest in this type of model, the cell model, appears to follow a sine wave with about a 25-year interval between peaks, and let me say that each peak has more sense than the last peak. I think I would like to ask Dr. Oparin for his comment.

Dr. Oparin: I would like to know whether these splendid photographs represent electron microscope photographs of sections of fixed objects or not.

Dr. Fox: Dr. Oparin, you have seen unpublished electron micrographs and I will show some of them in the next paper, for the first time at this conference. The sections are from specimens fixed by osmium tetroxide.

DR. OPARIN: This is very impressive, but they had so many disappointments with fixed material, that it would be better to see these things in unfixed conditions.

DR. FOX: Similar observations have been made with the optical microscope without fixing the microspheres.

DR. OPARIN: There was at one time a Mexican investigator by the name of Herrera, who before the war sent me a series of microscopic slides which were obtained by him artificially and in some cases even from inorganic materials. The slides were given to a very eminent microscopist. He not only decided that they were living things, but even classified them. However, they were real artifacts.

I am far from thinking that these pictures can be in any way compared with Herrera's presentation. But I still suggest the necessity of being careful about it.

Since the pictures are beautiful one has to be especially critical in their evaluation.

Comments

SIDNEY W. FOX, CHAIRMAN

*Institute for Space Biosciences, Florida State University,
Tallahassee, Florida*

I shall take advantage of this time and place to express some appreciations. I would like to declare my thanks to that scholar in public office, Dr. Freeman H. Quimby, who provided the stimulus, the financial endorsement, and much of the advice for this conference. I also want to thank Mr. M. E. Dockendorf, the various wives, and especially the attending students for their help.

While preparing this paper, I found I was inundated by the need to oversee details of the conference, and I am afraid that my paper might, as a result, be somewhat disconnected. In this kind of paper, I feel it is unwise to leave many large gaps, so at the moment, I am really less concerned with the folly of probability, to quote Dr. Mora, than with the probability of folly.

I would like to say also that in my view the most that any of us at this or any similar conference can hope to do is generate not probabilities but possibilities, prebiological possibilities. Beyond that, we may hope to learn from experiments which possibilities are sequentially compatible.

This brings us back to an emphasis on Dr. Akabori's remark about the real meaning of Wakulla. I am also sure that if we succumb to vitalism in its varied guises, and I think there are many, we then do not do any experiments, we consequently do not learn, and we are placing ourselves in a position that tends to reinforce the negative preconceptions which immobilized us at the outset.

SIMULATED NATURAL EXPERIMENTS IN SPONTANEOUS ORGANIZATION OF MORPHOLOGICAL UNITS FROM PROTEINOID

SIDNEY W. FOX

Institute for Space Biosciences,
Florida State University,
Tallahassee, Florida

This paper will concern itself with a review of the properties of micro-spheres from thermal proteinoid. The significance and attributes of these structured units are in an intimate way a function of the material from which they arise. The properties of the thermal proteinoids have been reviewed many times (Fix, 1960, 1963; Harada, 1961; Fox *et al.*, 1962); these properties will not be catalogued here again.

Approximately two dozen attributes of protein are found in thermal proteinoid, including some of each of the eighteen common amino acids in peptide linkage, a susceptibility to proteolysis, nutritive quality (Krampitz and Knappen, 1962), and a tendency to form cell-like multi-macromolecular structures. Antigenicity and helicity have not yet been observed in thermal proteinoids. These attributes are, however, found in synthetic polyamino acids (Stahmann, 1962).

A synthetic polyamino acid with so many attributes of protein, and which arises simply under such widespread conditions (Fox, 1964), is a candidate for a model of primordial protein. Inasmuch as these attri-butes include a unique kind of *morphogenicity*, the model serves to resolve a paradox which has been an intellectual deterrent to experi-ments in the area of abiogenesis. The paradox has been stated clearly by Blum (1951) as follows:

> The riddle seems to be *How, when no life existed, did substances come into being which today are absolutely essential to living systems yet which can only be formed by those systems?* It seems

361

begging the question to suggest that the first protein molecules were formed by some more primitive "nonprotein living system" for it still remains to define and account for the origin of that system.

The thermal experiments have demonstrated how a *nonliving* system could give rise to polymers which are sufficiently protein-like that they could form a protocellular or precellular system (Fox, 1964) with which natural experiments could continue.

In attempting to develop models of precellular organization, we have largely restricted our experiments to those processes which plausibly in our view might occur naturally in abiotic environments. Although part of the original interest in thermal copolymerization of amino acids was in terms of the synthesis of protein models, this emphasis was supplanted by studies of a model of primitive, or primordial, protein. The proteinoids, in fact, represent a means by which all of the eighteen amino acids common to protein, or indeed a smaller number of amino acids, might have been copolymerized in a simple way. This mode is so simple, in fact, that it has represented for some an outrageous heresy of the carbobenzoxy tradition. For others it has represented a heresy to suggest that protein-like materials, particularly with some degree of nonrandomness, could be obtained by the brutal process of heating. On the other hand, the simplicity is compatible with a geologically plausible set of phenomena.

Demonstrable ways in which the reactant amino acids might arise have been many. Dr. Harada has shown one new kind of possibility.

It is possible to produce from these thermal polymers, also in a very simple way, a model of precellular organization. Here again we must reemphasize that contemporary cells are indeed very complex, and not to be considered easily susceptible to valid modeling. In the light, however, of a truly evolutionary premise, complexity must be preceded by simplicity, and the simplest models deserve attention in a context of which properties can be included experimentally within them. Complexity can be introduced in the laboratory in a stepwise fashion as perhaps it might similarly have been introduced in natural experiments. This philosophy has also been expressed by Philip Morrison under the title "Carbonaceous Snowflakes and the Origin of Life" (Morrison, 1962) on the basis of some of the formed units to be described here.

In detaching ourselves from the evolved and easily bewildering complexity in which we find ourselves, we are led to think in the context of simple systems in a primitive environment. This context is a truly evolutionary one with its capacity for stepwise empirical progression from simplicity to complexity.

In contrast to the situation pertinent to any other cell model of which I am aware, these studies use material which is not found in cells but which instead arises from a matrix that we can entertain as geologically plausible. This distinction is a crucial one in attempting to simulate pre-biological systems.

As a demonstration of these relationships, experiments were performed with the aid of Mr. Robert McCauley. A mixture of dry amino acids, containing sufficient aspartic acid and glutamic acid, was placed in the depression of a piece of lava from the beds on the Kapoho field on the island of Hawaii. The reaction vessel, i.e., the piece of lava, was then placed in an oven at 170°C for several hours. The powder was thereby converted to a light amber-colored liquid so viscous that it remained *in situ*. The rock and polymer was then laved by hot 1% sodium chloride solution. The liquid, which was slightly turbid, now contained large numbers of microspherical units. Other experiments used water in the form of artificial rain in the laboratory. Results are as in Figs. 1–3 of Dr. Young's paper.

The similarity to some of the formed elements found in meteorites will be apparent to those who have seen the latter. The conditions which exist in a meteorite containing carbonaceous material and some water and having a thermal gradient (Mason, 1962) are perhaps even more conducive than lava to the formation of such microparticles.

The fact that the polymerization proceeds on a piece of lava helps to affirm that the reaction is rugged over a range of conditions. The amino acids need not survive very long, in fact hardly at all, inasmuch as all experiments reporting the formation of amino acids by heat also reveal their immediate condensation (Fox, 1963). Before the thermal poly-amino acids could disintegrate chemically, they would need to be washed from the site of their formation, an act which could also occur rapidly.

It is now clear, then, that the amino acids, their preprotein polymers, and the formed sequelae of these polymers can emerge in the same locale in a continuum in which a wide range of simple conditions would yield these prebiological phenomena. For an idea of the widespread nature of such locales on the Earth, Bullard's book on volcanoes should be consulted (Bullard, 1962).

Under controlled laboratory conditions the proteinoids have been made in a wide variety in hundreds of experiments. Also under controlled laboratory conditions, the microparticles have been made in thousands of experiments. When so produced, they have many properties which can be studied and varied. These microspherical particles have been made by dissolving approximately 15 mg proteinoid in 2.5 ml hot water or hot salt solution and allowing the clear liquid to cool for a few minutes. In many experiments, the proteinoid was crude.

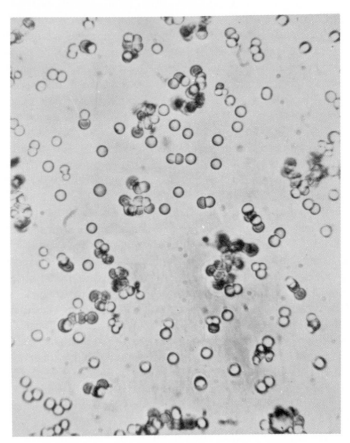

FIG. 1. Proteinoid microspheres.

For Fig. 1, the polymer was a purified preparation, and the microspheres were centrifuged and washed. The individual units are approximately 2 μ in diameter. In general, they are most easily produced in a bacterial size, not to mention the coccoid shape. The comments of Dr. Lipmann (p. 259) are recalled at this point. In this figure may also be seen two sizes, as often observed. Also seen are filaments which are assemblies of individual small microspheres. One may also see in this field forms which resemble budding yeast.

The uniformity of the units makes possible experiments in hypotonic and hypertonic solutions. The results are swelling and shrinking, respectively, although the responses are less marked than for biocells.

The units are very numerous, 10^8-10^9 resulting typically from 15 mg of polymer. The facts that they are so numerous and that some individuality is occasionally recognizable suggest that nature had much opportunity to perform vast numbers of experiments.

The microparticles can be made more or less stable than true cells. Some of this stability is apparent in the fact that these units retain their shape over many weeks and presumably indefinitely. They may be, and usually are, centrifuged in a clinical centrifuge at 3000 rpm; they retain their integrity under such conditions. Their stability is further demonstrated by their sectionability, as originally observed by Young and Munoz. This property has made it possible to produce the electron micrographs to be shown later. The need for such stability in precellular forms has been stressed by Prof. Oparin (Oparin, 1957).

Although compositional components such as ribonucleic acid (RNA) are definitely missing, unless they be intentionally added, the protein-like nature of the material is sufficiently like the substance of a bacterial cell that the microsphere accepts the Gram stain. Furthermore, by controlling the proportion of acidic proteinoid and of basic proteinoid used in the preparations of microspheres, one can produce them in the gram-positive or in the gram-negative state (Fox and Yuyama, 1963a). The gram-positive microspheres contain a sufficient proportion of basic proteinoid (Fox et al., 1962). The solubilities in dilute alkali of the gram-negative and gram-positive microspheres exactly parallel those of gram-negative and gram-positive bacteria (Fox and Yuyama, 1963a).

When produced under slight pressure the microspheres may associate in algae-like chains (Fig. 2) (Fox and Yuyama, 1963b). This effect raises questions about some of the objects of micropaleontology.

The evidence that the microspheres have a membrane has accumulated from studies under the optical microscope, the electron microscope, and from time-lapse pictures (Fox and Yuyama, 1964).

Membranes are suggested in Fig. 3 taken under the optical microscope.

The appearance of a microsphere stained with osmic acid, sectioned, and examined under the electron microscope is seen in Fig. 4. One may compare a section of Bacillus cereus (Murray, 1960).

When the microspheres are placed in aqueous suspension they typically set a pH of 3. If buffer of pH 5.5–6.5 is added, they begin to hollow out, and "double membranes" can be seen. These were stained, caught in the methacrylate block, sectioned, and examined by electron micrography, by Takeshi Fukushima with the help of Mrs. C. Dockery.

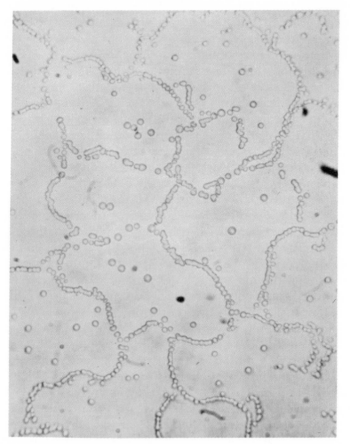

FIG. 2. Associated proteinoid microspheres.

In Fig. 5 are two views of double layers, an unexpected feature, in the same kind of preparation. Perhaps one should expect the unexpected if reason exists for believing that the trial is a true sequence of evolutionary experiments. These double layers require no phospholipid as such, but the polymer contains hydrophobic side chains. Recently D. Green and co-workers (Richardson, et al., 1963) have found that the mitochondrion owes its shape to lipid-free "structural protein" (Green, 1964).

Figure 6 shows microspheres in which buffer of pH 6.0 has diffused slowly into a suspension. The interior diffused out through the boundary, but the boundary remains, as in the electron micrographs. One may

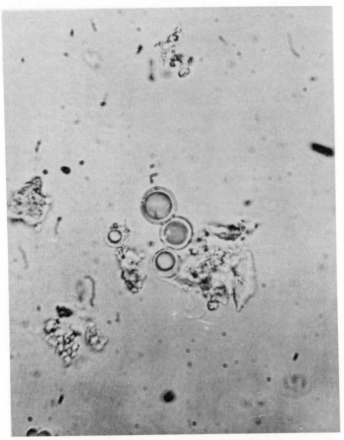

FIG. 3. Microspheres with double boundaries.

also note here a simulation of cleavage of a septate type (Fox and Yuyama, 1963b).

Figure 7 shows frames from a time-lapse study. Until these were available one could not decide whether these units were the result of fusion or fission. Frames 60 and 111 show clearly that the process is fission in the uppermost microsphere in the upper left-hand quadrant.

Other evidence consistent with a membrane is found in the large microsphere near the center. The polymer in the interior diffuses out while the polymer in the boundary remains. This is, of course, selective action.

The way in which catalytic activity might have entered by natural experiments into formed microparticles has been investigated with David

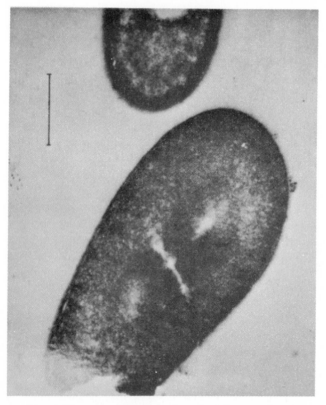

Fig. 4. Electron micrograph of section of microsphere.

Joseph and Elizabeth Wiggert. The starting point for this was the known catalytic activity of zinc, magnesium, and other salts for the hydrolysis of adenosine triphosphate (ATP). Attempts to introduce Zn into proteinoids and other thermal polyamino acids gave highly erratic results until freshly prepared zinc hydroxide was used. The materials behaved as in Fig. 8.

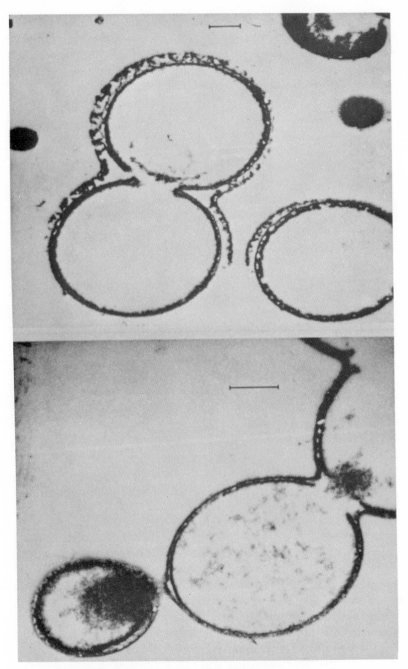

FIG. 5. Electron micrographs of double layers in microspheres.

After proteinoid and zinc hydroxide are heated in aqueous solution to give a clear liquid, the solution deposits on cooling microspheres containing zinc. When washed with water, the wash liquids show successively less activity. The washed microspheres, however, maintain activity. Since the zinc-microspheres are changed in the experiment with ATP,

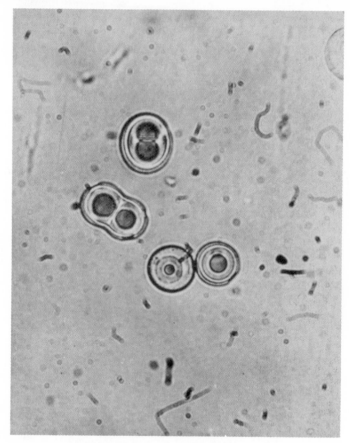

Fig. 6. Twinned microspheres from raised pH.

the activity cannot be referred to as catalytic, in the full sense of that term.

A large part of what can now be visualized as having occurred thermally, according to this model, is shown in Fig. 9.

The aspects which have received study in the largest spectrum of variations are the polymerization and the formation of a kind of "pro-

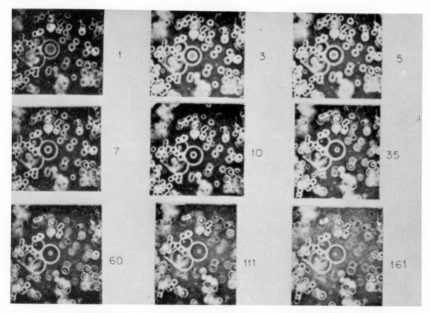

FIG. 7. Time-lapse study showing several phenomena.

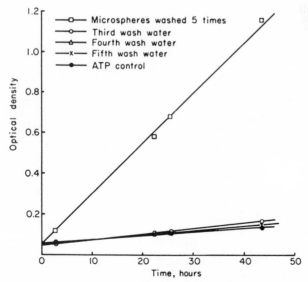

FIG. 8. Adenosine triphosphate-splitting activity in Zn-microspheres. Optical density is molybdate color intensity measuring release of phosphate.

teinaceous" "membranous" spherule. Thousands of the latter type of experiment have been performed. Study of the possibilities in glassware and review of the necessary conditions on the Earth, through field investigation and through the library, indicate that such sequences must have occurred innumerable times.

A principal significance is the demonstration of the emergence of both complex materials and complex microstructures, reminiscent of cells, by simple processes. At the least the dilemma posed by Blum is resolved

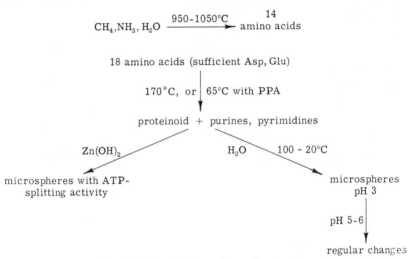

Fig. 9. Thermal theory, November, 1963.

in at least one fashion. The explanation has been extended to permit us to visualize a spontaneous synthesis of protein-like material sufficiently similar to yield a protocell which could spontaneously include ATP-splitting ability. One might thus visualize a natural evolution to cells and subsequently to cellular synthesis of macromolecules.

ACKNOWLEDGMENTS

This study is contribution no. 029 of the Institute for Space Biosciences. It was aided by grant NsG-173-62 of the National Aeronautics and Space Administration. *Manuscript received October 30, 1963.*

REFERENCES

Blum, H. (1951). "Time's Arrow and Evolution," p. 170. Princeton Univ. Press, Princeton, New Jersey.
Bullard, F. M. (1962). "Volcanoes." p. 55, *et seq.* Univ. of Texas Press, Austin, Texas.
Fox, S. W. (1960). *Science* **132**, 200.

Fox, S. W. (1963). *In* "Protein Nutrition and Metabolism" (J. Kastelic, H. H. Draper, and H. P. Broquist, eds.), p. 141. Special Publ. No. 4, Univ. of Illinois College of Agriculture.

Fox, S. W. (1964). *Nature* **201**, 336.

Fox, S. W., and Yuyama, S. (1963a). *J. Bacteriol.* **85**, 279.

Fox, S. W., and Yuyama, S. (1963b). *Ann. N.Y. Acad. Sci.* **108**, 487.

Fox, S. W., and Yuyama, S. (1964). *Comp. Biochem. Physiol.* **11**, 317.

Fox, S. W., Harada, K., and Rohlfing, D. L. (1962). *In* "Polyamino Acids, Polypeptides, and Proteins" (M. Stahmann, ed.), p. 47. Univ. of Wisconsin Press, Madison, Wisconsin.

Harada, K. (1961), *Protein, Enzyme, and Nucleic Acid* (Tokyo, in Japanese) **6**, 65.

Krampitz, G., and Knappen, F. (1962) *Nature* **195**, 385.

Mason, B. (1962). "Meteorites." Wiley, New York.

Morrison, P. (1962) *Science* **135**, 663.

Murray, R. G. E. (1960). *In* "The Bacteria" (I. C. Gunsalus and R. Y. Stanier, eds.), Vol. I, p. 55. Academic Press, New York.

Oparin, A. I. (1957). "The Origin of Life on the Earth," pp. 321 and 354. Academic Press, New York.

Richardson, S. H., Hultin, H. O., and Green, D. E. (1963). *Proc. Nat'l. Acad. Sci. U.S.A.* **50**, 821.

Stahmann, M., (1962). "Polyamino Acids, Polypeptides, and Proteins." Univ. of Wisconsin Press, Madison, Wisconsin.

DISCUSSION

DR. BLOIS: Was the lava used in the experiment, in which the amino acids were placed, cleaned chemically?

DR. FOX: No. The reactions were also carried out in the open air of the laboratory.

DR. QUIMBY: I would call the layers in the electron micrographs boundaries. I believe that they are about ten times as thick as the usual semipermeable membrane in living systems. Is there anybody able to comment on this point?

DR. GROSSENBACHER: I think that is true, but the basic forces that produce a double layer would still be of interest.

MR. YUYAMA: The distance between the membranes is about 100 Å. It is very thin.

DR. FOX: The two views in Fig. 5 demonstrate the experimental variability which conceivably might permit making microspheres with boundaries that are closer together or further apart.

DR. GROSSENBACHER: I would like to suggest the use of the term "layer" from the electron microscope point of view. They have a finite thickness. Calling them layers gets around the whole business of what membranes have meant to some people.

Dr. Ponnamperuma: You mentioned the release of inorganic phosphate from ATP by the zinc hydroxide microsphere. Wouldn't you expect that from any of your proteinoids on account of the acidic character?

Dr. Fox: No. We ran many controls and we don't find ATP-splitting activity in proteinoid at pH 5. In fact, in these experiments and in a companion set that was run subsequently, we had that kind of control; there was no activity beyond that of the autohydrolysis of ATP.

Dr. Sagan: These results are quite stimulating, and I think it is not impossible that they may have some relevance to the origin of life; but I wonder if perhaps you could help me understand, in a general way, your proposed sequence of thermal synthetic reactions.

Dr. Fox: The reactions in a purely thermal sequence are as follows:

(a) CH_4, NH_3, $H_2O \xrightarrow{\text{ca. } 1000°C}$ volatile amino acid intermediates (perhaps amino acid nitriles): a rapid vapor phase reaction.

(b) Hydrolysis to amino acids, at 20–100°C in water. A small amount of water might be present in the rapidly formed condensation product after the reaction and be used up by hydrolysis to give dry amino acids. A larger amount of water might be present from rain or otherwise, and then it would evaporate.

(c) Copolymerization must occur when temperature is at 100–200°C (or much less with PPA, other phosphates) and with sufficient aspartic acid or lysine.

(d) Microspheres form when water enters the reaction locale (rain, tides, etc.).

The amino acids might, however, arise in other ways, as by Miller's synthesis, Abelson's syntheses, Oró's syntheses, Hasselstrom's synthesis, etc., instead of by (a) and (b) above.

The understanding of how water must have entered and left the scene is crucial to understanding the sequence. If it is now clear to you, it will also be apparent that these changes are realistically imputed to a natural environment.

Dr. Sagan: This scenario is geophysically implausible. You need temperatures of the order of 1000°C to make your intermediates, and temperatures less than 100°C to make the amino acids. Even if the intermediates are stable indefinitely at 1000°C—which I doubt—you require the juxtaposition of high-temperature volcanic environments and low-temperature aqueous environments. The proposed synthesis occurs only at the interface of these environments. In any given epoch, the fraction of the Earth's surface covered by such interfaces would be very small.

That's simply to *make* the amino acids. Then, the amino acids made in aqueous phase have to somehow be deposited anhydrously so that they can subsequently copolymerize. To form microspheres, they have to be put back into aqueous solution. This sequence may be convenient in the laboratory; whether it occurs frequently in nature is less clear. The temperatures required to synthesize the amino acid intermediates rapidly pyrolyze amino acids, depolymerize polypeptides, and degrade microspheres. I would like to see an order of magnitude calculation in which a probability is assigned to each scene of the scenario, and a total polypeptide abundance over geological time derived. It seems to me that this abundance will be much less than the large concentration of polypeptides in the primitive seas apparently required for the origin of life, Strecker synthesis of amino acids seems much more likely in primitive times, but the problem of the large-scale production of polypeptides remains, I believe, unsolved.

Dr. Fox: Your statements include many assumptions which we might continue to discuss. The geophysical plausibility of the scenario is, however, explained and documented in *Nature* (1964), **201**, 335, 336.

Dr. Oró: I would like to make just one point for the record, that a synthesis of amino acids by heating simple gas mixtures at high temperatures is being referred to in this conference as Harada's method. I want the record to be clear that this synthesis has been suggested in a paper of mine [Oró (1961), *Nature* **190**, 389], and that it has been carried out by Mr. Skewes and me in our laboratory about 1 year ago. The results have been presented in a number of lectures.[1]

Dr. Fox: We are glad to be informed of these contributions of Dr. Oró's. It is also true, however, that in our laboratory thought has been given to thermal synthesis of amino acids for many years as part of the developing total thermal theory. Amino acids from solids were reported in 1955 (Fox, Johnson, and Middlebrook, *J. Am. Chem. Soc.* **77**, 1048). In 1961, Dr. Harada discussed the possible formation of amino acids in the reactions of gases of the primitive atmosphere on floating lava [Harada, K. (1961), *Protein, Nucleic Acid, Enzyme (Tokyo)* **6**, 65].

Dr. Gaffron: Are the spherules as easily dissolved as they have been formed?

Dr. Fox: Some of them are and some of them are not. Much depends on the constitution. Many of the zinc-containing spherules are less soluble than the individual components.

Dr. Gaffron: If they cannot be easily dissolved, they must have changed, and the question of composition comes up at the moment when

[1] *Second National Meeting of Biochemistry,* Univ. of Santiago, Spain, August 1, 1963. *A Symposium on Organic Geochemistry: The Origin of Petroleum,* Univ. of Texas, Austin, October 11, 1963.

you are able to centrifuge them down. In which way did they change from the composition of the liquid in which they have formed? Evidently they do not dissolve easily again.

DR. Fox: We haven't done definitive experiments on that. I can make some guesses on this and we can work this out for you by calculations. The composition would vary, depending upon which experiment one is focusing his attention upon.

Now, the change in solubility is very marked, if one mixes the acidic type and the basic type, each being soluble, and then makes microspheres which now contain both and are of the gram-positive type. These have less solubility than the components and the composition of the mother liquid would be relatively richer in the basic . . .

DR. GAFFRON: The next question is which of your amino acids then would be responsible for structure if you call that structure? This is an important point, I believe.

DR. Fox: Yes. The answer to your question can be approached systematically, because of the ease of controlling these thermal copolymerizations. In this connection thermal poly (glycine, anhydroaspartic acid) is the only polyamino acid of many studied which yields erythrocyte-shaped particles. These, incidentally, form rouleaus like red blood cells.

MR. ROHLFING: Dr. Young has revealed that microspheres can be formed from proteinoid at low temperatures. Spherical bodies are produced at room temperature from the imide-free form of either proteinoid or polyaspartic acid by exceeding solubility of the polymer in water, or by salting out a concentrated solution of polymer.

Dr. Gaffron has inquired about the structural basis of microsphere formation. In partial answer, the finding that microspheres are formed from a homopolymer (polyaspartic acid) limits to one the number of kinds of amino acid residue that can be considered essential for this morphogenic process. A further indication of the importance of acidic amino acid residues in microsphere formation is the fact that microspheres have not been formed from lysine proteinoid unless acid proteinoid is present.

MR. PIRIE: How many enzymes have you looked for? Have you looked for various enzymes and failed to find them?

DR. Fox: No. We have looked for four or five kinds of catalytic activity. We got into a rather systematic study of p-nitrophenyl acetate, partly because that makes a suitable Ph. D. thesis, or a more suitable one than a survey kind of operation. Dr. Krampitz is now looking at quite a number of possibilities with natural substrates. We have had some indications which on rigorous attack haven't held up.

All I can tell you about rigorously is the *p*-nitrophenyl acetate and, I think with a considerable degree of rigor, the effects on localizing the ATP-splitting activities in the microspheres by combining zinc ions with the substance of the microsphere.

DR. GAFFRON: I missed something here. This increased activity towards ATP, what have you there? Does it go exclusively with the spheres or do you find it already in the initial starting material in the proteinoid?

DR. FOX: We find it with the zinc salts of the proteinoid made in various ways, or, for example, with zinc polyasparate, and I emphasize again that we cannot report enhancement of activity in the combination of zinc and polymer over that which is due to zinc content alone. So the significance of these results so far is solely with respect to localizing ATP-splitting activity, which zinc can, in a primitive way or crude way, confer upon the organized unit. This doesn't mean, of course, that we are not looking for enhanced activity. We are. While I can not yet say anything rigorous about enhancement of the activity of the zinc, an organized unit which happens to incorporate ATP-splitting activity has, I believe, prebiological significance.

DR. SAGAN: Dr. Ponnamperuma and I had some discussion elsewhere on the question of thermal synthesis. I would like to try to clarify one point.

There is a range of energy sources available in primitive times for the synthesis of organic molecules, and many of them, such as electric discharges, high-energy electrons, or heat, are very likely interchangeable. But whatever the energy source, it is important that there be a large-scale production of polypeptides. A large-scale production of polynucleotides, for example, is not required, because polynucleotides presumably were able to self-replicate; a polypeptide will just sit there.

If there is ever to be a coupling between polynucleotides and polypeptides, so that a specific polynucleotide codes for a specific polypeptide, there must be some general process for synthesizing large quantities of polypeptides in the primitive oceans. The most important polypeptide synthetic pathway is then the pathway which produces the most polypeptides, unless some energy sources make better polypeptides than others. The problem reduces to a simple question of production rates and stabilities. If any proposed synthetic sequence gives rise to large amounts of polypeptides in the primitive environment, that is very exciting, and likely was relevant for the origin of life. If a proposed synthetic sequence gives, all in all, very small amounts of polypeptides, then perhaps it was not so significant.

DR. FOX: The assumption that synthesis of polypeptides had to occur in the primitive oceans is not favored by rudimentary principles of chemical thermodynamics. The equation

$$H_2NCHRCOOH + H_2NCHR'COOH = H_2NCHRCONHCHR'COOH + H_2O$$

proceeds to the right more readily in the absence of water [for a fuller treatment, see Fox, Vegotsky, Harada, and Hoagland (1957), Ann. N.Y. Acad. Sci. 69, 328]. Accordingly, the reaction goes best at temperatures above the boiling point of water or under conditions which remove water. The many extensive volcanic regions referred to earlier are hot and dry, so that the spontaneous production of thermal polyamino acids must have been widespread, provided amino acids were available. Also, the thermal synthesis in the laboratory gives yields in the range of 10–40%. The limitation of amounts would thus be mainly in the amino acids.

When the thermal polyamino acids are covered with water they are simultaneously converted to spherules and are protected from destructive influences by layers of water.

DR. PONNAMPERUMA: We seem to accept the current idea that only a polynucleotide can replicate. We do not know. There may be some primitive proteins which had the capacity of replicating.

DR. FOX: As a matter of fact, this is a suggestion that Joshua Lederberg has made [see "Science in Space" (1961), p. 415, McGraw-Hill, New York). I don't argue for it. I would like to keep all the books open.

DR. SAGAN: If either primitive polypeptides were weakly self-replicating, or if primitive polynucleotides were weakly catalytic, many of our present difficulties would be removed. Or even if there were a way of making your proteinoid microspheres directly in a liquid water solution at moderate temperatures.

DR. FOX: Thermodynamic studies and interpretations [Borsook, H., and Huffman, H. M., (1944). In "Chemistry of the Amino Acids and Proteins," C. L. A. Schmidt (ed.), pp. 865–866. "Charles C Thomas, Springfield, Ill.] show that synthesis of a small proportion of peptide bond in aqueous solution is thermodynamically feasible without imparting energy to the system, whereas production of large polypeptides would be expressed by numbers such as $(1/20)^{30}$. Both theoretically, and experimentally, our systems have (must have) some water or some phosphoric acid or other phosphate. The aqueous systems are *hypohydrous*. Many moles of water per mole of amino acid cannot be present unless an energy yielding reaction is coupled to the peptide bond synthesis. Terrestrial cells, of course, have evolved to do this, but one must first explain how such cells came into existence. The material of the microspheres arose in the absence of cells, and provide a way out of the dilemma.

DR. VALLENTYNE: I have no desire to prolong this discussion, but having taken Sagan a little bit to task before, I am in agreement with one point. I don't think these conditions are really geologically plausible. That was a good term, but one might better say geologically not impossible. The point I want to make, though, is not that at all. This work is nice work and is of interest for its own sake. I think, if one attempts to justify it on the basis of geology, which is a little bit hard to do, to make it meaningful or probable, that's where one gets into difficulties with it. I have no objection to the work itself. I think it's leading somewhere that is in an interesting direction, and I am happy to see it continue, but to try to create an analogy for it in terms of Earth history—well, every time a geologist hears it, it pricks him under the skin, and that's why you get such reaction to it from people who think in terms of Earth history.

There's one question I would like to ask about your work. Since you have the possibility open, to form these proteinoids as microspheres or in solution, does it make any difference with regard to enzymatic activity whether they are organized in microsphere form or in solution? Perhaps this is what Dr. Gaffron was asking.

DR. FOX: To respond to the second comment first, our experiments with the zinc are too young to answer that with any surety. The preliminary indication is that it does make a difference.

As for the questions of thermal polymerization of amino acids in a geological locale, I have encountered geologists and others who do not accept the picture. I have also met many geologists who have positive reactions. Some of these, for instance, were at the Woodring Conference in 1961. Several suggested field work in volcanic zones and made specific proposals. I am grateful to them, particularly Dr. Garrels and Dr. Zies. I have done some field work on temperature ranges and organic compounds, and, in the laboratory, reactions on heated lava. These are the evidence for the geophysical plausibility of the laboratory conditions. A paper has been submitted to Nature [Fox, S. W. (1964), Nature 201, 336].

DR. ORÓ: Rather than making a destructive criticism, I would like to make a constructive one. Professor Oparin in his presentation has mentioned that in the Kola peninsula, which is an igneous rock formation having no connection with sedimentary deposits, methane and heavier hydrocarbons are continuously being released into the atmosphere. This is an instance of organic matter of supposedly abiogenic origin. I think we should look for other instances.

I would like to suggest that in the boundary layers of lava flows and other magmatic ejecta there may be some evidence of organic compounds entrapped at the time in which the lava or magma was cooled down to a sufficiently low temperature.

DR. FOX: I have looked for organic compounds in hot zones in cinder cones, and I can say that we have found them, with Mr. Windsor's help on the analyses. But I am not sure we can rule out the presence of amino acids due to contamination by terrestrial organisms. Some of the analyses are remarkably like the analyses from Harada's experiments with gases.

DR. ORÓ: I think there are methods and criteria that may allow one to differentiate. In a lava flow, the only place I would think one may find organic molecules that have survived is at the boundary layers. One cannot expect to find any organic molecules in the internal part of the lava flow because the organic compounds would have been charred. If organic compounds are found entrapped in the silicate of the outer layers of the lava flows, or other igneous formations, one may be able to exclude contamination.

DR. FOX: I can't agree with this. When I think of the difficulty of excluding contamination, it is extreme. I think that this was brought out very clearly at the symposium on meteorites [Nagy, B. (1963), Ann. N.Y. Acad. Sci., 108, 339], where at least quite a number of us were quite sure that no real evidence of the elimination of terrestrial contamination was brought forward.

One other way of getting boundary conditions in the sense of Oró is to have rain which does come on the Earth rather frequently, and I think the premise that it does not rain on volcanoes can not be defended.

DR. YOUNG: I just wanted to make a statement in an attempt to generalize a little more on the geological possibilities. We don't need some special sort of environment to do this. You don't need a volcano. I think the same reaction could have occurred on the primitive Earth where amino acids were present, if the proper catalysts were present.

DR. SAGAN: Including solution of the reaction products in the oceans?

DR. YOUNG: Anywhere there was an accumulation of amino acids in a dry condition, and perhaps even in the oceans. It doesn't have to be on the hot volcano. These reactions can go on at lower temperatures.

DR. SAGAN: If they can occur at lower temperatures, then the probabilities are greatly enhanced.

DR. YOUNG: That is my point. Also there is no reason to feel that the synthesis of nucleic acids is excluded as being simultaneous with this event.

DR. QUIMBY: Dr. Fox spoke of 170°C as being a "brutal" temperature. My feeling is that 170°C is no more brutal than any of the other energies that have been employed to synthesize the various molecules which we have been talking about. That includes points near the spark gap, γ-irradiation, the linear accelerator at Berkeley, and or germicidal lamps.

DR. Fox: I would like to respond to Dr. Young's remarks. The points that Dr. Young makes about the breadth of terrestrial conditions for spontaneous chemical reactions is one that is often overlooked, and his emphasis is one that is endorsed by the evidence. The problem is not so much one of finding terrestrial conditions to match laboratory conditions but rather one of selecting the appropriate conditions from the vast variety of geophysical possibilities. A hopeful approach in this direction is that of determining which geologically possible reactions are sequentially possible.

Another aspect that deserves close attention is the way in which water must be present or absent at various stages.

Fundamentally, uncoupled chemical polymerization of amino acids to a substantial degree in aqueous solution is thermodynamically contraindicated, as brought out several times in the literature. [See, for instance, Fox, Vegotsky, Harada, and Hoagland (1957), Ann. N.Y. Acad. Sci. 69, 328.] Understanding of this relationship can be crucial and the fact that chemically the energy barrier can in effect be surmounted by raising the temperature above the boiling point of water, or by using anhydrizing agents like polyphosphoric acid is also crucial. The latter permits polymerization at temperatures below the boiling point of water, e.g., 70°C, as we reported in 1960.

Now, the fact that polymerization can occur at 70°C as well as at 170°C is no reason to conclude that the polymerization on the Earth at lower temperatures is more probable or more plausible.

Any judgment which does not take into account Dr. Young's emphasis and the thermodynamic considerations could, if taken seriously, preclude meaningful experiments.

Of course, organisms have an intricate, evolved biochemical system for supplying energy for peptide bond synthesis. The model shows how amino acids could yield polyamino acids which in turn could yield structured units which split ATP and could conceivably evolve to synthesizers of cellular protein. The limitation might not have been polypeptides or amino acids at all but adequate amounts of suitable phosphoric anhydride compounds.

To develop a valid judgment on these matters, I believe that one must at least (a) take into account the thermodynamic problem, (b) familiarize himself thoroughly with laboratory experiments, (c) research the present and past terrestrial geophysical conditions in the field and in the library, (d) determine the terrestrial distribution of various forms of phosphate, etc. We have been reviewing these aspects and others over 6 years and are led to believe by these studies that polymerization of amino acids on the surface of the Earth might, or rather must, have occurred at temperatures both below and above the boiling point of water. If one must state an opinion, my opinion is that the syntheses at higher temperatures occurred more often. These outlooks have been developed in full view of the well known fact that models tend to have a hypnotic quality for their proponents. As yet, however, the significant finding is that a simple process at one of many possible temperatures can, demonstrably, explain the origin of polymers similar to, and as complex as, proteins and possibly nucleic acids.

DR. PONNAMPERUMA: I think the remarks Dr. Quimby has made about the energies are really valid if applied to the actual position where the reactions take place. In all these experiments, however, any molecules synthesized were swept away from the scene of the reaction. The place where the molecules accumulate is perhaps found under very ordinary conditions. The parallel is not quite true.

DR. QUIMBY: I wasn't thinking so much of the experiments, I was thinking of the primeval UV flux.

DR. PONNAMPERUMA: Under the water?

DR. QUIMBY: That is right. The products of synthesis by UV in the primeval atmosphere must reach water in some depth to prevent photochemical decomposition.

Part V

PERSPECTIVES II

THE RECOGNITION OF HEREDITARY ORDER IN PRIMITIVE CHEMICAL SYSTEMS

H. H. PATTEE

Biophysics Laboratory, Stanford University,
Stanford, California

If you choose to consider hereditary transmission as one of the unique characteristics of life, then this paper does not belong in a conference on prebiological systems. However, I endorse Dr. Pirie's skeptical attitude expressed at the opening session, that we really do not know if the systems we are discussing are prebiological or not. At the same time, I am also very optimistic, along with Dr. Buchanan, in expecting that the next 5 years will see almost all types of biochemicals produced abiogenically from simple, possible, primitive earth compounds. In fact, at the next origin of life symposium we may hear of fissioning proteinoid microspheres and nonenzymatic replication of nucleic acids. Perhaps someone will stir them together and get division, but I hate to think of the discussions these papers will generate. It is going to be increasingly difficult to interpret such results without agreement, or at least a statement, of our ground rules.

The fundamental problem which still confronts us is that even if we imagine we have all the biochemicals we could use, the nature of the most primitive, evolving, hereditary structures remains quite obscure. Although Oparin (1938) has from the beginning emphasized the essential continuity of evolution from the very simplest molecular levels of aggregation, most recent suggested hypotheses for the earliest hereditary systems reflect the newly acquired knowledge of highly evolved present organisms. They are extrapolations backward to the simplest conceivable collection of nucleic acid and protein which replicate, transcript, and synthesize just well enough to assure biological evolution by natural selection (e.g., Miller, and Urey, 1959; Crick, 1961; Rich, 1962). Now of course it is clear that there certainly was an earlier stage of life involving nucleic acid coupled specifically to protein synthesis so that

385

such units could evolve by natural selection very much by the same basic process that they do today. What is not at all clear is that this stage should absorb our primary interest.

I think it may not be the best strategy so early in our thinking to divide the origin of life problem into the two stages called *chemical evolution* (e.g., Calvin, 1956; Blum, 1961) which implies only stochastic reactions without hereditary order or replication, and *biological evolution*, which begins with self-replication and evolves by natural selection. These may be suitable categories for the description of matter on the earth at different stages separated by several billion years, but they may not be at all suitable for the time in between, which is where we should soon begin looking. In fact, this distinction appears to confound us from the beginning, since we say that a mutable, self-replicating system is a prerequisite for natural selection, and we are consequently prevented from calling upon natural selection to reduce the improbability of the occurrence of the first self-replicating system. From this point of view, the appearance of the first nucleic acid memory, coupled to protein enzymes in such a pattern as to assure persistent replication and synthesis, is a very serious problem. To many writers this is the place to invoke auspicious, but random, events to push chemical evolution over the crucial hump.

The apparent simplicity of the Watson-Crick (1953) replication scheme, together with the geological time-span which is assumed to be available for these auspicious events to occur, has produced enough confidence in those who accept this approach so that for some the problem no longer exists. We never hear of the ominous, but equally random, events which might push evolution back over the hump. In any case, as Bridgman (1956) points out, to invoke chance as an explanation for any event is the worst possible strategy, since it leads to no experiments. Operationally it means we do not choose to go into the matter further. In the long run, we shall learn more by accepting the Laplacian attitude which reserves the chance hypothesis only for those situations where, after many trials, the strange effects finally destroy each other (Laplace, 1820). It is better to be pessimistic and find out you are wrong, than be optimistic and find out nothing.

I believe that a new point of view may be needed for the design and interpretation of origin of life experiments beyond the stage of showing that biochemicals can be synthesized from small molecules without detailed control by the experimenter. The nature of the primitive evolutionary process will not be understood by believing that the end state of such a chemical synthesis always represents a spontaneous or chance event simply because this end state is demonstrated to occur repeatedly, when in fact this label only means that the details of the process are unknown to the experimenter. Events can be safely dismissed as "spontaneous" only when the details are incidental to the results, or when no large informational control is involved. For example, in the case of a living cell we prefer to explain its behavior as largely the result of its parental hereditary information, rather than calling it a spontaneous event. This is simply an expression of our belief that it is far more probable that the particular states of these molecules which we recognize as living will occur through a hereditary process than by spontaneous trials from the set of all possible states of these same molecules. But this belief should also affect our attitude toward all levels of organization, and that is why the idea of depending on spontaneity to produce crucial events such as self-replication, is not a satisfactory answer. I have tried to state this more generally, though as yet imprecisely, as a parallel to the evolutionary principle of Simon (1962) which is that *hierarchic systems will evolve far more quickly than nonhierarchic systems of comparable size* (also cf. Bernal, 1959). Whereas this concept relates to the stability of intermediate structures in evolution, I would also suggest the principle that *hereditary organization occurs with a higher probability (or more frequently) than nonhereditary organization resulting in the same degree of complexity.*

The new approach to origin of life experiments which I am proposing, is directed at the simplest possible level of hereditary propagation in macromolecules which may arise after a stage of spontaneous chemical evolution, but well before self-replicative biological evolution, which progresses by natural selection. This intermediate level of organization I would call the stage of *molecular automata,* or to paraphrase Charles Babbage, the stage where polymers begin to "feed on their own tails." Evolution at this prereplicative stage would progress initially by direct feedback selection processes which correspond logically to what we call "training" in computers or individuals. I am proposing that hereditary transfer is accomplished in growing copolymers by conformation-dependent propagation rules. Well-trained aggregations of such growing copolymers may gradually gain more self-control and less direct interaction with the environment leading finally to what we call self-replication and the completely indirect interaction with the environment which we call natural selection. I hope to make these ideas clearer as I proceed.

I have introduced this discussion with some words which have many usages, often controversial. Dr. Dobzhansky has suggested that we hold another symposium to discuss the origin of life terminology which already has led us into some confusion. That is not our only trouble. In any case I shall at least try to define my own usages as applied in this discussion.

The terms *hereditary order, replication, selection,* and *evolution* all have associated with them a variety of more or less historical definitions which originated in the description of highly evolved living organisms. Therefore it is not surprising that these usages may be ambiguous or not directly applicable to the most primitive molecular organizations. However I believe that the concept of "hereditary process" is fundamental at all levels and for all types of organization. The common definition refers to the transmission of characteristics or properties from parent to heir. I shall extend this meaning slightly and by *hereditary process* I shall mean any process by which information is transmitted from one structure (the parent) to another structure (the heir) so as to result in a net increase in the physical order of the total system (comprising parent, heir, and environment). The three elements of this system must themselves be defined unambiguously in any given situation. The distinction is usually clear enough in higher organisms, but requires some clarification for more primitive processes such as may occur in bacteria and viruses. In the case of even more elementary interactions the definition must be made somewhat arbitrarily. By this definition, simple crystal growth, tactic polymerization, and cell division are examples of hereditary processes, the differences being in the definition of parent and heir, and in the amount of hereditary information transferred—the latter difference being perhaps as much as 10^{10} bits (e.g., Linschitz, 1953; Muller, 1958). This is an enormous quantitative difference, but it should not obscure the identity of the basic process.

The idea of *replication,* which is often assumed to be the key to the origin of life, has recently had a large number of interpretations (e.g., von Neumann, 1951; Allen, 1957; Pontecorvo, 1958; Anker, 1961; Crick, 1961; Muller, 1961; Wigner, 1961; Commoner, 1962). I shall consider replication as only a special case of hereditary process in which the parent and heir are (1) similar, and (2) separated. If in addition the parent and heir are (3) isolated from environmental sources of information I shall speak of *self-replication.* These three conditions are fulfilled, for the most part, in higher organisms, but they are by no means necessary for hereditary transmission, for acquisition of information, or for evolution.

The term *evolution* also has a wide range of meanings, but I use it in the general sense of the propagation and gradual increase of hereditary information in the course of time. From the definition of information

(Shannon, 1949), it follows that creation of any type of information requires some choice or *selection* of a particular state from a set of alternative states. The measure of information, H, is the base 2 logarithm of the number of equiprobable states, or more generally, $H = -\Sigma p_i \log_2 p_i$ where p_i is the probability of the ith alternative. This measure assumes that the act of selection is accomplished by an agent which is independent of p_i, and which is not itself a stochastic process (i.e., the act of selection occurs with probability one). As most of us recognize and as the discussions generated in this meeting demonstrate, the concept of selection is not simple. More often than not, an imprecise definition of the details of the process we denote by this term leads to some confusion. This is understandable since by definition the only event which can generate information is called a selective process. Consequently if the exact process of selection is not explicitly defined, there will be an ambiguous measure of the information generated.

The problem may be illustrated by a very simple molecular example: consider the growth under fixed conditions, of a linear copolymer made up of alternating subunits, A B A B A B A B . . . , which is completely determined except for the initiating subunit. One description of this growth is that there exists an obvious rule, assumed to rest on some natural but unspecified physical laws, which prevents the formation of alternative sequences. The initiating subunit is a random event. Therefore no information is involved in this pattern. It is the result of inherent restrictions in the laws of nature. On the other hand, an alternative description might assume that there is an equal probability of an A or B subunit colliding with the growing end of the polymer but that the last subunit *selects* one of the two alternatives. The process could be called a first-order Markov chain with the following transition probability matrix:

	A	B
A	0	1
B	1	0

where the left column is the last subunit and the top line is the added subunit. This implies that with this rule of selection, one of two sequences of N subunits (depending on the initiating subunit) will occur with probability one, which in the absence of this rule of selection would occur with a probability of 2^{-N}. Therefore, by the logarithmic measure of information, this selective process requires one bit of information per added subunit to produce this surviving order.

This may sound like an unnecessary use of the concepts of information and selection. However, consider the other extreme of complexity in living organisms. In estimating the amount of information accumulated by natural selection in adaptive evolution, Kimura (1961) uses the following reasoning: If the individuals which are to be eliminated by natural selection were to be kept reproducing at the same rate as the surviving individuals, their number would be $N = N_0 e^{Lt}$, where N_0 is the starting number, t is the number of generations, and L is the measure of decrease in population fitness (substitutional load). This implies that with natural selection, an event will occur with probability one, which in the absence of natural selection would occur with probability e^{-Lt}. Therefore, by the logarithmic measure of information, the process of natural selection requires $L/ln2$ bits of information per generation to produce the surviving order. The form of these arguments is similar, and both fit the definition of a hereditary process. In fact it would not be incorrect to use the same alternative description used for the copolymer growth, and represent the process of adaptive evolution as the result of natural, but unspecified, physical laws which prevent the survival of the alternative species. But to describe the process of evolution, or the origin of a replicating nucleic acid, or even the simplest order in a copolymer, as the result of inherent restrictions in the laws of nature is no more productive than attributing them to random events. The point I wish to make is that there is no essential difference between hereditary processes except in the *memory capacity* and the corresponding *memory delay*. In the copolymer where there are only two equiprobable initiating subunits, there is only a one-bit memory capacity, whereas in an organism replicating by direction of a deoxyribonucleic acid (DNA) molecule there may be a 10^{10} bit memory capacity. Therefore the copolymer growth process can only *transmit* one bit, and must do so at each subunit selection, while the DNA molecule can *accumulate* information through each successive generation. Both classes of molecule could evolve to the extent of their memory capacity, which in the case of an autonomous fixed-rule copolymer, is not a very exciting prospect.

However, I have chosen these extreme examples of *hereditary* and *selective* processes only to emphasize their generality and continuity from the simplest organization to the most complex. In my view, it is the intermediate levels of macromolecular structure in between these extremes which hold the greatest promise for future origin of life experiments. This is the level at which macromolecules have enough potential memory capacity and delay to behave in a logical sense as molecular computers (e.g., see von Neumann, 1951). Very little experimental work directed toward the origin of life problem has been done with this approach, but recent discoveries in the general field of polymer chemistry suggest a degree of complexity in the control of even the simplest polymers which is more than enough to justify a careful look at macromolecular order and its relation to self-organizing systems and evolution. This possibility has been largely overlooked in the past since most laboratory studies of polymerization were carried out under conditions in which the principle of equal reactivity of functional groups (Flory, 1953) is a good approximation. Even in more complex reactions the propagation rules are often adequately treated as simple c-order Markov chains, where c is a small integer. Physically this means that added monomers interact strongly only with chain-end monomers, penultimate, or pen-penultimate monomers (e.g., Birshteĭn *et al.*, 1961; Ham, 1962).

However it is unrealistic to expect a primeval earth environment, such as existed on a sterile seashore, to support only such idealized reactions. As a general rule, polymer kinetics, composition, and probably sequence are extremely sensitive to all types of local environmental conditions. Not only do the initiation and propagation reactions depend on type of solvent, temperature, concentration, and pressure, but also on particle size, particle size distribution, crystal structure, and chemical nature of catalysts and inhibitors. Since the discovery of simple catalysts which promote eutactic polymerization, by Ziegler (1952) and by Natta and his co-workers (1955), it is becoming increasingly clear that the truly random polymer is about as rare as the perfect crystal. Not only is some degree of sequence control from nearest neighbors a common occurrence, but specific steric control of the propagation step is exhibited by a wide variety of small molecules (e.g., see Gaylord and Mark, 1959).

But most important for the evolution of hereditary order must be the interactions of growing polymer chains with themselves. It is the nature of physical forces that the strongest effects result from short-range interactions, and that forces produce their effects (in small, nonrelativistic systems) with insignificant time delay. These general properties of physical interaction allow us to describe most events by differential equations, or statistically, by simple Bernoulli or Markov models. However, the flexible growing molecular chain is the simplest organization of matter which can, in a sense, escape these conditions. Of course short-range interactions are still the strongest, but in a folded, growing chain the strong, short-range interactions may not occur between nearest linear neighbors, and may consequently involve significant time delays.

In other words, the linear sequence and three-dimensional conformation at a given time are related only through a finite set of time-dependent, intermediate states. Such a propagation process is often called a hereditary system since we need to know some "history" in order to predict its future (e.g., see Feller, 1957). This is therefore the level of molecular structure where we should approach the organization and evolution of hereditary systems.

To illustrate this idea by a very simple example, consider a solution of two types of monomer, A and B, which can form linear copolymers according to some propagation rule which involves only the two nearest neighbors to the added monomer. The nature of the rule may or may not depend on a catalyst. One of the nearest neighbors may be the chain-end monomer to which the added monomer will form a strong bond, but the second nearest neighbor may depend on the conformation of the chain at the time of the propagation reaction. For example, if the chain is straight or not tightly folded the penultimate monomer will be the next nearest neighbor; or if the chain coils into a helix, the second nearest neighbor will be the monomer one turn of the helix back along the chain. For simplicity and ease of illustration I shall assume only two-dimensional conformations, and pick arbitrarily a very simple rule of addition which may be represented as a Markov chain with the transition matrix

	A	B
A	A	B
B	B	A

which means that if the two nearest-neighbor monomers are the same type, an A-type monomer is added, or if a different type, a B-type monomer is added. In describing an actual physical process, the entries in the matrix would be transition probabilities which would not be equal to one, would generally be asymmetric, and might change with the conformation and sequence of the chain. However, the present simplified rule will still illustrate the type of behavior we may expect from more complex systems.

The first stages are very simple. We may assume the equiprobability of the initiating dimers AA, AB, BA, and BB. From the rule we see that the AA dimer leads to a homopolymer made up of the A-type monomer, while the AB, BA, and BB dimers lead to the same periodic copolymer, $(ABB)_n$, except for the initiating sequence. As long as no sharp folding occurs, this pattern will depend only on the last two additions, and may therefore be called a second-order Markov chain. As the polymer concentration increases, it is reasonable to expect self-interactions. The possible varieties of folding are enormous for any long polymer, but again for simplicity of description, I shall limit the possible folds to plane zigzags or fakes, which occur in many polymer single crystals such as polyethylenes (e.g., see Lindemeyer, 1963). Suppose now, that the propagation reaction takes place while the polymer is folded in a tight zigzag so that the penultimate monomer is replaced as second nearest neighbor by a monomer further back along the chain. If there are M monomers in one zigzag fold, then the propagation reaction will become an $(M + 2)$-order Markov process, and even if the reaction probabilities remain the same, the sequence generated may have a much longer period which may be of the order of $2^{(M+2)}$ monomers. For example, if a fold occurs every three monomers, the second monomer in the fold has a nearest neighbor three monomers back, and the last monomer in the fold has a nearest neighbor five monomers back in the linear sequence. Thus, starting with the BB dimer we would propagate the following folded pattern:

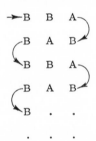

which gives a linear sequence $(BBABAB)_n$. The same period (with 3-unit phase shift) is initiated by the BA dimer, while the AB dimer generates the sequence $(ABB)_n$. Of course many other rules and conformations could be imagined which might correspond more closely to known polymer systems. For example, Szwarc (1958) has interpreted the kinetic studies of Idelson and Blout (1958) on the polymerization of amino acid N-carboxyanhydrides as suggesting a propagation dependent on a helical conformation of the growing polymer. He also proposed that tactic polymerization in general is enhanced by poor solvents which allow strong intrachain interaction. I have described in another paper (Pattee, 1961) how a helical structure could in principle propagate sequences which have statistical complexity as great as that observed in proteins, although no experimental verification of this particular example exists. In any case, I must emphasize that the exact nature of these examples is not relevant to the basic argument, which is that linear sequences in simple copolymers may be expected to depend in some way not only on nearest linear neighbors, but also, as the result of folding, on parts of the chain many subunits away. In other words, the *linear* sequence of a macromolecule may reflect in some detail the *three-dimensional* conformation of the macromolecule during its growth. The converse of this relationship need not be emphasized since in effect this is the end result of evolution. We know that the linear amino acid sequence in proteins largely determines the precise three-dimensional conformation necessary for enzyme activity. Furthermore, it is likely that the active site requires the close proximity in a three-dimensional configuration of several amino acid residues which may be widely separated in the linear polypeptide chain. However, this relationship in living systems is not symmetric. This fact is usually expressed as the Central Dogma (Crick, 1958), which states that the information follows a one-way path starting with linear base sequences of DNA and ending with the three-dimensional conformation of proteins. It is precisely this asymmetry which makes present living systems depend largely on *natural* selection and *self*-replication for the accumulation of hereditary information, for these two terms imply that neither in the selection process which generates information nor in the process which transmits this information is there any simple, direct information input or feedback *from* the environment *to* the linear sequences. In complex living organisms, only through blind errors of transmission followed by a kind of stochastic contest among all the heirs for many generations can a surviving linear sequence finally be said to have acquired some new information.

I do not wish to minimize in any way the large information-generating power and error-correcting variability of a random trial and statistical selection process. Indeed, as estimated by Kimura (1961), the amount of information accumulated by natural selection from the Cambrian period is of the order of 10^8 bits, which would appear more than adequate to account for the increase in phenotypic complexity in present organisms from the Cambrian jellyfish and crustaceans. But the fact remains that all of the evidence on which we base evolutionary theory comes from biochemically highly developed organisms which in spite of many structural and functional differences, depend on the same fundamental and very complex molecular control processes. There is simply no evidence that mutation and natural selection have ever produced significant changes in the basic pattern of nucleic acid synthesis transcription, amino acid coding, and protein synthesis which form what we call a self-replicating unit. Consequently, in considering the evolution of this basic pattern of self-replication we are not limited to the extremes of stochastic chemical evolution on the one hand, or to the mutation and natural selection hypothesis of higher organisms on the other. A whole spectrum of hereditary selective, and evolutionary processes lie in between.

Returning to the hypothetical illustration of how a simple propagation rule in a copolymer may lead to a conformation-dependent linear sequence, we may now consider the converse process of conformation *control* by linear sequence, which is a characteristic of proteins. In this hypothetical example, we have already postulated that certain neighboring monomers, if similar, favor association with A-type monomers, and if dissimilar, favor association with B-type monomers. Suppose then, that those physical constraints which favor such association in the growth process will also favor similar associations in a sequential folding process in a completed polymer. For example, the $(ABB)_n$ polymer if generated in a pattern with folds only at the last B monomer in the period would continue to generate the same linear sequence thus:

$$\longrightarrow A \quad B \quad B \quad A \quad B \quad B \quad A \quad B \quad B$$
$$B \quad B \quad A \quad B \quad B \quad A \quad B \quad B \quad A$$
$$A \quad B \quad B \quad . \quad . \quad . \quad \text{etc.}$$

A fold at any other monomer will produce different linear sequences, as may be directly verified. Consequently, we might expect the most probable conformation pattern in an $(ABB)_n$ polymer generated with this rule to fold only at the last B monomer of a period. Under the same propagation rule, other linear sequences would produce other folding patterns and, conversely, other folding patterns would generate other linear sequences. Again let me emphasize that the exact rules are for concrete illustration, but the only essential condition is that *some* type of rule exists so that there is sequence dependence on conformation, and conformation dependence on sequence. With this condition, it is not difficult to show, without attempting any rigor at this point, that such macromolecular systems are a representation of a Turing machine (Turing, 1936), where the internal states of the machine are defined by the propagation rule and the folding instructions, and the tape is represented by the linear sequence (e.g., Pattee, 1961; Stahl and Goheen,

1963). From a more physical point of view, we may consider the propagation rule as coupling the information in the linear order to the information in the folding order. In the absence of any such rule the linear order and folding order would be completely independent, and therefore the propagation rule reduces the total potential information capacity of the copolymer in return for the direct coupling with the source of information (i.e., the environment). Finally, anticipating the biological interpretation, we may consider the linear sequence as a hereditary memory, while the sequence-dependent folding represents the functional expression of this memory which couples with the environment. But unlike higher organisms, this coupling works in both directions. It is clear that, in polymers propagating under these restrictions, the information contained at any time in the linear sequence may be acquired from the environment just as well as from a parental sequence. Both types of information are equally heritable, and in fact they are indistinguishable without knowledge of the full history of a particular sequence. It is also possible that sequences change by random mutations either during growth or after completion. In both cases, some mutations can produce new sequences which will be equally heritable. Insofar as a selective process produces extinction of certain sequences without at the same time directly altering their conformation or sequence, such a process may be called *natural* selection.

To review the argument briefly, I am proposing that known properties of simple tactic polymer growth and conformation suggest an elementary type of hereditary process in which information may be both propagated in linear sequences and converted into structure which in turn may exhibit specific control of monomer addition. The essential requirement for this behavior is some *conditional rule of propagation* which in effect constrains the possible linear sequence to some functional dependence on the three-dimensional structure of the growing polymer. In such a primitive type of polymer growth, the influence of the local environment is capable of producing heritable changes in the linear sequence. In other words, the Central Dogma of higher organisms does not apply, and information may flow from the local environment into the hereditary memory as well as the other way. Primitive evolution, that is, the earliest gradual increases in hereditary information, occurs in this case in the same way as information or learning may be said to increase in computing machines or in living individuals: that is, by direct feedback rather than by natural selection. The analogy of the learning process to higher evolution has often been noticed (e.g., Pringle, 1951; Ashby, 1952; Turing, 1956), but I am proposing that primitive hereditary molecular evolution may have actually started with a kind of training by direct, selective feedback interaction with the local environment, and developed only gradually by a range of less and less direct and increasingly *delayed* selective processes to the final stage of completely indirect natural selection. From this point of view, it is not productive to ask when hereditary propagation of order became replication or self-replication, or when direct feedback interactions with the environment became natural selection. The difference is only in degree, and both evolved continuously. The only useful activity is to study the detailed behavior of such systems, both experimentally and theoretically, to see what can be predicted and what can be explained by this general approach.

In support of this hypothesis for the origin of life, I shall here give only brief arguments, although a more detailed analysis is certainly necessary. At this point, however, it is my only intention to make the theory plausible enough, in comparison with other theories, to generate some enthusiasm for more thought and a few experiments along the lines I suggest, or hopefully, along better lines.

In the first place, this hypothesis does not require any crucial event, unless it is the occurrence of copolymers with conformation influence on linear sequence. Although this may be extremely probable, one may also take the position that replication of nucleic acids has already been demonstrated, and that the gradual evolution of a polymerase-type catalyst is all that is necessary. However, as Commoner (1962) and others have repeatedly pointed out, this is not *self*-replication with the autonomous persistence necessary to assure evolution by natural selection. The cell remains the smallest known unit of *self*-replication. In spite of the conceptual simplicity of template copying, no one has formulated a threshold model for a nucleic acid–protein system capable of persistent replication and natural selection which does not draw heavily on fortuitous events. Furthermore, all reasonably careful considerations about the essential logical and physical details of this process, such as that of von Neumann (1951) and Wigner (1961) do not tend to stimulate confidence in spontaneity as an explanation for the origin of self-replication.

Secondly, as we know from personal experience, and as others have derived from the design of learning machines (e.g., Newell *et al.*, 1960), in the initial stages of any learning process the stimulus-response interaction with the environment is reasonably quick and direct. Much of our early training, and most of the training in lower animals may be considered as rote learning, where success or failure is simple and direct.

After we have gradually accumulated some good heuristic rules or patterns based on more or less direct interaction with the environment, the immense number of possible states of our brains have been conditionally structured enough to allow what we call more "creative" thought. Our thinking process now becomes increasingly similar to blind search and selective survival (Hadamard, 1945; Campbell, 1960), although there is much to be learned about this type of selection too. This general learning strategy has itself been selected as the most efficient process for training organizations from men to machines, and it is just as reasonable at the primitive molecular computer level. It has often been pointed out (e.g., Pattee, 1961) that a blind or random search and selection process for finding even the simplest protein sequence, assuming equiprobability of isomeric sequences, is physically unreasonable. We have learned that premature random searching, without basic training, is not likely to be creative or productive in the brain, or in a chess-playing machine program; and no reason has been proposed why random search for polymer sequences should give such remarkable consequences. First there must be a gradual evolution of patterned structure, or as in our extremely simple copolymer example, propagation rules which amount to conditional constraints on the otherwise hopelessly immense number of possible unrelated configurations. If the concepts of self-organizing systems (e.g., von Foerster, 1960; Ashby, 1962) have any degree of general validity, then we should expect random search and natural selection from self-reproducing units to be the latest, and probably the last, pattern of all hereditary evolution processes.

Finally, from a simple physical point of view, can we expect the most primitive molecular aggregations, which undergo reactions in a heterogeneous and variable local environment, to behave as independently as a nucleic acid in the isolated, buffered environment of a cell? Even if polynucleotides and polypeptides were the first hereditary macromolecules, both the sequence behavior and the selective processes affecting them on the primitive earth would have been quite different from their present behavior within the living cell.

These arguments should convince no one that molecular automata exist or that they were the ancestors of present living systems. But perhaps they suggest a new approach and some new experiments. The first reasonable place to look for heritable order is in the sequence of synthetic polymers, and in their propagation rules and conformation. Along these lines Fox and Harada (1960) have shown that the thermal copolymers of amino acids are not random, as judged by total composition and N-terminal composition. The composition ratios were also markedly different from the reaction mixtures. Simha and Zimmerman (1962) have also reported evidence of penultimate effects on the sequence of natural and synthetic polynucleotides. Since the phenomenon of tactic polymerization is not well understood even in the simplest polymers, there remains much fundamental work to be done before the question of the possibility of molecular computation can be resolved. Although a great effort is being made to improve the properties of plastics by discovering techniques for programmed tacticities, there is virtually no polymer chemistry research aimed at the origin of life problem.

A second place to look for simple hereditary order may be in proteins, although current thinking may discourage this possibility. The known sequences of amino acids in proteins show a statistical order in di- and tripeptide sequences Williams *et al.*, 1961) and in c-order Markov chains of certain types (Pattee and Thiebaux, 1964) which is indistinguishable from random sequences drawn from a similar nonuniform population of amino acids. The only proper conclusion from this evidence is not that randomness has survival value, but that as yet we are totally ignorant of the significance of protein sequences. If these sequences were translated back into base sequences from where they presumably originated, there is still no way to distinguish by what types of selective process this order was generated. It is quite reasonable that many changes in base sequence have no selective advantages (Freese, 1962), and at the same time it is also likely that some base sequences are generated by very elementary selective rules, as for example, the light fraction of crab testes DNA which is largely an alternating AT polymer (Sueoka, 1961). The appearance of this sequence in the enzymatic synthesis of DNA without any primer DNA (Schachman *et al.*, 1960) is strong evidence that this order is not determined by natural selection. Until much more is known of the details of nucleic acid and protein sequence relationships, the possibility of more primitive types of hereditary order in these molecules cannot be ruled out. It is worth noting in this respect that an experienced statistician, given only a sequence of a few hundred monomers generated by the very simple propagation rule of the earlier example, and generated in folds of only ten monomers, would be extremely lucky to find evidence that this was not a random sequence.

A third type of experiment is suggested by the hypothesis that the simplest levels of macromolecular order have hereditary properties, and acquire heritable information by direct interaction from the environment. Since this is a comparatively mechanistic model compared to any proposal which depends on a fortuitous threshold event, such as replication, the details of the environment assume much greater importance.

This is based on good evidence that the initiation, propagation, and conformation of even the simplest polymers may be strongly and specifically influenced by the detailed nature of the local environment. If the earliest hereditary order was of this nature, then the complexity of the environment is essential for generating complex behavior in macromolecules. We all have a feeling that no deterministic system can evolve complexity unless it starts at a certain minimum level of complexity itself. Szent-Györgyi (1948) expressed this feeling by his comment that you will find it difficult to build any mechanism out of marbles. Von Neumann (1951) felt that this "concept of complexity" had the significance of a general principle which as yet no one has been able to formulate clearly. In any case, we should not allow fear of overcomplexity to prevent us from doing careful experiments which simulate realistically the complexity of primitive Earth environments. For all the inevitable inaccuracies in detail, a sterile simulated seashore, with waves, tides, sand, rain, and intermittent sunlight, is a more accurate primitive earth environment than the well-defined but oversimplified reactions studied so far. Of course, any general attempt at chemical analysis in such a system is impossible, but on the other hand, perhaps nothing really significant can be expected to occur in the way of macromolecular order unless it is a reflection of the complexity of the environment from which it arose. The discovery in such an experiment of any type of macromolecular homogeneity, either in ultrastructure which might be seen by high resolution electron microscopy or by chemical characterization of any kind would be one obvious starting point for closer scrutiny.

The simple hereditary hypothesis which I am proposing places the origin of life problem in what is presently a physical no-man's land between macroscopic mechanical systems where complete specification of the constraints and dynamic variables is possible, and statistical systems where incomplete specification of states is an essential postulate. However, statistical models have very limited value when hereditary memories propagate and enhance Laplace's strange effects which would otherwise destroy each other by averaging out. Perhaps some of the most profitable lines of theory and experiment will be suggested by analogies to automata and computers which possess the highest order of logical and structural complexity which man has produced artificially, although at present there is still a barrier in language and technique between chemical and automata studies. It was also Laplace who recognized the fault of our minds in classifying complex systems as either well-ordered and deterministic, if we understand them, or chaotic and random, if we do not. Even though we know that present living systems possess an irreducible molecular complexity where the smallest events may not be insignificant, perhaps where we lose sight of the continuity between what we call living biological organizations and nonliving chemical reactions may simply be the Laplacian illusion of classifying some chemical effects as chance events when in fact we are only observing an evolving molecular automaton which we do not yet understand.

Revised manuscript received February 3, 1964.

REFERENCES

Allen, G. (1957). *Am. Naturalist* **91**, 65.

Anker, H. S. (1961). *Perspect. Biol. Med.* **5**, 86.

Ashby, W. R. (1952). "Design for a Brain." Wiley, New York.

Ashby, W. R. (1962). *In* "Principles of Self-Organization" (H. von Foerster and G. W. Zopf, Jr., eds.), p. 255. Pergamon Press, New York.

Bernal, J. D. (1959). *In* "The Origin of Life on Earth" (F. Clark and R. L. M. Synge, eds.), p. 38. Pergamon Press, New York.

Birshteïn, T. M., Gottlib, Y. Y., and Ptitsyn, O. B. (1961). *J. Polymer Sci.* **52**, 77.

Blum, H. F. (1961). *Am. Scientist* **49**, 474.

Bridgman, P. W. (1956). *Science* **123**, 16.

Calvin, M. (1956). *Am. Scientist* **44**, 248.

Campbell, D. T. (1960). *In* "Self-Organizing Systems" (M. C. Yovits and S. Cameron, eds.), p. 205. Pergamon Press, New York.

Commoner, B. (1962). *In* "Horizons in Biochemistry" (M. Kasha and B. Pullman, eds.), p. 319. Academic Press, New York.

Crick, F. H. C. (1958). *Symp. Soc. Exptl. Biol.* (Great Britain) **12**, 138.

Crick, F. H. C. (1961). *In* "Growth in Living Systems" (M. X. Zarrow, ed.), p. 3. Basic Books, New York.

Feller, W. (1957). "An Introduction to Probability Theory and Its Application," p. 369. Wiley, New York.

Flory, P. J. (1953). "Principles of Polymer Chemistry," p. 102. Cornell Univ. Press, Ithaca, New York.

Fox, S. W., and Harada, K. (1960). *J. Am. Chem. Soc.* **82**, 3745.

Freese, E. (1962). *J. Theoret. Biol.* **3**, 82.

Gaylord, N. G., and Mark, H. F. (1959). "Linear and Stereoregular Addition Polymers: Polymerization with Controlled Propagation." Wiley (Interscience), New York.

Hadamard, J. (1945). "The Psychology of Invention in the Mathematical Field." Princeton Univ. Press, Princeton, New Jersey.

Ham, G. (1962). *J. Polymer Sci.* **61**, 9.

Idelson, M., and Blout, E. R. (1958). *J. Am. Chem. Soc.* **80**, 2387.

Kimura, M. (1961). *Genetical Research* **2**, 127.

Laplace, P. S. (1820). "Théorie analytique des probabilities" 6th ed. (translated by F. W. Truescott and F. L. Emory), 6th ed. Reprinted (1951) by Dover, New York.

Lindemeyer, P. H. (1963). *J. Polymer Sci.* Pt. C, **1**, 5.

Linschitz, H. (1953). *In* "Information Theory in Biology" (H. Quastler, ed.), p. 251. Univ. of Illinois Press, Urbana, Illinois.

Miller, S. L., and Urey, H. C. (1959). *Science* **130**, 245.
Muller, H. J. (1958). *Bull. Am. Math. Soc.* **64**, 137.
Muller, H. J. (1961). *Perspect. Biol. Med.* **5**, 1.
Natta, G., Pino, P., Corradini, P., Danusso, F., Mantica, E., Mazzanti, G., and Moraglio, G. (1955). *J. Am. Chem. Soc.* **77**, 1708.
Newell, A., Shaw, J. C. and Simon, H. A. (1960). *In* "Self Organizing Systems" M. C. Yovits and S. Cameron, eds.), p. 153. Pergamon Press, New York.
Oparin, A. (1938). "The Origin of Life." Macmillan, New York.
Pattee, H. (1961). *Biophys. J.* **1**, 683.
Pattee, H., and Thiebaux, H. J. (1964). *8th Ann. Meeting, Biophys. Soc. Chicago.*
Pontecorvo, G. (1958). *Symp. Soc. Exptl. Biol.* **12**, 38.
Pringle, J. W. S. (1951). *Behavior* **3**, 174.
Rich, A. (1962). *In* "Horizons in Biochemistry" (M. Kasha and B. Pullman, eds.), p. 103, Academic Press, New York.
Schachman, H. K., Adler, J., Radding, C. M., Lehman, J. R., and Kornberg, A. (1960). *J. Biol. Chem.* **235**, 3242.
Shannon, C. (1949). "The Mathematical Theory of Communication" C. E. Shannon and W. Weaver, eds.), p. 19. Univ. of Illinois Press, Urbana, Illinois.
Simha, R., and Zimmerman, J. M. (1962). *J. Theoret. Biol.* **2**, 87.
Simon, H. A. (1962). *Proc. Am. Phil. Soc.* **106**, 467.
Stahl, W. R., and Goheen, H. E. (1963). *J. Theoret. Biol.* **5**, 266.
Sueoka, N. (1961). *J. Mol. Biol.* **3**, 31.
Szent-Györgyi, A. (1948). "Nature of Life. A study on Muscle." Academic Press, New York.
Szwarc, M. (1958). *Chem. and Ind.* p. 1589.
Turing, A. M. (1936). *Proc. Lond. Math. Soc.* **2-42**, 230.
Turing, A. M. (1956). *In* "The World of Mathematics" (J. R. Newman, ed.), Vol. IV, p. 2099. Simon and Shuster, New York.
von Foerster, H. (1960). *In* "Self-Organizing Systems" (M. C. Yovits and S. Cameron, eds.), p. 31. Pergamon Press, New York.
von Neumann, J. (1951). *In* "Cerebral Mechanisms in Behavior" (L. E. Jeffress, ed.), p. 1. Wiley, New York.
Watson, J. D., and Crick, F. H. C. (1953). *Nature* **171**, 964.
Wigner, E. P. (1961). *In* "The Logic of Personal Knowledge," p. 231. Routledge and Kegan Paul, London.
Williams, J., Clegg, J. B., and Mutch, M. O. (1961). *J. Mol. Biol.* **3**, 532.
Ziegler, K. (1952). *Angew. Chem.* **64**, 323.

DISCUSSION

DR. MORA: My remarks after Dr Schramm's presentation may apply here too. I cannot see the gradual evolution of selection of molecules which have persistent copy-forming ability (reproducibility) unless one postulates to start with a high enough degree of copy-forming ability to persistently overcompensate the randomization tendencies; and I cannot see how this type of molecular property can be accounted for by our current ideas about physics and chemistry.

Dr. Pattee brings forth in his model a certain influence that neighboring groups might have on the sequence in copolymerization and proposes that a linear sequence order might be the result. This is indeed a feasible proposition, based on polymer principles. But, and I think Dr. Pattee also points this out, this means only that you have a tactic polymer crystal, and it does not mean that the order is heritable, or that the system has self-reproducibility or evolutionary ability.

DR. PATTEE: Dr. Mora is concerned with the problem of the origin of persistent self-replication from the chaos. This is certainly the central question. The level of complexity of the mutable, self-replicating unit evolving by natural selection which concerns Dr. Mora is still a very long way off in the terms of my discussion. Before anyone can say how such complex organisms function, we must know the basic operations of macromolecules. I have proposed that the observed behavior of simple polymers in forming tactic sequences and intricately folded crystals could provide a sufficiently rich interplay of sequence, structure, and function to account for a gradual evolution by hereditary processes, culminating in self-replicating systems. Just as all computers, no matter how complex, require certain minimal basic structures and functions to serve as general problem-solving devices, so do living systems require some minimal set of molecular operations to assure their propagation. I have suggested that these basic operations are logically quite similar in both cases, although their physical representation is different. To substantiate this idea would require experimental evidence of conformation-dependent sequence control in simple copolymers. This does not appear physically improbable, and if it occurs we have the necessary basic operations for a molecular automaton which in a very primitive way could learn, remember, and evolve. I believe it will be experimentally more productive to think of these questions in terms of polymer chemistry than of primitive biology.

DR. ORÓ: Although we use the terms chaos, absolute randomness, and maximum entropy as if these conditions existed, they actually do not exist. Perhaps the universe is moving toward such conditions, but at present they are not real. As someone has said, chaos is misunderstood order. By this what is meant is that if we make an effort to study in more detail a system which we may have labeled chaotic or random we will eventually find in it a certain degree of order. I want to give a practical illustration of this statement which I think is quite relevant to the points of Dr. Pattee's lecture and to the experimental observations of Professor Schramm. Professor Schramm has synthesized branched polynucleotides which contain 3',5'- and 2',5'-phosphate diester bonds.

Our first reaction would be to call these polynucleotides random poly-mers. However, this would be a wrong conclusion. For, let's suppose that we have a branched polyuridylic acid (poly-U) and that in a section of the molecule we have, let's say, 30 Us linked by 3′,5′-phos-phate diester bonds. Although small, this represents a certain degree of order in the molecule and it is quite conceivable that this small nonrandom section, within the so-called random poly-U, could act as a template for the formation of a polyphenylalanine containing ten phenylalanine residues. If this was the case, the synthesis of a poly-phenylalanine molecule containing only ten amino acid residues would result in a significant increase (about tenfold) of order over that pre-existing in the free amino acid molecules. In summary, the so-called random polymer has some degree of order, and in addition this order is, in principle, transmittable to less ordered molecules.

DR. SZUTKA: Dr. Pattee in his discussion mentioned the crystals as nonrandom products of certain processes. I disagree because there are no such formations as perfect crystals. A crystal always contains im-perfections. For such a crystal, an equation can be derived that will give the number of imperfections per unit of volume. However, the position of imperfections cannot be located mathematically.

I might just close by saying that generally speaking we do not ob-serve a nonrandom distribution. It is always random in whatever process you are thinking of.

DR. PATTEE: I began by using probability notations, but changed over to using zeros and ones just for illustration. I didn't mean to imply that anything had a probability of either zero or one. I might make another point, since you raised the problem of crystals. Of course, there are mutations in crystals just as in anything else. There is also in normal crystallization the process known as polytypism, which is a very remark-able long-range periodic order that may be as many as twenty to thirty atomic lattices, and which is very regular, even in a simple diatomic crystal type.

This indicates the propagation of long-range order even in very simple systems like that. I don't mean to imply that dislocations are not random but only that dislocations can still produce very long-range regularity.

DR. ORÓ: If I understood you right, you said that mutations imply loss of information. Did you mean it in the strictly mathematical sense or in the biological sense?

DR. PATTEE: I was talking about accumulation of organic information by mutation, and I just made the point that by the definition of informa-tion that the mutation, at the moment of mutation, represents a loss of information, but that the selective process in populations of replicating systems is where the information is gained, and here again I refer you to the paper of Kimura (1961) which expresses this the way I meant it.

DR. ORÓ: Could you accept as an additional definition of mutation, a change or modification of information? In order to express biological realism, a mutation can also be considered as the change of a triplet into another one, and so actually a mutation in some cases may mean a modification of the information rather than a loss.

DR. PATTEE: I accept your definition. I understand what you mean. This has been discussed previously, but because I want to use here the standard definition of information, I cannot accept noise-producing events themselves as information.

CODING TRIPLETS IN THE EVOLUTION OF HEMOGLOBIN AND CYTOCHROMES C GENES

T. H. JUKES

Space Sciences Laboratory, University of California, Berkeley, California

The subject of this talk differs from the main theme of the meeting in that it deals with the evolution of living organisms rather than with prebiological systems. This disparity may be excused, since information regarding the chemistry of early forms of life is needed in speculating on the nature of prebiological systems.

The composition of proteins is dependent upon information supplied by the genes. The sequence of bases in the genetic molecule of deoxyribonucleic acid (DNA) supplies this information. This sequence is subject to mutational changes which take place during evolution and, indeed, are a part of the evolutionary process. Such changes affect the composition of proteins through the translation of the DNA base sequences into the amino acid code.

Current knowledge of the amino acid code depends almost entirely on biochemical experiments with the contents of bacterial cells. These experiments are designed to produce the enzymatic synthesis of polypeptides in systems containing amino acids, transfer ribonucleic acid (sRNA), ribosomes, and the various cofactors and crude enzymes necessary to bring about the formation of peptides in ordered sequences. Synthetic polyribonucleotides are used as "templates," following the discovery by Nirenberg and Matthaei (1961) that polyuridylic acid led to the production of polyphenylalanine in a cell-free system prepared from *Escherichia coli*. This discovery was followed by experiments in which synthetic polyribonucleotides containing various proportions of the bases A, C, G, U, and H (adenine, cytosine, guanine, uracil, and hypoxanthine) were used as templates or "artificial messengers" in the biological synthesis of polypeptides (Lengyel *et al.*, 1961; Matthaei *et al.*, 1962; Speyer *et al.*, 1962; Wahba *et al.*, 1963a,b; Jones and Nirenberg, 1962). The results have been summarized elsewhere (Jukes, 1963a), and the

408 T. H. JUKES

coding triplets that have been suggested as a result of the studies are listed in Table I. It is generally thought that groups of 3 consecutive bases, "triplets," in the synthetic polyribonucleotides or in natural messenger RNA are each responsible for coding a single amino acid. The experiments did not indicate the sequence of bases in each triplet except possibly for AUU (tyrosine) and GUU (cysteine). However, a

TABLE I
AMINO ACID CODE TRIPLETS[a]

Amino acid	Messenger RNA code triplets	Shared doublets
Ala	CAG, CCG, CUG	C*G
Arg	GAA, GCC, GUC	G*C
AsN	CAA, CUA, UAA	*AA, C*A
Asp	GCA, GUA	G*A
Cys	GUU	. . .
Glu	AAG, AUG	A*G
GlN	AAC, UAC, GGA	*AC
Gly	GAG, GCG, GUG	G*G
His	ACC, AUC	A*C
Ilu	AAU, CAU, UUA	*AU
Leu	UAU, UGU, UUC, CCU	. . .
Lys	AAA, AUA	A*A
Met	UGA	. . .
Phe	UCU, UUU	U*U
Pro	CAC, CCC, CUC	C*C
Ser	ACG, CUU, UCC	. . .
Thr	ACA, CCA, UCA, CGC	*CA
Try	UGG	. . .
Tyr	ACU, AUU	A*U
Val	UUG	. . .

[a] From Wahba and co-workers (1963b) with subsequent additions. These sequences must all be read from right to left if the code for valine is GUU (Leder and Nirenberg, 1964).

proposal for the sequences in the other triplets was made, depending on the findings with certain mutations in which single amino acids were found to be changed in proteins. Some of these changes are found in nature and others were brought about by chemical mutagens or by ultraviolet light. They are summarized in Table II, which includes results from a number of investigations from various laboratories (Hunt and Ingram, 1959; Wittmann, 1961, 1963; Wittmann and Wittmann-Liebold, 1963; Tsugita and Fraenkel-Conrat, 1962; Yanofsky, 1962, 1963; Yanofsky et al., 1964; Pierre et al., 1963; Smith, 1964; Gottlieb et al., 1964; Jones *et al.*, 1964; Kalan *et al.*, 1964) that have been reviewed elsewhere (Jukes, 1963a). Some of the changes were the result of treatment of tobacco mosaic virus (TMV) with nitrous acid. This deaminates the TMV RNA so that cytosine forms uracil, and adenine forms hypoxanthine, which behaves like guanine in a coding triplet. These changes in a number of

TABLE II

SINGLE AMINO ACID CHANGES IN MUTATIONS COMPARED WITH
SINGLE BASE CHANGES IN MESSENGER RNA IN TERMS
OF PROPOSED CODING TRIPLETS

Protein[a]	Amino acid change	Corresponding base change	Protein	Amino acid change	Corresponding base change
Hb, TMV[b]	Lys/asN	A/C, A/U	TMV	Thr/ser	A/G, A/C
Hb	Lys/asp	A/G	TMV	Thr/met	C/G
Hb	Lys/glu	A/G	TMV, TS	Thr/ilu	C/U, C/A
TMV	AsN/ser	A/U	TMV	Pro/leu	C/U
TMV[b]	AsN/arg	C/G	TMV	Pro/ser	C/U
TMV[b], Hb	AsN/asp	C/G	L, AP	Ala/val	C/U
Hb	His/tyr	C/U	TMV, TS	Ser/leu	C/U
Hb	His/arg	A/G	TMV	Ser/phe	C/U
L	His/glN	C/A, U/A	TMV	Asp/ala	(G*A/C*G)
Hb	GlN/arg	G/A	TMV, Hb, L, TS	Asp/gly	A/G
TS	Glu/ala	A/C	TS	Gly/val	G/U
Hb	Glu/glN	C/G	TS	Gly/cys	G/U
Hb, TMV, TS	Glu/gly	A/G	TMV, TS	Arg/gly	C/G, A/G
Hb, TS, TMV	Glu/val	A/U	TS	Arg/ser	C/G
TS	Tyr/cys	A/G	TS	Arg/leu	G/U
TMV	Tyr/phe	A/U	TS	Arg/thr	?
Cyt c	Met/leu	A/U	TMV	Ilu/val	A/G
TMV	Leu/phe	C/U	TMV	Ilu/met	U/G

[a] Hb = hemoglobin, TMV = tobacco mosaic virus protein, TS = tryptophan synthetase, L = β-lactoglobulin, bovine, AP = alkaline phosphatase, Cyt c = cytochrome c.
[b] Spontaneous changes in TMV.

instances produce a measurable substitution in a single amino acid locus in the TMV coat protein, such as proline to leucine, interpretable as a change of C to U in a coding triplet.

The biological synthesis of polypeptides is believed to take place in polysomes, groups of ribosomes that are held together by single strands of messenger RNA, or synthetic polyribonucleotides in the case of the "artificial" cell-free systems. If the synthetic polyribonucleotides become cross-linked, they lose the single-stranded character that is presumed to be necessary in the formation of polysomes and in the synthesis of polypeptides. Since polyribonucleotides containing G may cross-link readily, such molecules are difficult to use successfully in experiments with cell-free systems that synthesize proteins. This circumstance is thought to be responsible for the difficulties encountered with poly-ribonucleotides high in G, thus accounting for the lack of results with the 16 unassigned triplets containing G. However, the 48 triplets with assigned functions include four codes for each of 6 amino acids, three for each of 8 amino acids, two for each of 6 amino acids, and one apiece for each of the remaining 4 amino acids. This is sufficient information to account for 34 of the 36 known single-amino acid mutational changes, including all mutations in the hemoglobins, on the basis of single base changes in triplet codes (Table II). Furthermore, the knowledge of the composition of 48 triplets enables considerable exploration to be made of the evolutionary changes in protein strands as related to mutational changes in DNA. Such an exploration is the subject of this article. The sequences shown in the triplets in Table I are based for the most part on speculation. If it is eventually necessary to rearrange many of the sequences, this will not affect the qualitative nature of the discussion presented in this article, although some quantitative adjustments of the proposed base changes may be necessary. For example, we have postu-lated that the codes for glutamic acid are ATG and AAG (written in terms of DNA bases) and for aspartic acid are GTA and GCA. A change from glutamic acid to aspartic acid therefore represents a code change in at least 2 bases. If it is eventually shown that there are other codes, or different sequences, for glutamic acid and aspartic acid, this change might be reduced to a single-base change. Such adjustments for erron-eous sequences or for currently unassigned codes would alter some of the calculations made below, but not to a great extent. Furthermore, it seems evident from statistical considerations that a number of the amino acid changes occurring in evolution should be the result of 2-base and even 3-base changes in the same coding triplet if it is assumed that mutational events take place at random in the genetic material. This matter will be examined below. Table III lists the possible amino acid changes that can occur as a result of single-base changes in the coding triplets in Table I.

The assumption is made that evolution is largely due to a series of mutational events in which DNA molecules are changed in length or in which the bases in DNA molecules are changed by substitutions. In a substitution any of one of the 4 bases may become replaced by another and a substitution may take place in either strand. The newcomer is paired by its complementary base during the next mitotic event, and thereafter the pair of intruders is faithfully copied in succeeding cell divisions until, perhaps many generations later, a second substitution or "hit" occurs in the same locus and produces a second change. These changes when occurring in structural genes will produce corresponding and related alterations in the amino acid sequences of proteins. Under

TABLE III

AMINO ACID INTERCHANGES THAT CAN OCCUR AS THE RESULT OF
SINGLE-BASE CHANGES IN THE CODING TRIPLETS POSTULATED IN
TABLE I

Amino acid	Possible interchanges[a]
Ala	AsN, *glu*, *gly*, ilu, leu, pro, ser, thr, *val*
Arg	*AsN*, asp, cys, *glN*, *gly*, *his*, *leu*, *lys*, pro, *ser*
AsN	*Asp*, glN, ilu, leu, *lys*, met, pro, *ser*, thr
Asp	GlN *gly*, ilu, *lys*, thr,
Cys	*Gly*, phe, ser, *tyr*
GlN	*Glu*, *his*, ilu, leu, lys, met, pro
Glu	*Gly*, his, ilu, *lys*, ser, tyr, *val*
Gly	Ser, *val*
His	Lys, pro, ser, thr, *tyr*
Ilu	*leu*, lys, *met*, phe, pro, ser, *thr*, tyr, *val*
Leu	*Met*, *phe*, *pro*, ser, thr, try, val
Lys	Thr, tyr
Met	Thr, try
Phe	*Ser*, thr, *tyr*, val
Pro	*Ser*, thr
Ser	*Thr*, tyr

[a] The italicized examples have been reported to occur in the mutations listed in Table II.

present conditions it is not possible to decipher genes by measuring their base sequences, but the order of amino acids in proteins may be determined, and when two proteins have evolved independently from a common ancestor, the differences in their amino acid sequences reflect the changes that have taken place in the base composition of the genes involved. It is instructive to examine from this standpoint the primary structures of a group of homologous proteins. Information of this type is available for the hemoglobins and myoglobin (Jukes, 1963b; Schroeder, 1963; Ingram, 1963). The single-amino acid mutations that have been described for the hemoglobins all correspond to single-base changes in the triplets in Table I; these changes are summarized in Table IV. The hemoglobins are a group of proteins that occur in the red blood cells of animals. The vertebrate hemoglobins, except for those occurring in a few primitive animals, the cyclostomes, consist of a tetrameric molecule containing four peptide chains (Ingram, 1963). Normal adult human hemoglobin contains two α chains and two β chains and is abbreviated as $\alpha_2^A \beta_2^A$; the A refers to its designation as hemoglobin A.

TABLE IV

MUTATIONAL CHANGES IN AMINO ACIDS IN HUMAN α- AND β-HEMOGLOBINS[a]

Location	Amino acid change	Postulated change in coding triplets
α-16	lys/asp	AUA/GUA
α-30, β-121	glu/glN	AAG/AAC
α-54	glN/arg	GGA/GAA
α-22, α-57	gly/asp	G*G/G*A (a)[b]
α-58, α-87, β-63	his/tyr	A*C/A*U (a)
α-68	asN/lys	C*A/A*A (b)[b]
α-116, β-6, β-7, β-26, β-121	glu/lys	A*G/A*A (b)
β-6	glu/val	AUG/UUG
β-7	glu/gly	A*G/G*G (b)
β-63	his/arg	A*C/G*C (a)
β-67	val/glu	UUG/AUG
β-79	asp/asN	GUA/CUA

[a] See Hunt and Ingram (1959), Ingram (1963), Jukes (1963a), Schroeder (1963), Pierre et al. (1963), Gottlieb et al. (1964), and Jones et al. (1964).
[b] (a)* = A or C; (b)* = A or U.

Fetal (F) hemoglobin is written as $\alpha_2^A \gamma_2^F$ because it contains two γ chains which are replaced in the adult by β chains. A second type of adult human hemoglobin (A$_2$) that occurs in smaller amounts is written as $\alpha_2^A \delta_2^{A_2}$; as the abbreviation implies, it contains 2 δ chains instead of the 2 β chains in hemoglobin A. The genes that are responsible for the production of the various peptides may be depicted as follows in the diploid cell (after Ingram, 1963).

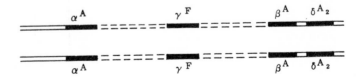

The paired genes depicted in this diagram are each presumed to be portions of a double-stranded molecule of DNA, each gene containing about 440 pairs of bases. One of the strands of the gene can give rise by a reaction catalyzed by RNA polymerase to a complementary single strand of messenger RNA, which in turn codes the biological synthesis of a polypeptide unit that becomes part of a molecule of hemoglobin.

The γ genes function during fetal life and the β genes are apparently "turned off" during this period. In the first 6 months of life, this situation is reversed; the γ peptides gradually disappear and their place is taken by β chains. This is thought to be due to a change in the rate at which the respective messenger RNA molecules are produced.

An individual can carry a heterozygous abnormality for one of the peptide chains, such as β^S (sickle cell trait) replacing one of the β^A chains, in which case this diagram would be written as:

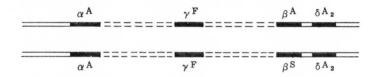

This individual would produce two types of hemoglobin molecules: $\alpha_2^A \beta_2^A$ and $\alpha_2^A \beta_2^S$. The presence of β^S chains gives rise to sickle cell anemia.

Another closely related protein, myoglobin, occurs in muscle. Its molecule is a single peptide chain, and its composition and genetic significance will be considered later.

The chemistry of the hemoglobins has been extensively studied and much information is available regarding their amino acid composition and sequence. The findings have led to theories concerning the evolution of the hemoglobin genes, and this question has been discussed at length by Zuckerkandl and Pauling (1962), by Ingram (1963), and others.

The following scheme follows largely the outline presented by Ingram. An original myoglobin-like molecule was the biochemical ancestor of present-day myoglobin and the hemoglobins. It consisted of a single polypeptide chain that carried a single heme group, thus resembling present-day myoglobin. The starting point of the period under discussion was when the gene for this molecule (which we shall term "P_1") underwent duplication and translocation to form two genes, one of which, the α-chain gene, has evolved "in such a way that its product, the α-chain, had the properties of dimerization in solution to form α_2

molecules" (Ingram, 1963). The next postulation is that genes of the α chain duplicated again to form the primitive γ gene (P₂), thus leading to the formation of tetramers (α₂γ₂); later the γ gene duplicated to form the primitive β gene (P₃), which more recently duplicated to form the primitive δ gene (P₄) so that the series of four hemoglobin genes shown in Fig. 1 now exists. During this period the myoglobin gene followed an evolutionary course without further duplication, but it underwent changes as a result of mutational events.

Furthermore, the period under discussion represents hundreds of millions of years, and includes the separation of various phyla, orders

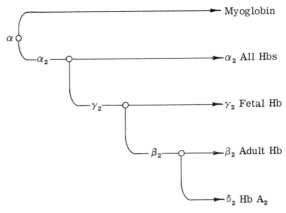

Fig. 1. Evolution of the hemoglobin genes. (From Ingram, 1961.)

families, genera, and species. Each species has its own set of hemoglobin genes which have evolved separately.

The polypeptide chains of myoglobin and the four normal human hemoglobins have been written side by side as a sequence of amino acids (Table V). The chains are not all of the same length, and they have been matched together on the basis of 21 positions at each of which the same amino acid occurs in all the molecules. It is necessary to leave gaps at a few points to complete the matching of the strands. This process appears somewhat arbitrary but is believed to have a genetic basis occurring from mutational excision of portions of the DNA molecule followed by reunion of the strands at each end of the excised and discarded portion. An example of such an event is depicted in Table V as having occurred between loci 50 and 51 in the α chain.

The amino acids at the 21 loci that do not vary are presumed to be essential to the structure and function of proteins in the globin group that combine with heme and are used for the transport of oxygen. The intervening amino acids can evidently vary to a considerable extent without such variations causing lethal effects, and these "variable" loci may be compared from chain to chain with reference to the possible coding triplets. As an example, the amino acids lysine at locus 138 in myoglobin, threonine at 134 in α-hemoglobin, asparagine at 139 in β-hemoglobin, and serine at 139 in γ-hemoglobin correspond to proposed coding triplets written in terms of DNA as follows: AAA and ATA, lysine; ACA, CCA, TCA, and CGC, threonine; CAA, CTA, and TAA, asparagine; ACG, TCC, and CTT, serine. Of these, the following

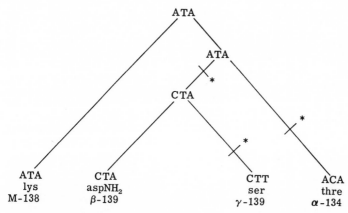

FIG. 2. Evolution of a coding triplet. * = single-base changes.

bear the simplest relationship in terms of single-base changes: ATA, ACA, CTA, and CTT, leading to the postulation that the triplets responsible for coding this site evolved as shown in Fig. 2.

These 4 amino acids which at first sight appear unrelated may now be seen as the result of 3 single-base changes in the DNA during evolution.

By applying procedures of this type throughout the amino acid sequences in these four proteins, it was possible to speculate on the composition of the corresponding genes. This was presented elsewhere (Jukes, 1963b). It may be inferred that the protein coded by the gene P_1 was intermediate in composition between present day myoglobin and hemoglobins. Similarly the primitive α-hemoglobin would be intermediate in primary structure between the present β- and γ-hemoglobins on the one hand and the present α-hemoglobin on the other, although

TABLE V

Amino Acid Sequences and Their Coding Triplets in the Hemoglobin Series

Lines 1 to 4, Amino acid sequences in human myoglobin and α-, β- and γ-hemoglobins (Hb); lines 5, 6, and 7, substitutions of β Hb in δ Hb (δ), α Hb in horse α Hb and other α Hb's. The subscripts are: horse = h, gorilla = g, orangutan = o-u, chicken = c, rabbit = r, beef = b, sheep = s; β Hb in other primates = + (Hill et al., 1963); human myoglobin in whale myoglobin = w (Hill, 1964). The next 5 lines contain a list of possible coding assignments for the amino acids in the columns above. P₁, P₂, P₃, and P₄ list hypothetical coding assignments for the primitive molecules that gave rise to the myoglobins and hemoglobins (P₁); to α-, β-, and γ-hemoglobin (P₂); to β- and γ-hemoglobin (P₃) and to human α- and horse α-hemoglobin (P₄). In a number of loci, alternate coding assignment are equally possible; for example, ala/ser as CTG/CTT or CCG/ACG (M-89), leu as any of its 4 codes (M-88), and leu/phe as TTC/TTT or CCT/TCT (M-71), etc. All sequences should be read from right to left.

Protein

Position markers: 152 · 146 · 141/146 · 140 · 130

Amino acid sequences

Protein																	
M	HOOC—glN	gly	tyr	gly	leu	glu	lys	tyr	asp	ser	ala	met	asp	lys	arg	phe	leu glu
α	HOOC—arg (141)							tyr	lys	ser	thr	val	ser	val	ser	val	ala (146)
β	HOOC—his (146)							tyr	lys	his	ala	leu	ala	asN	ala	val	gly ala
γ	HOOC—his (146)							tyr	arg	ser	ser	leu	ala	ser	ala	val	gly thr
δ, etc.	phe_w							lys8_w	ala8_w		ilu_w						ser

Coding triplets

Protein												
M	ATA	A*T	GTA	ACG	CCG	TGA	GTA	ATA	TTT	TTC	ATG	
α	GTC	A*T	AAA	ACG	ACA	TGT	TTG	ACA	ACG	TTG	TCC	CTG
β	ATC	A*T	AAA	ACC	CCG	CTA	CCG	TGT	CTG	GTG	CCG	
γ	ATC	A*T	GAA	ACG	ACG	CTG	CTT	CCG	TTG	GTG	CCA	
δ etc. (T*T)		ATA	CCG			TTA					CTT_h	

	C,T			C,T								
*	ATC	A*T	AAA	ACG	ACG	ACG	TGT	GTG	ATA	GCG	TTG TTC CTG	

P₁												
P₂ if different from P₁	CTG	CTA	CCG						GTG	CCG		
P₃ if different from P₁												
P₄ if different from P₁												

416

TABLE V (*Continued*)

Protein

					130											120					111	
M	leu	ala	lys	asp	met	ala	gly	glu	ala	asp	ala	gly	phe	asp	ala	pro	his	lys	thr	asN	leu	val
										116						115					
α	leu	phe	lys	asp	leu	ser	ala	his	val	ala	pro	thr	phe	glu	ala	pro	his	leu	his	ala	ala	leu
									126	121								117	116		
β	val	val	lys	glN	tyr	ala	ala	glN	val	pro	pro	thr	phe	glu	ala	gly	his	phe	his	his	ala	leu
										δ	δ				δ			δ	δ		
γ	val	met	lys	glN	try	ser	ala	glN	val	glu	pro	thr	phe	glu	met	gly	his	phe	his	ilu	ala	leu
										glN					asN			asN	arg		
δ, etc.		lys	met	glN	asN	asN		asp		lys				lys				arg_w	val		
																			his_w		

M	TTC	CTG	A*A	G*A	TGA	CTG	G*A	C*G	ATG	G*G	C*C	A*C	T*T	GTA	G*G	C*C	A*C	ATA	ACA	CTA	CCT	TTG
α	TTC	TTT	A*A	G*A	TGT	CTT	C*G	ATC	TTG	CAG	C*C	ACA	T*T	ATG	C*G	C*C	TTC	ATC	CTG	CCG	TTC
β	TTG	TTG	A*A	GGAATT	CTG	C*G	AAC	A*A	CAC	C*C	ACA	T*T	AAG	A*A	G*G	A*C	TTT	ATC	ATC	CTA	CCG	TTC
γ	TTG	TGA	A*A	GGATGG	CTT	C*G	AAC	C*C	ACA	T*T	AAG	C*C	ACA	A*A	G*G	GAA	CTA	GTC
δ, e·c.					TGA	AAC		AAC		AAA	C*A_h		AAC			TTG_h						
										GTA_h						ATC						

*		A,T C,T		A,C,T		A,T,A,C,T	C,T	A,T A,C,T C,T

P₁   TTC TTG A*A G*A TGT CTT C*G ATC TTG CAG C*C ACG T*T GTG A*G C*C A*C AAT ATC CTG CCG TTC

P₂ if different from P₁   GGA   ACA   ATG A*A   TAT TTT

P₃ if different from P₁   ACA   C*G   TTC

P₄ if different from P₁

417

TABLE V (Continued)

Protein																						
			110									100										
		107	ilu	105								ilu										
M	ser	his		ala	glu	ser	glN	phe	glu	leu	tyr	lys	pro	ilu	lys	his	lys	thr	—	ala	his
α	thr	val	leu	110 leu	cys	his	ser	leu	lys	phe	asN	val	asp	val	arg	leu	lys	his	ala	his
β	val	cys	val	leu	val	asN	gly	leu	arg	phe	asN	glu	asp	val	his	leu	lys	asp	cys	his
γ	val	thr	val	leu	val	asN	gly	leu	lys	phe	asN	glu	asp	val	his	leu	lys	asp	cys	his
δ, etc.	his_w	ser	ilu_w																		tyr

M	ACG	ATC	TTA	CTG	ATG	CTT	AAC	TTT	ATG	TAT	ATT	A*A	TTA	C*C	TTA	ATA	A*C	ATA	ACA	CTG	A*C
α	ACA	TTG	TTC	TTC	GTT	ATC	ACG	TTC	AAA	TTT	C*A	TTG	C*C	GTA	TTG	G*C	TTC	A*A	CTG	A*C
β	TTG	GTT	TTG	TTC	CTA	GCG	TTC	GAA	TTC	C*A	ATG	C*C	GTA	TTG	A*C	TTC	A*A	GTT	A*C
γ	TTG	TCA	TTG	TTC	CTA	GCG	TTC	AAA	TTT	C*A	ATG	C*A	GTA	TTG	A*C	TTC	A*A	GTT	A*C
δ, etc.	ACC	ACG_h			AAT															A*T

*						A,T				A,C,T		C,T			A,T	C,T		C,T

P₁	ACC	TTC	TTG	CTC	TTG	CTC	AAG	TTT	TTG	AAA	TTT	C*A	TTG	C*C	GTA	TTA	A*A	TTA	A*A	CTG	A*C
P₂ if different from P₁		TTT			ACG								TTG			TTC					
P₃ if different from P₁	TTG	TTT			CTA	GCG				ATG			TTG			TTC				GTG	
P₄ if different from P₁		TTT																		

418

TABLE V (*Continued*)

Protein																						
		90										80										70
M	ser	glN	ala	leu	pro	lys	ala	glu	ilu	glu	his	his	gly	lys	lys	lys	leu	ilu	ala	gly	leu	ala
		85			82				78		76			73		71			68			65
α	leu	asp	ser	leu	ala	ser	leu	ala	asN	pro	met	asp	asp	val	his	ala	val	ala	asN	thr	leu	ala
		90										80				76						
β	leu	glu	ser	leu	thr	ala	phe	thr	gly	lys	leu	asN	asp	leu	his	ala	leu	gly	asp	ser	phe	ala
		90																				
γ	leu	glu	ser	leu	glN	ala	phe	thr	gly	lys	leu	asp	asp	leu	his	lys	ilu	ala	asp	gly	leu	ser
δ, etc.					asN				gly		leu			leu		gly	val	glu	lys			gly
									leu$_w$							glu	thr	asp	leu			
																pro						
M	TCC	GGA	CTG	TTC	CAC	ATA	CTG	ATG	TTA	A*G	ATC	ATC	G*G	ATA	ATA	A*A	TTC	TTA	CTG	GCG	TTC	CTG
α	TTC	GTA	CTT	TTC	CAG	CTT	TTC	CCG	CTA	C*C	TGA	GTA	G*A	TTG	ATC	C*G	TTG	CTG	CTA	ACA	TTC	CTG
β	TTC	ATG	CTT	TTC	CCA	ATG	TTT	CCA	GTG	A*A	TGT	CTA	G*A	TTC	ATC	C*G	TTC	GTG	GTA	ACG	TTT	CTG
γ	TTC	ATG	CTT	TTC	AAC	CTG	TTT	CCA	GTG	A*A	TGT	GTA	G*A	TTC	ATC	A*A	TTA	CTG	GTA	GCG	TTC	CTT
γ. etc.					CAA$_h$				GTG$_h$		TGT$_h$			TTC$_h$		G*G$_h$	TTG^{+}	ATG	ATA			GTG$_h$
																			TTC$_h$			
									TTC							A*G^{+}	TCA^{+}	GTA^{+}				
																C*C^{+}						
*										A,T			C,T			A,T						
P_1	TTC	GTA	CTT	TTC	CAC	ATA	TTC	CCG	GTG	A*A	TTT	ATA	G*A	TTA	ATC	A*A	TTC	TTG	CTG	GCG	TTC	CTG
P_2 if different from P_1														TTC				CTG	CTA			
P_3 if different from P_1														TTC				CTG	GTA			
P_4 if different from P_1					CAG									TTC		G*G						

TABLE V (*Continued*)

Amino acid alignment

Protein				60				57												50		48
M	thr	leu	val	thr	val	gly	his	lys	lys	leu	asp	glu	ser	ala	lys	met	glu	asp	glu	ser	lys	leu
α	asp	ala	ala	lys	val	gly	his	gly	lys	val	glN	ala	ser			gly				his	ser	leu
			67				63			60										50		
β	gly	leu	leu	lys	lys	his	gly	lys	val	pro	asN	gly	met	val	ala	asp			asp	thr	ser	leu
γ	thr	leu	val	lys	lys	his	gly	lys	val	pro	asN	gly	met	ilu	ala	ser			ser	ala	ser	leu
δ, etc.	glu			glu		tyr		asp			arg							glu		ser		glu
			ala			arg		ala										ala_w		thr_w		

Codon alignment

Protein																						
M	ACA	TTC	TTG	ACA	TTG	G*G	A*C	ATA	A*A	TTC	GTA	A*G	CTT	C*G	ATA	TGA	A*G	GTA	A*G	ACG	ATA	TTC
α	GCA	CTG	TTG	A*A	ATA	G*G	A*C	GTG	A*A	TTG	GGA	C*G	CTT			G*G				ACC	CTT	TTC
β	GCG	TTC	TTG	A*A	ATA	G*G	A*C	CTG	A*A	TTG	AAA	C*C	CTA	G*G	TTG	C*G		GTA	C*C	ACA	C*C CTT	TTC
γ	ACA	TTC	TTG	A*A	ATA	G*G	A*C	CTG	A*A	TTG	AAA	C*C	CTA	G*G	TTA	C*G		TGA	C*G	ACG	CTT	TTC
δ, etc.	AAG^+	ATG	ATG_b	A*T	GTA_{o-u}			GAA										ATG^+		ACG	ATG^+	
			CTG_s	G*C	CTG_h													CTG			ACA	
*				A,T	A,C,T C,T			A,T								A,T		A,T				

P₁	ACA	TTC	TTG	A*A	ATG	G*G	A*C	CTG	A*A	TTG	GTA	C*G	CTT	G*G	TAA	TTA	C*G	GTA	A*G	ACA	CTA	TTC
P₂ if different from P₁											AAA	C*C	CTA							G*G	CTT	
P₃ if different from P₁																TGA				C*G	CTT	
P₄ if different from P₁																						

TABLE V (Continued)

Protein																									
													35		37				30					26	
					40																				
M	his	lys	phe	lys	asp	phe	lys	glu	leu	thr	glu	pro	his	gly	lys	phe	leu	arg	ilu	leu	ilu	asp	asp	gly	his
α	asp	phe	his	pro	tyr	thr	thr	try	phe	ser	met	arg		glu	leu	ala		leu	ala	glu	asp	ala	gly	tyr	
		45																	30						
β	asp	gly	phe	ser	glu	glu	thr	try	val	phe	leu	leu		ala	leu	glu		leu	ala	glu	glu	gly	gly	val	
γ	asN	gly	phe	ser	asp	glu	thr	try	val	phe	leu	leu		ala	thr	glu		leu	thr	glu	glu	gly	gly	ala	
δ, etc.					argw				serw	gly					glN				glN			lys		gluw	

M	ATC	A*A	T*T	ATA	AAG	TAT	ACA	ATG	C*C	A*C	GCG	ATA	TTT	TGT	G*C	AAT	TTC	TTA	GTA	GTA	G*G	ATC
α	GTA	T*T	ACC	CTC	T*T	ATT	ACA	ACA	C*C	T*T	ACG	TTC	TTT	TGA	G*C	AAG	CTG	ATG	CTG	G*G	ATT
β	GTA	G*G	T*T	ACG	ATG	T*T	GAA	AAC	ACA	C*C	A*T	TTG	TTC	TTC	G*C	GAG	ATG	CCG	ATG	GTG	G*G	TTG
γ	CTA	G*G	T*T	ACG	GTA	T*T	GAA	AAC	ACA	TGG	C*C	A*T	TTG	TTC	TGT	G*C	GAG	CCA	ATG	GTG	G*G	CTG
δ, etc.	TTC+GAA						C*Gr	ACG	GCGh							AAC	ACG	ATA	ATG			

| * | A,T,C,T | C,T | | | | A,C,T,C,T | | | | | A,C,T C,T | | | | C,T | | | | | | A,C,T |

P₁	GTC	A*G	T*T	GAA	GTA	T*T	ATT	AAA	TAA	ACA	ATG	C*C	A*T	ACG	TTA	TTT	TGT	G*C	AAG	TTC	CCG	ATG	GTG	G*G	ATG
P₂ if different from P₁	GTA	G*G							AAA																
P₃ if different from P₁	TCC					TTT	GAA	AAC								TGG				TTG	TTG	TTC			GAG
P₄ if different from P₁	GTA	G*G																							TTG

421

TABLE V (Continued)

Protein

Amino acid sequences (position numbers shown above residues):

M: gly(23) ala val asp(20) pro glN(19) val lys ala(15) try ala lys leu val glu(10) try glu gly gly(5) leu(2) gly-NH₂(1)

α: glu ala gly his(19) ala gly val lys(12) gly try gly ala ala val asN thr(9) lys ala(6) pro(4) ser(3) leu(2) val-NH₂(1)

β: glu asp val asN(19) val lys leu try gly leu ala val ala ser lys glu glu(6) thr(4) leu(2) his val-NH₂(1)

γ: asp glu val asN val lys gly try ser leu ser thr ilu thr ala lys asp glu glu(4) thr phe(2) his gly-NH₂(1)

δ, etc.: δ ... asp ... gly ... asN ... thr ... gly lys ala thr thr(3) val-NHAc(1)
   ala asp ... ala_w ... asN ... δ ... lys val ... ala glN val-NH₂w(1)

DNA codon assignments:

M: GTG CTG TTG GTA C*C AAC TTG ATA CCG TGG CTG ATA TAT TTG AAG ? TGG ATG GTG TTC GTG

α: ATG GTG CTG ATC C*G GAG TTG ATA GCG TGG CTG CTG AAA TTG CAA ACA ATA GTA CTG CTC TCC TCC TTC TTG

β: ATG GTA TTG CTA TTG ATA GCG TGG CTG TTC CTG TCA TTG CAG ACG ATA GTA ATG ATG CTC TCA TTC ACC TTG

γ: GTA ATG TTG CTA TTG ATA GCG TGG CTG TTC CTT TCA TTA CCA CCG ATA GTA ATG ATG TCA TTT ACC GTG

δ, etc.: CTG GTA G*G_h GTA ACG_h TAA ACA GTA ATA CTG_h ACA_c TTG_c
          GTA_g C*G TTG AAC_b TTG

* A,C,T

P₁   GTG GTG TTG GTA C*G AAG TTG ATA GCG TGG CTG CTG TAA TTA CAG ACG ATA GTG ATG CTC TCC TTC ACC TTG
P₂ if different from P₁   CTA
P₃ if different from P₁   TCA
P₄ if different from P₁   CTA

422

the difference between primitive α and present α would be less than the difference between primitive α and present β and γ because β and γ have tended to change more rapidly than α (Ingram, 1963).

The difference between the amino acid sequences in the hemoglobins are due to corresponding differences in the base sequences in the respective hemoglobin genes and reflect a prolonged series of mutational events that have caused base replacements. If we consider as a model a linear row of 300 bases randomly distributed between A, C, G, and T, we may calculate the possibilities for a succession of random events that will change any of the bases to any other. As the number of events increases, the chances for a locus being "hit" twice will increase. The average probabilities in terms of the Poisson distribution are given in

Total hits in 300 loci	Loci hit				
	Once	Twice	3 times	4 times	5 times
90	66	10	1	0.1	0
180	99	30	6	1	0.1
300	110	55	18	5	1

the accompanying tabulation. Loci that are hit 2 or more times will be changed again and there will be one chance in four that each hit subsequent to the first hit will change the base back to the original base.

The apparent hits or actual base changes will therefore be as follows: for 90 hits, 75 base changes; for 180 hits, 127 base changes; for 300 hits, 169 base changes.

Let us now view these base changes in terms of changes in 100 consecutive coding triplets. The base changes produced by the hits will be statistically distributed among the triplets approximately as shown in the accompanying tabulation.

Hits	Base changes	Changes per 100 triplets		
		Single-base	2-base	3-base
90	75	35	13	3
180	127	36	24	11
300	169	34	29	18

Four or more base changes per triplet will appear as 1, 2, or 3-base changes. As the number of mutational events increases, the amino-acid changes will tend more and more to correspond to 2-base changes in the code. This enables a rough test of the postulations concerning hemoglobin to be made in terms of the data in Table VI, as shown in Table VII.

TABLE VI

BASE CHANGES AND AMINO ACID CHANGES IN THE RELATIONSHIP
BETWEEN HUMAN α-, β-, γ-HEMOGLOBINS AND MYOGLOBIN (M),
HUMAN AND HORSE α-HEMOGLOBIN (α/h), AND HUMAN
AND WHALE MYOGLOBIN (M/W)

	α/M	β/M	γ/M	α/β	α/γ	β/γ	α/h	M/W
"Variable" loci	116	120	120	118	118	125	121	131
Apparent base changes in variable loci:								
None	12	12	12	42	38	86	104	115
One-base	62	55	56	54	57	25	13	13
Two-base	40	51	50	22	23	12	4	3
Three-base	2	2	2	0	0	2	0	0
Base changes[a]	1.22	1.36	1.35	0.83	0.87	0.44	0.17	0.14
Amino acid changes[a]	0.90	0.90	0.90	0.64	0.68	0.31	0.14	0.12

[a] Average per variable locus.

TABLE VII

COMPARISON OF ESTIMATED BASE CHANGES IN HEMOGLOBIN AND
MYOGLOBIN GENES WITH PREDICTED DISTRIBUTION

		Calculated base changes per 100 coding triplets				
		From Table 5			From Poisson formula	
Polypeptide chains compared	Amino acid changes per 100 loci	1-base	2-base	3-base	1-base	2 or more bases
α/M	90	53	35	2	40	50
β/M	90	46	42	2	"	"
γ/M	90	47	42	2	"	"
α/β	64	46	19	0	45	19
α/γ	68	48	19	0	46	22
β/γ	31	20	10	2	27	4

We shall assume that amino acid changes take place with the minimum of necessary changes in the base composition of the triplets involved. For example, a change of arginine to serine could be represented more economically in terms of base changes by GCC/TCC then by GTC/TCC, GTC/CTT, or GCC/ACG.

We shall also assume that base changes in the gene can more readily be tolerated when no amino acid changes result therefrom than when this is not the case. For instance, a change of GCC/GTC, arg/arg, would take place without any disruption of protein structure. Such "silent" mutational changes can hence take place frequently and imperceptibly. If these assumptions are combined, it may be postulated that a mutation of arg/ser, GCC/TCC can most readily take place when the arginine at a given site is being coded by GCC, and arg/leu, GTC/TTC when the same genetic site is occupied by GTC. This leads to the assumption that the amino acid interchanges in the hemoglobins took place when each coding site was in the configuration that permitted the change with a minimum of alteration. This assumption reduces the number of 2-base and 3-base changes that need postulation. As an example, if a site is occupied in three chains by ala, asN and leu, we shall therefore assume that, for example, a change from ala to asN takes place when the ala site is occupied by CAG or CTG which can be changed to CAA or CTA (asN) and if the same ala site mutates to leu, this takes place when the ala site is occupied by CCG which can be changed to CCT (leu) by a single-base change. These assumptions markedly reduce the total numbers of 2-base and 3-base changes in coding triplets that are needed to interpret the amino acid changes at all the homologous sites in the globins. The numbers of these changes that were postulated in an earlier publication (Jukes, 1963b) may therefore be reduced to the numbers shown in Table VII. Further information on the unassigned coding triplets may enable these numbers to be reduced even further.

If it is assumed that nearly all mutational events in the evolution of a single hemoglobin gene are single-base changes, the exceptions being additions and excisions of one or more bases, we may estimate the number of such changes in the hemoglobin series by comparing the unchanged "variable" loci (Tables V and VI) with the Poisson formula. This has been done in Table VII. The agreement is excellent for α/β and α/γ, but there ought to be more single base changes and fewer 2-base changes in the β/γ comparison. A calculation of this type for the myoglobin/hemoglobin comparisons is difficult because the average correspondence between the myoglobin chain and the hemoglobin chains is only 9% in terms of "variable" loci. This is within the range of random coincidence if the relationship between the coding triplets is equivalent to a difference of not more than 12%. This is the figure obtained by examining all possible single-base changes in the triplets in Table I. One in eight of such changes results in the production of another code for the same amino acid and there is no reason to believe that the coincidence would be less if all 64 triplets were assigned to coding functions, in view of the fact that there are only 20 different amino acids. Nevertheless, the calculations in Table VI for α/M, β/M, and γ/M are of interest since they appear to indicate a more rapid rate of change in β and γ hemoglobins than in α hemoglobin, which has been noted elsewhere (Ingram, 1963; Hill et al., 1963).

The Cytochromes

The amino acid sequences in this group of proteins have been studied by Tuppy and co-workers, and by Emil Smith and co-workers (Paleus and Tuppy, 1959; Margoliash et al., 1961; Kreil and Tuppy, 1961; Matsubara and Smith, 1962). There is a remarkable similarity in the sequences in the cytochromes c from different species. Each contains about 104 amino acids and, even in the case of cytochrome c from yeast, 54 sites are identical with those in the other cytochromes c. The evolutionary significance of this homology was discussed by Margoliash (1963) and by Smith (1964). Table VIII was compiled by procedures similar to those employed in Table V and elsewhere (Jukes, 1963b) for the hemoglobins, and the comparison is summarized in Table IX.

It seems probable that all, or nearly all, of the 54 sites that are identical in the protein sequences shown in Table VIII are occupied by amino acids that cannot be changed because they are essential to the function of cytochrome c. This conclusion is reached from the low order of probability that all 6 amino acids at any single site would be identical by chance (1 in 20^6) and from the fact that "variable" and nonvarying amino acids are juxtaposed to some extent in blocks rather than being randomly interspersed.

However, it is also possible that evolutionary changes have not yet proceeded for a significant length of time to have changed more than 50 of the 104 sites to amino acids that differ from those in the "parent" molecule which we assume to have been the progenitor of the cytochromes c. In this second case, let us suppose that 100 of the 104 sites are "variable," excluding sites 14, 17, and 18 and 19 which we may assume to be needed to combine with heme.

If only 50 sites are "variable" as in the first case, then the average of 40 sites at which yeast cytochrome c differs from the vertebrate cytochromes c represents 80% of the "variable" sites. Each of the 40 sites corresponds in the gene to a base triplet which has received one or more "hits." For 40 out of 50 3-base sites to be hit, the Poisson distribution should be as follows: sites hit once, 16; sites hit 2 or more times, 24. In the second case, 40 out of 100 variable sites have been hit, so there should

TABLE VIII

Amino Acid Sequences in 6 Cytochromes c and a Few Amino Acid Substitutions in Dog, Rhesus Monkey (R) and Human Mutant (HM) Cytochromes c[a]

The next seven lines list the proposed coding assignments, based on minimum changes at each site. Lines 2 to 6 are left blank where the amino acids are identical with those in line 1. All sequences should be read from right to left.

Cytochrome c

	104				100								92		90			
1 Human	HOOC—glu	asN	thr	ala	lys	lys	leu	tyr	ala	ilu	leu	asp	ala	arg	glu	glu	lys	lys
2 Horse	HOOC—glu	asN	thr	ala	lys				ala	ilu			glu		glu	thr	lys	
3 Yeast	HOOC—glu	cys	—	ala	lys				thr	ilu			asN		asp	lys	glu	
4 Tuna	HOOC—ser	ala	thr	ser	—				ala	val			glN		glu	gly	lys	
5 Chicken	HOOC—ser	thr	ala	asp	lys				ala	ilu			val		glu	ser	lys	
6 Beef and Pig	HOOC—glu	asN	thr	ala	lys				ala	ilu			glu		glu	gly	lys	
7 Others		lys_{dog}															thr_{dog}	
1 Human	A*G	CTA	CCA	CCG	A*A				CCG	TTA			CAG		ATG	A*G	A*A	
2 Horse	A*G	CTA	CCA	CCG	A*A				CCG	TTA			AAG		ATG	ACA	A*A	
3 Yeast	A*G	GTT	—	CCG	A*A				CCA	TTA			CAA		GTA	A*A	A*G	
4 Tuna	ACG	CTG	CCA	ACG	—				CCG	TTG			AAC		ATG	G*G	A*A	
5 Chicken	ACG	CCA	CCG	GCA	A*A				CCG	TTA			TTG		ATG	ACG	A*A	
6 Beef and Pig	A*G	CTA	CCA	CCG	A*A				CCG	TTA			AAG		ATG	G*G	A*A	
7 Others		ATA															ACA	
*	A,T				A,T											A,T	A,T	

TABLE VIII (Continued)

Cytochrome c

	lys	ilu	gly	val	phe	ilu	met	lys	thr	gly	pro	ilu	tyr	lys	lys	pro	asN	glu	leu	tyr	glu	met	leu
							80										70						
1 Human		ilu	ilu																		glu	met	leu
2 Horse		ala	ilu																		glu	met	leu
3 Yeast		leu	ala																		thr	ser	met
4 Tuna		ilu	ilu																		glu	met	leu
5 Chicken		ilu	ilu																		glu	met	leu
6 Beef and Pig		ilu	ala																		glu	met	leu
7 Others																		glN	leu		glu	leu	
																		R	HM				

1 Human	TTA	TTG	CAU	A*G	AAG	TGA	TGT
2 Horse	TTA	CTG	CAU	A*G	AAG	TGA	TGT
3 Yeast	TTC	GTG	CAG	ACA	AAG	TCC	TGA
4 Tuna	TTA	CTG	CAU	A*G	AAG	TGA	TGT
5 Chicken	TTA	CTG	CAU	A*G	AAG	TGA	TGT
6 Beef and Pig	TTA	CTG	CAU	A*G	AAG	TGA	TGT
7 Others					AAC	TGT	

* A,T

428

TABLE VIII (*Continued*)

Cytochrome c

Amino acid block

	58						50		47	46				
	thr	asp	glu	gly try	ilu	gly	lys asN	lys asN ala	ala thr	tyr	ser	tyr gly	pro ala	glN gly
1 Human	thr	asp	glu	gly	try	ilu	gly	lys asN	lys asN ala	asp	ser	tyr	pro
2 Horse	thr	glu	glu	lys	thr	ilu	gly	asN	lys asN	asp	thr ser	phe	glN
3 Yeast	asN	asN	glu	asp	leu	val	asN	lys ilu	ilu lys	asp	ser	tyr	glu
4 Tuna	thr	asp	asN	val	val	ilu	gly	asN	lys asN	asp	ser	tyr	glu
5 Chicken	thr	asp	glu	gly	thr	ilu	gly	asN	lys asN	asp	ser	phe	glu
6 Beef and Pig	thr	glu	glu	gly	thr	ilu	gly	asN	lys asN	asp	ser	phe	pro
7 Others													

Codon block

										50	47	46	
1 Human	CCA	GTA	A*G	GTG	TTA	TTA	G*G	CTA	ATA	C*G	ACG	A*T	CAC
2 Horse	CCA	ATG	A*G	ATA	TCA	TTA	G*G	CTA	ATA	G*A	ACA	T*T	CAC
3 Yeast	C*A	CTA	A*G	GTA	TTC	TTG	C*A	ATA	TTA	G*A	ACG	A*T	AAC
4 Tuna	CCA	GTA	C*A	CTA	TTG	TTA	G*G	CTT	ATA	G*A	ACG	A*T	AAG
5 Chicken	CCA	GTA	A*G	GTG	TCA	TTA	G*G	CTA	ATA	G*A	ACG	T*T	AAG
6 Beef and Pig	CCA	ATG	A*G	GTG	TCA	TTA	G*G	CTA	ATA	G*A	ACG	T*T	CAC
7 Others													
*	A,T		A,T									C,T	

TABLE VIII (Continued)

Cytochrome c

Positions 40 … 30 … 20. Reference sequence (reading left to right):
thr lys arg gly phe leu gly his leu asN pro gly thr lys his lys gly lys glu val thr his cys

	thr	lys	leu	his	thr	lys	lys	lys
1 Human	thr	lys	leu	his	thr	lys	lys	lys
2 Horse	thr	lys	leu	his	thr	lys	lys	lys
3 Yeast	ser	his	ilu	his	val	pro	lys	lys
4 Tuna	thr	lys	leu	try	val	lys	lys	asN
5 Chicken	thr	lys	leu	his	thr	lys	lys	lys
6 Beef and Pig	thr	lys	leu	his	thr	lys	lys	lys
7 Others								

1 Human	ACA ATA	TTC	A*C	TCA	A*A	A*A
2 Horse	ACA ATA	TTC	A*C	TCA	A*A	A*A
3 Yeast	ACG ATC	TTA	A*C	TTG	C*C	A*A
4 Tuna	ACA ATA	TTC	TGG	TTG	A*A	C*A
5 Chicken	ACA ATA	TTC	A*C	TCA	A*A	A*A
6 Beef and Pig	ACA ATA	TTC	A*C	TCA	A*A	A*A
7 Others						
*			C,T		A,T	A,T

430

TABLE VIII (*Continued*)

Cytochrome c

Amino acid sequence (positions):

		15			12		10										
1 Human	glN	ser	cys	lys	met	ilu	phe	ilu	lys	lys	gly	lys	glu	val	asp	gly	NHAc
2 Horse	glN	ala		lys	glN	val		ilu	lys	lys			glu	val	asp	gly	NHAc
3 Yeast	leu	glu		arg	thr	lys	leu	thr	ala				lys	ala	ser	gly	ala lys phe glu thr NH₂
4 Tuna	glN	ala		lys	glN	val		thr	lys	lys			ala	val	asp	gly	NHAc
5 Chicken	glN	ser		lys	glN	val		ilu	lys	lys			glu	ilu	asp	gly	NHAc
6 Beef and Pig	glN	ala		lys	glN	val		ilu	lys	lys			glu	val	asp	gly	NHAc
7 Others																	

Codons (positions 15, 12, 10):

		15			12		10						
1 Human	TAC	ACG	AAA	TGA	TTA	TTA	A*A	A*A	A*G	TTG	GTA	G*G	
2 Horse	TAC	CCG	AAA	GGA	TTG	TTA	A*A	A*A	A*G	TTG	GTA	G*G	
3 Yeast	TTC	A*G	GAA	CCA	ATA	TTC	ACA	C*G	A*A	CTG	CTT	G*G	. . .
4 Tuna	TAC	CCG	AAA	GGA	TTG	TCA	A*A	A*A	C*G	TTG	GTA	G*G	
5 Chicken	TAC	ACG	AAA	GGA	TTA	TTA	A*A	A*A	A*G	TTA	GTA	G*G	
6 Beef and Pig	TAC	CCG	AAA	GGA	TTG	TTA	A*A	A*A	A*G	TTG	GTA	G*G	
7 Others													
*	A,T					A,T	A,T		A,T			A,C,T	

a See Margoliash *et al.* (1961), Matsubara and Smith (1962), Kreil (1963), Chan *et al.* (1963), Yasunobu *et al.* (1963), and Smith (1964).

432 T. H. JUKES

be 30 sites hit once and 10 sites hit 2 or more times. In terms of the coding triplets in Table I, Table IX indicates in the yeast:vertebrate comparison that about 23 sites have been hit once and 16 sites have been hit more than once. However, about 9% of the sites that have actually been hit more than once will appear to have been hit only once due to being changed to a code for the preceding amino acid (Jukes, 1963b),

TABLE IX

COMPARISONS OF CYTOCHROMES C

	Amino acid differences	Coding triplet changes			Total base changes	Mutational events
		1-base	2-base	3-base		
Horse/beef	*3*	*2*	*1*	—	*4*	*4*
Human/horse	12	8	4	—	16	
Human/beef, pig	9	7	2	—	11	
Human/chicken	14	10	4	—	18	
Horse/chicken	12	7	5	—	17	
Beef/chicken	10	5	5	—	15	
Avg	*11*	*7*	*4*	*0*	*15*	16
Human/tuna	21	14	6	1	29	
Horse/tuna	19	12	5	2	28	
Beef/tuna	17	10	6	1	25	
Chicken/tuna	18	9	7	2	29	
Avg	*19*	*11*	*6*	*1.5*	*28*	32
Human/yeast	38	26	11	1	51	
Horse/yeast	39	23	14	2	57	
Beef/yeast	38	21	17	—	54	
Chicken/yeast	40	23	17	1	60	
Tuna/yeast	44	24	17	2	64	
Avg	*40*	*23*	*15*	*1.2*	*57*	70

so that if 40 out of 50 sites have been hit, 18 will show single-base changes in the code and 22 will show 2-base changes. Evidently the first assumption is closer than the second and we may conclude that there are only about 60 "variable" amino acids in the cytochromes c. This would give a ratio of 1-base changes:2-base changes of about 22:18. About 2 of the 2-base changes will appear to be 1-base changes, so that the apparent ratio would be 24:16, as found in the calculation shown in Table IX. The calculated base changes in Table IX may be expressed in terms of mutational events. If 60 amino acids are "variable," there are 180 bases for coding them, and 57 of these have been changed in the yeast:vertebrate comparison. To produce 57 changes in 180 sites, about 70 mutational events are required, allowing for 2 or more hits on each of 13 sites, 3 of which will be changed back to the original base. Similarly in the comparison between tuna and the warm-blooded species there have been 28 changes in 60 sites, corresponding to 32 mutational events, and between man and horse, 16 base changes corresponding to 17 mutational events.

If it is assumed that 130 million years have elapsed since the man: horse separation (Zuckerkandl and Pauling, 1962), the fish:warm-blooded separation should be about 230 million years and the vertebrate: yeast separation should be about 540 million years if the mutation rate is constant in terms of base changes in the cytochrome c gene, which may not be the case. The comparison between human/horse and vertebrate/ yeast is somewhat wider than that deduced by Margoliash (1963) who based the comparison on amino acid differences alone.

The changes in the primary structure of the 6 cytochromes c shown in Table VII are similar in frequency to the Poisson distribution in spite of the nonrandomness of the locations which are changed. The sites with no amino acid changes are 56; sites with one change, 30; 2 changes, 13; 3 changes, 2; 4 changes, 3. The Poisson distribution is: unchanged sites, 58; one change, 34; 2 changes, 10; 3 changes, 2; 4, changes 0. This is similar except for the presence of "hot spots" at positions 89, 92, and 103 in the cytochromes c.

Discussion

It seems probable that many base changes occurring as mutational events will produce intolerable amino acid substitutions even in the "variable" sites in proteins because it is likely that only a limited number of amino acid interchanges are possible without disturbing the secondary and tertiary structure of a protein to an unacceptable extent. The recipients of unacceptable substitutions will presumably be eliminated. The treatment of the data in Table V and VII is necessarily restricted to an examination of nonlethal changes. It is remarkable that so many changes can take place in the globins and cytochromes without interfering with their functions. The average number of amino acid changes in the hemoglobins and myoglobins (Table V) is 1.6 per locus excluding abnormal variants and 1.7 in the cytochromes c (Table VI). Interchanges in which "hydrophilic" amino acids are replaced by "hydrophobic" amino acids (Margoliash, 1963) and *vice versa* are quite frequent.

The parent molecule of the hemoglobins and myoglobins is deduced to have been intermediate in composition and primary structure between myoglobin and α-hemoglobin, rather than being a strange "primitive" molecule. Similarly, the archetypal cytochrome c was intermediate in composition between yeast and vertebrate cytochromes c. By the same token, human α-hemoglobin and the hemoglobin in lampreys both may well have diverged far from the parent "protoglobin," each having been subjected to mutational events over a period of several hundred million years.

The separation of the myoglobins from the hemoglobins is an unusually favorably circumstance for the examination of evolution in terms of amino acid changes and base changes. It will be possible to study this example more completely and with accuracy when more information is available concerning the composition of the amino acid code.

The comparison will not be truly satisfactory, however, until the actual sequence of bases can be compared in the myoglobin and hemoglobin genes.

The report by Leder and Nirenberg (1964) that valine is coded by GUU, and the finding of Yanofsky (1963) that the direction of poly-peptide synthesis is co-polar with the valine coding sequence in the val x arg cross, indicate that the sequences in tables V and VIII should be read from right to left.

Revised Manuscript received February 10, 1964.

REFERENCES

Chan, S. K., Needleman, S. B., Stewart, J. W., Walasek, O. F., and Margoliash, E. (1963). *Federation Proc.* **22**, 658.
Gottlieb, A. J., Restrept, A., and Itano, H. A. (1964). *Federation Proc.* **23**, 172.
Hill, R. (1964). Private communication.
Hill, R. L., Buettner-Janusch, J., and Buettner-Janusch, V. (1963). *Proc. Natl. Acad. Sci. U.S.* **50**, 885.
Hunt, J. A., and Ingram, V. M. (1959). *Nature* **184**, 640.
Ingram, V. M. (1963). "The Hemoglobin in Genetics and Evolution." Columbia Univ. Press, New York.
Jones, O. W., and Nirenberg, M. W. (1962). *Proc. Natl. Acad. Sci. U.S.* **48**, 2115.
Jones, R. T., Coleman, R. D., and Heller, P. (1964). *Federation Proc.* **23**, 173.
Jukes, T. H. (1963a). *Am. Scientist* **51**, 227.
Jukes, T. H. (1963b). *Advan. Biol. Med. Phys.* **9**, 1.
Kalan, E. B., Greenberg, R., Walter, M., and Gordon, W. G. (1964). *Biochem. Biophys. Res. Comm.* **16**, 199.
Kreil, G. (1963). *Z. Physiol. Chem.* **334**, 154.

Kreil, G., and Tuppy, H. (1961). *Nature* **192**, 1123.

Leder, P., and Nirenberg, M. W. (1964). *Proc. Natl. Acad. Sci. U. S.* **52**, 420.

Lengyel, P., Speyer, J. F., and Ochoa, S. (1961). *Proc. Natl. Acad. Sci. U.S.* **47**, 1936.

Margoliash, E. (1963). *Proc. Natl. Acad. Sci. U.S.* **50**, 672

Margoliash, E., Smith, E. L., Kreil, G., and Tuppy, H. (1961). *Nature* **192**, 1125.

Matsubara, H., and Smith, E. L. (1962). *J. Biol. Chem.* **237**, PC3575.

Matthaei, J. H., Jones, O. W., Martin, R. G., and Nirenberg, M. W. (1962). *Proc. Natl. Acad. Sci. U.S.* **48**, 666.

Narita, K., Titani, K., Yaoi, Y., and Murakami, H. (1963). *Biochim. Biophys. Acta* **77**, 688.

Nirenberg, M. W., and Matthaei, J. H. (1961). *Proc. Natl. Acad. Sci. U.S.* **47**, 1588.

Paleus, S., and Tuppy, H. (1959). *Acta Chim. Scand.* **13**, 641.

Pierre, L E., Rath, C. E., and McCoy, K. (1963). *New Engl. J. Med.* **268**, 862.

Schroeder, W. A. (1963). *Ann. Rev. Biochem.* **32**, 301.

Smith, E. L. (1964). *Federation Proc.* (In preparation).

Speyer, J. F., Lengyel, P., Basilio, C., and Ochoa, S. (1962). *Proc. Natl. Acad. Sci. U.S.*, **48**, 441.

Tsugita, A., and Fraenkel-Conrat, H. (1962). *J. Mol. Biol.* **4**, 73.

Wahba, A. J., Gardner, R. S., Basilio, C., Miller, R. S., Speyer, J. F., and Lengyel, P. (1963a). *Proc. Natl. Acad. Sci. U.S.* **49**, 116.

Wahba, A. J., Miller, R. S., Basilio, C., Gardner, R. S., Lengyel, P., and Speyer, J. F. (1963b). *Proc. Natl. Acad. Sci. U.S.* **50**, 581.

Wittmann, H. G. (1961). *Naturwissenschaften.* **48**, 729.

Wittmann, H. G. (1963). "Informational Macromolecules" (H. J. Vogel, V. Bryson, J. O. Lampen, eds.), p. 177. Academic Press, New York.

Wittmann, H. G., and Wittmann-Liebold, B. (1963). *Cold Spring Harbor Symp. Quant. Biol.* **28**, 589.

Yanofsky, C. (1962). *Proc. Natl. Acad. Sci. U.S.* **48**, 195.

Yanofsky, C. A. (1963). *Cold Spring Harbor Symp. Quant. Biol.* **28**, 581.

Yanofsky, C., Carlton, B. C., Guest, J. R., Helinski, D., and Henning, V. (1964). *Proc. Natl. Acad. Sci. U.S.* **51**, 266

Yasunobu, K. T., Nakashima, T., Higa, H., Matsubara, H., and Benson, A. (1963). *Biochim. Biophys. Acta.* **78**, 791.

Zuckerkandl, E., and Pauling, L. (1962). In "Horizons in Biochemistry" (M. Kasha and B. Pullman, eds.), p. 189. Academic Press, New York.

DISCUSSION

MR. PIRIE: Jonathan Swift promised to write a "Panegyrical essay upon the number three." Had he written it, it would probably, like his "Meditation upon a broomstick," have tended to make fun of writers like Robert Boyle. For Boyle would have been more appreciative of the paper we have just heard than I am. Having lived through such episodes as Wrinch, and Bergmann and Niemann, I am hostile to this *a priori* approach to biochemistry.

At this meeting, unlike the meeting in Moscow, we seem to have agreed that viruses have nothing to do with the problem. I have maintained that for a long time, because viruses are wholly dependent on the metabolism of their hosts. But they are useful tools for studying specific synthesis because they are to some extent host-controlled. If you grow certain strains on different hosts, a different type of virus protein is made. This is demonstrated by amino acid composition and serology.

DR. JUKES: The same protein is made each time if the strain that has been treated with a chemical mutagen is put back in the same host.

MR. PIRIE: That may be all right.

DR. JUKES: That was done.

MR. PIRIE: If you put it in a different host, the host controls what is made, as well as the infecting agent. So it is not just the sequence of nucleotides in the nucleic acid that has control; the host affects the result as well.

The two effects are superimposed. The infecting agent is not in sole control of the structure of what is made; the host also has control.

DR. JUKES: Suppose one always obtains the same amino acid sequence from the untreated virus RNA in using the same host, then one at that point treats the RNA with nitrous acid and obtains a different amino acid sequence: what then?

MR. PIRIE: Then you have a different state of affairs. I am not saying the nucleic acid has no role. All I am saying is it hasn't a total role. The host affects what happens, too.

DR. JUKES: The same isolated tobacco mosaic virus RNA, using the same host, will always produce the same amino acid sequence. The variable is the mutagen.

MR. PIRIE: In that experiment you would have changed the infecting agent with a mutagen. You can also get a different product by changing the synthetic mechanism—that is, by using a different host.

DR. JUKES: It is the RNA and not the host that is in sole control of the amino acid sequence.

THE ROLE OF LIGHT IN EVOLUTION: THE TRANSITION FROM A ONE QUANTUM TO A TWO QUANTA MECHANISM

HANS GAFFRON

Institute of Molecular Biophysics and Department of Biological Sciences
(Fels Fund), The Florida State University,
Tallahassee, Florida

When in this discussion I shall speak of light, I mean the narrow portion of solar radiation from λ 360 to λ 900 mμ, which living beings make use of. Most of this spectral region is visible to us humans, except the part below λ 400 mμ which is visible, though, to limulus and insects, and that above λ 700 mμ, which is visible to purple bacteria.

Visibility means that the light-absorbing living pigments do not merely get warm—as any spot of paint does—but that they initiate a sequence of reactions which affect the life of the organism. Evolution has seen to it that these responses to light are beneficial for the respective organisms. Compared with the number of biochemical reactions which keep a living cell alive, the number of known photochemical reactions is very small. And again among these few, all are catalytic in the sense that they start a process which is driven by an energy source which is not light; all except one, and this one is photosynthesis. The evolutionary importance of photosynthesis stems from the fact—known for over a century—that all forms of life we are acquainted with depend ultimately on the efficient photochemical transformation of carbon dioxide into organic food. To point out that some microorganism can do the same trick without light—by reducing, for instance, carbon dioxide with hydrogen or sulfide or ferrous iron—does not invalidate the statement because oxygen from the air is always involved; the abundance of free oxygen in the atmosphere is the other important consequence of photosynthesis. It is very remarkable that the reaction which sustains life on Earth depends exclusively on one class of pigments, namely, the porphyrin magnesium

437

complexes called chlorophylls. The similarly constructed iron porphyrins, the hemes, are useless as photochemical agents but serve instead in numerous ways as electron transfer catalysts. If there have been chlorophyll-free organisms which could make use of other light-absorbing pigments to synthesize food from carbon dioxide and water, they have completely disappeared. We distinguish at the present time two kinds of photosynthetic reactions which depend on chlorophylls, one with, the other without an evolution of oxygen. The anaerobic process, photoreduction, appears to be a less advanced or earlier form of photosynthesis (For literature before 1963, see books edited by Pirson, 1960; Gest et al., 1963; Kok and Jagendorf, 1963). With the transition from one to the other, large quantities of oxygen began to accumulate on the surface of the Earth. I shall discuss first the molecular mechanism which brought this change about and then summarize again the reasons why I believe that the porphyrin pigments antedated the earliest living cell (Gaffron, 1957, 1958, 1960, 1962a,b). If so, they must have had a part in the interactions among the substances of the Miller-Urey soup, which we have mentioned so often at this meeting (Oparin, 1959, 1961; Pirie, 1959).

The oldest organisms on Earth of which we have some geological knowledge are said to have belonged to the blue-green algae. Their age is estimated, according to the rock formation they have been found in, at 2 billion years. We may conclude, therefore, that Darwinian evolution began to accelerate at about half time, measured in terms of the present age of our planet, which has been set at 5 billion years. If it has taken a long time for this planet to cool down to temperatures below boiling water, much less than 2 billion years are left for the hypothetical organochemical evolution ending in the appearance of the first living cell. Should it be confirmed that this Earth was formed at very low temperatures, the favorable period becomes, of course, longer.

We are agreed that radiation with light quanta of sufficient energy to break H—O or H—C bonds, or any other equivalent method of radical formation, caused or contributed to the accumulation of many moderately complex organic substances on the surface of the Earth. After listening to the reports on spontaneous chemical synthesis at this meeting, it appears as if nearly all smaller organic molecules (below molecular weight 1000) which play the role of metabolic building stones and catalysts in living cells, might have arisen spontaneously and in large quantities by one way or another, and, therefore, served for either biopoesis or as food for organisms intruding from outer space. Since the second possibility, entertained by some who believe in the significance of organized structures seen in certain meteorites, makes a discussion of a special biopoesis on Earth rather pointless, we shall leave it aside.

There is no evidence, however, that a mere accumulation of low molecular weight organic material is sufficient to bring about the mysterious emergence of self-reproducing entities (Landsberg, 1964), and such an accumulation would suffice even less without a continuous influx of free energy. The only uninterrupted supply of useful energy has been daylight.

It follows that we have to reconstruct the relevant part of the missing evidence by studying all kinds of light-driven reactions. There are, of course, two approaches. One is to invent artificial organic systems which might be elevated by light onto levels of greater complexity; the other to take apart the most efficient photobiological reaction we know of, until we find the essential core of the photochemistry around which the living cell developed to its present form.

The rough outline of the photosynthetic process is, of course, familiar to all of you. But we have been slow in recognizing the importance of two rather general points. The one is that any fossil plant or microorganism which is recognizably related to contemporary photosynthetic forms must have contained all fundamental sets of enzymes and pigments that make photosynthesis possible. Biochemically, these organisms were up to date, and if they did evolve oxygen it means that the anaerobic or partially anaerobic period on Earth dates farther back than 2 billion years. The second point is that photosynthesis requires the cooperation of a few basic and ubiquitous biological processes which in themselves are not photochemical at all. It follows that already 2 billion years ago life was an old invention with a long period of evolution in its past. Figure 1 may illustrate what I mean. Generally, it suffices to call "photochemical" all those biological processes which would not proceed without light. This definition covers all events from the initial absorption of light to the deposition of the final products. For our purposes here we need a stricter definition, and a sharper description of what we mean by photochemical. No biological light reaction is known which does not consist of a sequence of photophysical, photochemical, and purely enzymatic steps, and most of the latter are of the kind that proceed nearly everywhere without light. Where, therefore, shall we draw the line between light and dark reactions? How many steps after the light absorption act do the truly biochemical processes begin? Should we divide physics and chemistry according to electronic excitation states which do not happen at normal temperatures unless light is present, or should we include those chemical steps which make immediate use of the energy of light quanta and would otherwise not proceed at ambient temperatures? Probably the latter definition is the most appropriate one for inquiries on photobiological processes. We have also to consider the possibility that biochemical specificity does not begin with the secondary enzymes, but even at the primary excitation level of the pigment.

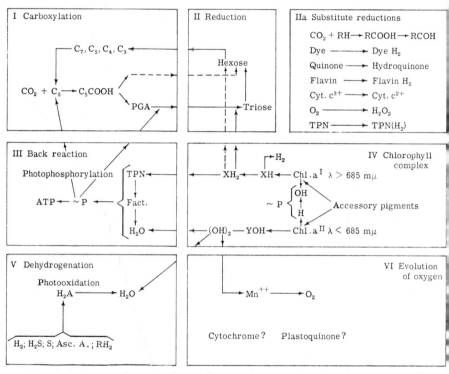

Fig. 1. Summary of present knowledge of photosynthesis as a set of at least five semi-independent reaction systems which have to cooperate in order to achieve the synthesis of organic matter from carbon dioxide.

The binding of the pigment in the organic matrix may be responsible for energy-rich states which are different from those of the naked chlorophyll molecules in solution. According to our definition, the parts of the complete photosynthetic system summarized in Fig. 1 which deal with the carboxylation of ribulose diphosphate, the reduction of phosphoglycerate, the Calvin-Benson cycle, the phosphorylation of intermediates, the production of adenosine triphosphate (ATP), the evolution of oxygen via a manganese catalyst or the equivalent utilization of hydrogen donors are all enzymatic dark reactions. We can keep them separate from the primary photochemical process, which is our main interest here. Most of the dark reactions have been found in chlorophyll-free cells and are well known as typical and ubiquitous steps of intermediary metabolism. Only the release of free oxygen from water is a reaction which seems to require direct interaction with light-excited molecules and has not been duplicated by any combination of enzymes and substrates. Yet it too must be a process containing a number of non-photochemical enzymatic reaction steps, simply because it cannot be accomplished in less than five such steps. In other words, we recognize a cluster of biochemical systems around a complex of pigments. Each system serves a different purpose, and together they solve the task of converting as much as possible of the 40 kcal available in the first singlet state of chlorophyll into chemical energy. This picture is based on experiments which show that some of the normal partial reactions can be eliminated or changed. We may have oxygen evolution without carbon dioxide reduction, or the reverse, namely, carbon dioxide reduction without oxygen evolution. We may observe a light-induced formation of ATP without any gas exchange, or instead the simultaneous evolution of hydrogen and carbon dioxide if synthetic processes are hindered. This complexity and variability forces us to assume that complete photosynthesis as it appeared in the blue algae 2 billion years ago must have had a long evolutionary history stretching still further back in time.

The central problem is the evolution of a pigment system which has the capacity to decompose water into its elements. The photolysis of water must be regarded as the primary achievement of the chlorophyll system. Everything else follows via reaction patterns which have become well known in general biochemistry. Thirty years ago van Niel pointed out that certain photosynthetic microbes, the purple and green bacteria, might represent remnants of an orginally much wider class of organisms having a photosynthetic system simpler than that known from green plants. The metabolism of purple bacteria could serve as an example for the kind of photochemistry which may have preceded that of the green plants on the evolutionary time scale. These organisms cannot evolve oxygen, though many tolerate oxygen. Because they require energy-rich hydrogen donors to reduce carbon dioxide, they do not contribute much to the store of free energy in the living world. Over-all light has only a catalytic function in these organisms. It lowers the entropy of the systems by producing a higher order of complexity—namely, the bacteria—but it does not serve to store chemical energy to be used later. Compared with the green plants and other aerobic organisms, purple bacteria seem primitive, because as obligate anaerobes they have no useful respiration, no useful fermentation, and grow therefore only in the light. But the pigment complex responsible for the utilization of light energy is strikingly similar to that of the green plants. It too contains chlorophylls, cytochromes, pyridine nucleotides, flavins, quinones, ferredoxin, and loosely bound metals. If the difference between the anaerobic purple bacteria and the unicellular aerobic algae signifies an evolutionary step forward, wherein does it consist? Why do the algae release free oxygen from water and the bacteria do not? One easy answer is the acquisition of new enzymes—and indeed the plants have a manganese catalyst, that the bacteria seem to lack, which is specific for the release of oxygen. Lack of manganese depresses oxygen evolution. Yet plants poor in manganese can still perform many of the other partial reactions. They can fix and reduce carbon dioxide, produce ATP, etc. The bacteria, on the other hand, need only one-thousandth of the amount of manganese which a healthy green plant requires. For a while I thought that this was the main difference between plants and bacteria. This idea was, however, not too convincing because manganese and an assortment of proteins must have been available to the purple bacteria and again to their predecessors. The hypothesis can be improved by combining the need for a special enzyme with the solution of the problem of how to decompose water in red light, where the energy of a single quantum cannot do the job. It is taken now as an axiom that it is impossible to separate H from OH (as in water) irreversibly and to release them as hydrogen and oxygen with the energy of only one red light quantum. Hence two quanta have to be used for this feat; any number of measurements of the efficiency of complete photosynthesis or of the intermediate electron transport steps have shown that two light absorption acts have to be coupled to achieve what the green plants but not the bacteria are able to do.

The transition from a one quantum to a two quanta mechanism looks *a priori*, therefore, as the kind of change one would choose if one had to explain a far-reaching evolutionary innovation.

To understand this transition, we must now distinguish between processes which over-all need the energy of more than one light quantum, but which require nothing better than a simple repetition of the same one-quantum step, and a process where the success of one light reaction depends on that of a second light reaction, and where the second is not identical with the first. A difference must appear already in the characteristics of the light-absorbing pigment. In other words, two times reactions 1 + 2 would not equal the sum of reactions 1, 2, 3, and 4.

$$A + Chl^I H \xrightarrow[\text{1st h}\nu] AH\cdot + Chl^I\cdot \tag{1}$$

$$Chl^I\cdot + BH\cdot \longrightarrow Chl^I H + B \tag{2}$$

$$B + Chl^{II} H \xrightarrow[\text{2nd h}\nu] BH\cdot + Chl^{II}\cdot \tag{3}$$

$$Chl^{II}\cdot + [OH_2] \longrightarrow [OH\cdot] + Chl^{II} H \tag{4}$$

The sequence 1 and 2 is possible when the molecule BH· (or BH$_2$) is a reducing agent or at least a hydrogen donor whose free energy is not much lower than that of the product AH· so that the difference can be easily covered by the energy of one absorbed light quantum. This would be the case of the anaerobic bacteria. But if BH· is not freely available and has to be made first by the dehydrogenation of a substance [OH$_2$] in which the hydrogen is as tightly bound as in water, a second light step has to be added for the reaction pair 3 + 4. Obviously, matters must be so arranged that the pigment system Chl^I covers the potential range between AH· and B, and the pigment system Chl^{II} that between BH· and [OH·]. There are at present two theories which claim to explain the interrelationship between Chl^I and Chl^{II}. The biochemists operate with the idea of a permanent difference, namely, two (or more) pigment systems whose potential and specificity are determined by the proteins to which the components are bound (the variation in oxidoreduction potentials of different cytochromes is the prime example; cf. Kamen, 1963; Gest et al., 1963). The physicochemists point out that the Chl^{II} may become Chl^I through the very circumstance that it has first changed B into BH·.

This bare outline of the twin pigment system given by equations 1–4 and Fig. 2 (p. 448) must suffice. We omit a discussion of why the final primary product of a one-electron step sequence will have to be stabilized by dismutation into fully reduced or oxidized compounds. We also omit a description of the "photosynthetic unit" which transmits photons to the reaction centers Chl^{I}H and Chl^{II}H. But in passing I wish to point out that the latter shows also an evolutionary change. In the green plants the unit is about ten times larger than in some of the photosynthetic bacteria.

Opportunities for coupled phosphorylation are of two kinds. One exists within reaction 2 when BH· is oxidized to B, and the other when reaction 1 is followed by a re-oxidation of AH· to A (or AH$_2$ to A). Because this back reaction is not built into the mechanism as is reaction 2, it permits a choice of electron acceptors.

The combined biochemical analyses of many workers have proceeded to the point where one can say that A represents a group of enzymes made up of ferredoxin, flavin, pyridine nucleotides on the reducing end of the photochemical mechanism; and $[OH_2]$, a system which includes cytochrome, oxygen precursors, manganese, and oxygen at the oxidizing end. Spectroscopic evidence, such as adduced by the work of Duysens, Witt, and others (cf. Kok and Jagendorf, 1963), supports the idea that B is either a quinone or a cytochrome, or a combination of both. Figure 2 I have taken from a paper I read 2 years ago at the Gif conference. It is one of many similar schemes intended to represent the working of a two-pigment–two-quanta mechanism, the details of which are at present the most discussed subject in the literature on photosynthesis (cf. Kok and Jagendorf, 1963).

It all started with Emerson's discovery that light of wavelengths longer than λ 690 mμ, although still absorbed by the chloroplast, is much less efficient in releasing photosynthetic oxygen than light in the main visible region reaching from λ 690 mμ toward shorter wavelengths in the near ultraviolet.

In going to longer wavelengths beyond λ 690 mμ, the rate of photosynthesis begins to decline faster than the light absorption itself, that is, faster than we would expect for ordinary physical reasons. It is not a matter of insufficient light absorption. For instance, green light is only weakly absorbed by chlorophyll. Nevertheless, per quantum absorbed, green light is usually just as efficient as blue or red. Thus we are in need of a special biochemical explanation.

The low efficiency of near infrared light is, however, only one-half the puzzle. The other half of Emerson's discovery is that the low efficiency of oxygen evolution in monochromatic light above λ 700 mμ tends to disappear when the inefficient light is offered together with light of shorter wavelengths. The effect is called "enhancement" and has been confirmed in numerous laboratories. The experimental results look somewhat like this: 1000 quanta of monochromatic light at λ 650 mμ release 100 molecules of oxygen from the absorbing green tissue; 1000 quanta of equally monochromatic light at λ 710 mμ release only 20. But both lights together do not produce 120 as one might expect, but, say, 160 molecules of O_2. The magnitude of such enhancements varies.

In nature all green plants are exposed to the entire daylight spectrum. The enhancement of photosynthetic reactions by superimposition of colors is always there. It is the normal case. And if the tail absorption on the long wavelength side of the chlorophyll spectrum is used for cyclic phosphorylation, we can be sure that it contributes in this way to the over-all process in photosynthesis. It saves some short wavelength light energy, so suitable for the evolution of oxygen, from being diverted into those phosphorylations which are a prerequisite for the reduction with water as hydrogen donor.

At the present time most of my colleagues in this field are looking for more direct evidence that would explain how short wavelength light helps the long wave light to become effective or, vice versa, how the latter may help the short wave light to produce more oxygen per quantum absorbed. The pigment complex must somehow be able to distinguish between these two colors. Either there is another pigment in addition to chlorophyll a, which absorbs more strongly around λ 720 mμ, or chlorophyll a itself deals differently with light quanta having less than 40 kcal of energy. No wonder that this appears to be a problem cut out for careful spectroscopic work.

Butler, Chance, Duysens, French, Kok, Myers, Rabinowitch, Witt, and others (cf. Kok and Jagendorf, 1963) have built particularly sensitive apparatuses—such as differential recording double spectrographs—which permit them to record slight changes in the absorption of various chloroplast pigments or to measure rates of photosynthesis under the influence of pure or mixed monochromatic radiations. Some of these absorption changes have been identified as due to pigments other than chlorophyll but associated with it.

The time sequence of spectral changes measured in fractions of a second is a way to follow electron transfer steps induced by the absorption of light, and to correlate them with the activity of known pigments. From this, one tries to construct a sequence of events amenable to interpretation in terms of the normal photosynthetic metabolism. There is no doubt that spectroscopic analysis is the one way to unravel the details of pigment interaction. But for the moment we want to know first of all what is the light energy in the near infrared good for, if it cannot promote regular photosynthesis?

This question can be approached in a simpler manner. In the presence of inorganic and organic hydrogen donors, purple and green bacteria make very effective use of light between λ 700 and 900 mμ to convert CO_2 into more bacteria without having to evolve oxygen simultaneously. From the point of view of evolution, it would be significant if it could be shown that this ability might still be a part of the photosynthetic mechanism of the algae. For all we know, the primary photoproducts formed in the main visible region may suffice for complete photosynthesis or they may need to be supplemented by the photoproducts of the mechanism which is activated in the near infrared. This will be difficult to ascertain because absorbed short wavelength energy easily migrates as such to absorption centers of lower energy levels, the same levels which correspond to direct light absorption at longer wavelengths. Until recently nothing had been seen in green cells which would suggest that light beyond λ 700 mμ, when used in isolation, might produce something useful for the plant. As far as the normal gas exchange is concerned, its energy could just as well be dissipated as heat. The task, therefore, consists in finding metabolic reactions which differ from normal photosynthesis but are promoted by light of this wavelength. One may study either partial reactions of photosynthesis with the aid of broken cells—and this has been done by Hoch (cf. Kok and Jagendorf, 1963) and by Arnon (Tagawa *et al.*, 1963)—or look for variants of the photosynthetic process in the intact cells, such as a bacterial type of metabolism where oxygen evolution is not a part of the over-all process. The latter has been our approach. We have found two such light-driven systems in intact cells, and our tests with near infrared light have fortunately been successful in both cases. These two metabolic processes in intact cells are the carbon dioxide photoreduction with molecular hydrogen in hydrogenase-containing algae such as *Scenedesmus* or *Chlamydomonas* (Bishop and Gaffron, 1962), and the photoassimilation of acetate in at least one alga, a volvocale called *Chlamydobotrys*. Pringsheim and Wiessner (1960) in Göttingen discovered that *Chlamydobotrys* does respire acetate in air, and yet is not a heterotrophic aerobic organism in the usual sense because it needs light for growth (Wiessner, 1963; Wiessner and Gaffron, 1964a,b). The light is absorbed by a normal, chlorophyll-containing green chloroplast. But it is acetate, not carbon dioxide, which is assimilated in the light, and correspondingly there is no oxygen evolution. In short, it is an organism with a double aberration from the normal metabolism of a green plant. Many photosynthesizing algae can grow with acetate in the dark. This one cannot. All photosynthesizing algae use carbon dioxide as their main carbon source and do this while releasing oxygen into the air. *Chlamydobotrys* does not grow with carbon dioxide. It has nevertheless some capacity for photosynthesis. But this ability becomes important only under anaerobic conditions as a mechanism to supply the missing oxygen. According to Wiessner, *Chlamydobotrys* grows at the expense of an oxidative mechanism in combination with photophosphorylation. I invited Dr. Wiessner, therefore, to my laboratory to look for an Emerson effect within this unusual metabolic pattern. The result, obtained just recently, is that the photoassimilation of acetate proceeds aerobically as well or better at λ 723 mμ as it does at λ 620 mμ, i.e., at wavelengths outside as well as inside the spectral range for normal photosynthesis. Two years earlier Dr. Bishop and I had found that the same is true for photoreduction in adapted algae (Gaffron and Bishop, 1963). It is a simple experiment to do. The same cells of *Scenedesmus* which had shown a very poor rate of photosynthesis at λ 705 mμ or λ 720 mμ, photoreduced carbon dioxide rapidly after 2 hours of adaptation to hydrogen.

This long discourse on the variations of the mechanism of green plant photosynthesis was necessary to make the point that the green chloroplasts evidently contain the components of a thermodynamically simpler synthetic process, very similar to, if not identical with, that of anaerobic photosynthetic bacteria.

The accident that the spectra of the responsible pigments are not quite alike made it possible to demonstrate the existence of a double system, which seems indeed to work according to the principle of equations 1–4 and Fig. 2. One more remark is necessary and we are finished with this chapter. You all know that phosphorylation, ATP formation, is a necessary part of any photometabolism of the synthetic kind. Apropos of Fig. 1, I also said that phosphorylation may be counted among the nonphotochemical reactions. Looking at equations 1–4, it is obvious that we have at least two possibilities for collecting the required energy— namely via an oxidation of AH to A and that of BH to B. These would correspond to what Arnon has named cyclic and noncyclic phosphorylation. Figure 2 indicates where these dark reactions may be located. It is important that the photoreducing mechanism of adapted algae and bacteria (reactions 1 and 2) offers these two choices independent of the possible coupling and extension to include reactions 3 and 4.

Further experimental support for the contention that part of the photosynthetic mechanism of green plants corresponds to that in the anaerobic purple bacteria is given by the selective effect of a series of metabolic poisons which interfere only with oxygen evolution and leave the part of the bacterial type of metabolism intact. Finally I ought to mention that Bishop (1962) found a mutant of *Scenedesmus* which is genetically unable to release oxygen. For the rest, however, the photometabolism of this mutant is again the bacterial type of photoreduction with hydrogen.

To sum up what I have said so far: the analysis of the parts of the photosynthetic mechanism as revealed in different and differently treated organisms has told us what must have happened more than 2 billion years ago. A new version of the already existing one-step photochemical mechanism appeared in which the over-all oxidation-reduction potential gradually shifted to the point where the old and the new mechanism barely overlapped. The two pigment systems combined and in this way formed an electron transport chain which spanned the potential gap

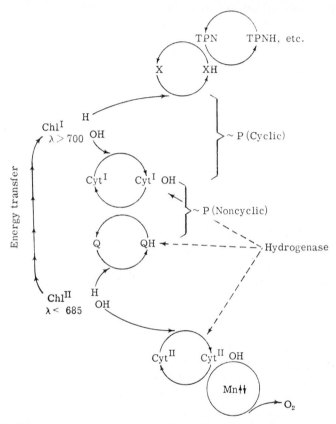

Fig. 2. Schematic attempt to explain the relationship between complete photosynthesis and photoreduction without oxygen evolution in normal green algae.

between an as yet unknown oxygen precursor (peroxide?) and reduced hydrogenase, with the result that water could now be decomposed photochemically into its elements in large quantites, something that had not happened since the time that high energy ultraviolet radiation had ceased to penetrate through the atmosphere to the surface of the Earth.

The last and aerobic era of the evolution of living beings is the true domain of Darwinian evolution (no multicellular obligate anaerobic organisms are known). After it had come about through the transition from one quantum light reactions to a very specific two quanta mechanism, there has been no need of further improvement. One quantum processes of the type indicated by reaction 2 in combination with 1, can be rigged up in the laboratory, and the question is now whether it may be possible to isolate still simpler physiological light reactions in living chloroplasts that will approach the mechanism of processes we are able to build up artificially.

The transition from mainly anaerobic to mainly aerobic conditions on Earth was brought about not by geochemical but by living forces. Since then only minor changes such as continental shifts, temperature fluctuations, or volcanic action have harassed the living world. At the present time we can easily see that another living force, our own activities, threatens the continued existence of man and beast alike. Man-made radiation, man-made poisons, etc., may bring us very rapidly to the next evolutionary crisis, perhaps comparable in general importance to the one we have dealt with at length. To return to my main theme: what has been the role of daylight in the times before the magnesium porphyrins became the center of protein-supported energy conversions?

I have used Table I on other occasions as a quick summary of now widely accepted beliefs concerning the steps of organic chemical evolution. I find it practical to distinguish five eras which follow each other after characteristic major irreversible environmental changes. Each such change brought some major evolutionary accomplishments to a stop because the supply of material formed exclusively during the past period disappeared. With several bridges burnt along this one-way trail, we cannot say how many statistically and thermodynamically promising beginnings of biopoesis got lost forever. We have to play this fascinating guessing game with the chips nature has left us and the general rules of physics and chemistry which seem to be valid everywhere in the cosmos.

The discussion of the first era we can skip entirely, because this conference has already reviewed practically everything that is worth saying about it. Eras IV and V, dominated by the chlorophyll-catalyzed photosynthetic reactions, have just been dealt with. What can we say about evolution after the loss of hydrogen and of ultraviolet? For our understanding these periods constitute the truly dark ages. And therefore I would like to make the point that without a successful use of visible light as the driving force during eras II and III not much more could have happened. The energy of visible light in the solar spectrum is twenty to thirty times that in the ultraviolet region. It is not reasonable to assume that this energy went unused until the complete living cells began to synthesize chlorophyll. To the contrary, we can be sure that iron, cesium or manganese compounds absorbed light according to their known absorption spectra in the near ultraviolet and underwent photo-

TABLE I

CURRENT BELIEFS ON THE SUCCESSION OF EVOLUTIONARY ERAS

Era	Environment	Energy source	Outcome
I	Anaerobic; CH_4, NH_3, H_2	UV; heat	Acetate, glycine, uracil, adenine, "organic soup"
	Loss of hydrogen		
II	Anaerobic; traces of O_2	UV; heat; visible light	Polyphosphates, peptides, POR-PHYRINS, oxido-reductions
	Loss of ultraviolet		
III	Anaerobic; traces of O_2; CO_2	Visible light	Surface catalysis, PHOTO-CHEMISTRY Synthetic reproduction cycles
	Loss of free food		
IV	Anaerobic; CO_2; traces of O_2	Photoreduction; fermentation	Multiplying metabolic units TWO-QUANTA PROCESS involving water Cells
	Loss of anaerobiosis		
V	Aerobic Anaerobic pockets	Photosynthesis; respiration	Autotrophic plants Darwinian evolution Mind

chemical changes. Larger amounts of oxygen must have been absent, otherwise autoxidation and photoxidation would have destroyed in a short time the raw material that our hypothesis of chemical evolution depends on.

That we have no living organism which makes use of the photo-chemistry of uranyl or rare earth salts is no reason to overlook the possibilities of their original usefulness. But in my opinion the search for a likely photosensitizer need not lead us so far outside the realm of the well-known. A photoactive pigment available long before the modern type of photosynthesis came into being might have been the precursor to the chlorophyll molecule itself. The inner skeleton of chlorophyll, the porphyrin ring, is a pigment of unusual stability, known to be able to catalyze numerous photochemical reactions *in vitro*. For the chemists the synthesis of such tetrapyrrole compounds has been a very difficult accomplishment. An evolutionary hypothesis based on the photochemistry of porphyrins seems not very promising because of the apparent improbability of the very first requirement—namely, the spontaneous appearance of such pigments. It is true, Shemin and his school at Columbia showed how the living cell is able to synthesize porphyrins in short shrift from the simplest of organic compounds such as acetate and glycine. But this, as we all know, happens with the aid of living enzymes—a far cry from what the chemist can do when he has to work without specific enzymes.

The difference between enzymatic and nonenzymatic reactions is regularly pointed out as the great, perhaps unsurmountable, barrier between organic chemical and organismic evolution. The standard answer to this, now given just as regularly, is to point out that thermodynamically time must be able to replace enzyme action because the latter does not change the energy relationships. And before modern enzymes evolved, less complicated models of cellular metabolism must have existed for every one of the basic reactions, which we are now accustomed to see coupled to catalytic proteins. Because the natural synthesis of porphyrins from the most abundant of compounds found in the original hypothetical organic soup is so astoundingly simple, I proposed in 1955 that the porphyrins have very likely been natural catalysts long before they became incorporated as important tools into the living cell (Gaffron, 1958). Most of the condensations which lead from acetate and glycine over δ-amino levulinic acid and porphobilinogen to porphyrins in the living cell seem to be exergonic. So far this natural synthesis has not been achieved artificially, probably because too few variations of the Miller experiment have been tried. Dr. Szutka here has given us an example—but his starting materials are not the ones I would like to see used in order to prove that under early earth conditions porphyrins arose from glycine and acetate.

It is often taken for granted that the main trick of evolution consisted in a grandiose process of autocatalysis—a general progress from rather insignificant beginnings toward a more specific, a more efficient, utilization of thermal and chemical sources of energy. For photochemical processes, however, this is not quite true. An absorption act is 100% efficient. The molecule either absorbs or does not absorb a particular light quantum. Evidently the problem consists in preserving the high efficiency of the primary act, which cannot be improved upon.

The light-absorbing molecule itself has to be stable not only against the impact of a high energy quantum, but also against chemical attack by its own reaction products. The latter must be of a kind that easily start a quick and progressing line of further transformations. Only in this way is it possible to avoid premature, i.e., useless, recombinations. May it be said in passing that photochemical reactions have the advantage of creating highly reactive or complex new molecules in cool surroundings and therefore guarantee them a lifetime a million or more times longer than they would have if they were synthesized by thermal reactions. And as long as protein-like substances were not around on Earth, photochemical reactions were the only ones which could, at least for the initial steps, dispense with the need for catalysts to lower activation energy barriers. In photochemical reactions most of these barriers are no hindrance because there is plenty of energy available on the forward move to overcome them easily. By the same token the photochemical steps are practically irreversible once the energy has been spent to produce molecular rearrangements.

These are my excuses for assuming that fluorescent organic dye stuffs must have been a great evolutionary force. And among them the porphyrins seem to be as appropriate as any. The possibility for an easy synthesis is given. Their stability is most remarkable, not only in the dark but also when they are used as sensitizers in artificial photochemical reactions. For comparison I might mention another natural class of fluorescent pigments, the flavins. Unprotected, they bleach easily and are often destroyed when exposed to light under aerobic as well as anaerobic conditions.

Porphyrin and its chelates, with magnesium and zinc, are among the most efficient sensitizers for photochemical reactions *in vitro*, for both photoreduction and photoxidation. In slightly exergonic reactions, it is easy to obtain quantum yields of one. At this meeting we have discussed how very plausible the notion has become that polyphosphates, or primitive nucleic acids, or polyamino acids, may have been formed under early Earth conditions, all of them substances with rudimentary catalytic powers which we find vastly amplified in the living state. It seems to me that the appearance of photochemically active organic pigments of the kind that are present in all living organisms and particularly in the photosynthetic ones, is one of the most plausible propositions we can make. The further development of the various ways through which porphyrin chelates have come to play such dominant roles in the basic mechanism of biochemical reactions must, of course, have depended on other simultaneous transformations within the available organic raw material. As I pointed out, porphyrin-sensitized oxidoreductions can be very efficient in concentrated solution. In order to maintain such high efficiencies when the dissolved substrates are not around in large quantities, living cells use the trick of adsorption at interfaces. Except for the work of Oster et al. (1962), there has not been a systematic search for characteristic influences of surfaces on organic photochemistry. The spontaneous polymerization of amino acids and of purines and pyrimidines we heard about at this meeting might quite possibly lead to compounds capable of supporting particularly efficient light reactions. No experiments along this line seem to have been done.

Until recently I believed that only reactions proceeding in the presence of macromolecules could show time course patterns which would deviate considerably from those dictated by the mass action laws which prevail in homogeneous solutions. A few years ago we came upon a strange photochemical reaction with which we are still occupied because it exhibits very peculiar kinetic characteristics (Habermann and Gaffron, 1962). It would take too long to describe in detail. Suffice it to say that it deals with the flavin sensitized photoxidation of ascorbic acid in neutral or slightly acid solution. The final end products are oxalic and threonic acids (Homann and Gaffron, 1963). Whenever the solution contains, besides ascorbate and flavin, also manganous ion and catalase, the process falls apart into two distinct steps which are not seen without these additions. In the presence of catalase and manganous ions, the first stable photoxidation product, diketogulonic acid, accumulates quantitatively until the last traces of the original ascorbate have been oxidized, then the photoxidation continues with the accumulated product as substrate—and the second reaction may run even faster than did the first. This quite unexpected sequence of events comes about because traces of ascorbate inhibit the manganese-catalyzed photoxidation of diketogulonate, and excess oxygen in turn slows down the photoxidation of ascorbate.

Such observations encourage us to search for reactions likely to have happened under early Earth conditions, not in simple well-defined and fully understood combinations, but in mixtures containing quite "unnecessary" additions. The latter might surprise us by their ability to act as regulating factors (Homann and Gaffron, 1964). I believe Dr. Fox would agree with this principle.

Students of sensitized photochemical reactions *in vitro* know of course that the greatest obstacle to a practical utilization of light energy in this manner is the tendency of the reaction products to recombine either directly or via a short detour of at most one or two intermediate steps. Under such conditions we find no permanent change, and no utilizable gain in energy. The living cell has solved the problem of premature and useless back reactions by making the detour longer and longer; in other words, by converting the back reactions into a cycle to which other metabolic processes can be coupled—a trick which also appears in many variations among nonphotochemical metabolic reactions. Perhaps—as I have said at greater length before, (Gaffron, 1962a)—some of the basic metabolic reactions such as phosphorylation and respiration arose first as partial reactions in the vicinity of the light-excited pigment. Only later did they develop into independent metabolic processes. It is also worth mentioning in this respect that in all photosynthetic organisms anaerobic fermentations in the dark not only are weak, but apparently useless. Fermentation of carbohydrates, the prototype of anaerobic dissimilation, may have appeared only after the plants had developed such an efficient way of producing carbohydrates in quantity. If the last phases of the development of photosynthetic organisms were as I have sketched them, it means that all organic light reactions have remained one-quantum processes from the very beginning, when they were initiated by single porphyrin molecules in solution, through the time they were going on in protein and lipid-bound pigment complexes, until the very last transformation produced the two-quanta mechanism of the green chloroplast. Very likely, therefore, the latter arose not before but after a complete cellular mechanism had already come into existence.

However plausible it may be that, in the course of organic chemical evolution, light has never ceased to be the most versatile energy source, it may not have had anything to do with the mysterious emergence of specific macromolecules; the transition from the open, Lamarckian system of continued and accidental acquisitions of new but lasting traits to the closed society of genes and enzymes is definitely another story. Yet careful comparison of the photochemical systems we can construct artificially with those which we may succeed in carving out of the living cell might help us to describe the conditions, and thereby to set the time, when a cell membrane became indispensable for the continuation of evolution.

ACKNOWLEDGMENTS

These studies were aided by contracts between the Office of Naval Research, Department of the Navy [NONR 988-(10)] and the United States Atomic Energy

Commission [AT-(40-1)-2687] and the Florida State University, and by Air Force Office of Scientific Research grant AF-AFOSR-62-190.
Revised Manuscript received April 8, 1964.

REFERENCES

Books on Photosynthesis and Photoreduction Containing References up to and including 1963
Pirson, A., ed. (1960). "Encyclopedia of Plant Physiology," Vol. V, Parts 1 and 2. Springer, Berlin.
Gest, H., San Pietro, A., and Vernon, L. P., eds. (1963). "Bacterial Photosynthesis." Antioch Press, Yellow Springs, Ohio.
Kok, B., and Jagendorf, A., eds. (1963). "Photosynthetic Mechanisms in Green Plants." Publ. 1145, U. S. National Academy of Science National Research Council.
Kamen, M. (1963). "Primary Processes in Photosynthesis." Academic Press, New York, New York.
Evolution of Photosynthesis
Bishop, N. I. (1962). *Nature* 195, 55.
Bishop, N. I., and Gaffron, H. (1962). *Biochem. Biophys. Res. Commun.* 8, 471.
Gaffron, H. (1957). In "Rhythmic and Synthetic Processes in Growth" (D. Rudnick, ed.), p. 127. Princeton Univ. Press, Princeton, New Jersey.
Gaffron, H. (1958). *Trans. Conf. Use of Solar Energy, Tucson, Arizona, 1955* Vol. 4, p. 145.
Gaffron, H. (1960). In "Evolution after Darwin" (Sol Tax, ed.), Vol. I, p. 39. Univ. of Chicago Press, Chicago, Illinois.
Gaffron, H. (1962a). In "Horizons in Biochemistry" (M. Kasha and B. Pullman, eds.), p. 59. Academic Press, New York.
Gaffron, H. (1962b). In "Beiträge zur Physiologie und Morphologie der Algen," p. 1. Fischer, Stuttgart.
Gaffron, H., and Bishop, N. I. (1963). In "La Photosynthese," p. 229. Editions du Centre National de la Recherche Scientifique, Paris.
Habermann, H., and Gaffron, H. (1962). *Photochem. Photobiol.* 1, 159.
Homann, P., and Gaffron, H. (1963). *Science* 141, 905.
Homann, P., and Gaffron, H. (1964). *Photochem. Photobiol.* In press.
Landsberg, P. T. (1964). *Nature* 203, 928.
Oparin, A. I. (1959). *Origin Life Earth, Rept. Intern. Symp. Moscow, 1957.*
Oparin, A. I. (1961). "Life: its Nature, Origin and Development." Oliver & Boyd, Edinburgh and London.
Oster, G. K., Oster, G., and Dobin, C. (1962). *J. Phys. Chem.* 66, 2511.
Pirie, N. W. (1959). *ICSU Rev.* 1, 40.
Pringsheim, E. G., and Wiessner, W. (1960). *Nature* 188, 919.
Tagawa, K., Tsujimoto, H. Y., and Arnon, D. I. (1963). *Nature* 199, 1247.
Wiessner, W. (1963). *Arch. Mikrobiol.* 45, 33.
Wiessner, W., and Gaffron, H. (1964a). *Nature* 201, 725.
Wiessner, W., and Gaffron, H. (1964b). *Federation Proc.* 23, 226.

DISCUSSION

Dr. Oró: I join Professor Gaffron's concern over the fact that very little work has been done with regard to pigments, and I think he is quite right that pigments should not be difficult to synthesize under reasonably simple conditions. In our laboratory we have evidence for the abiotic synthesis of yellow and pink pigments, some of which are photo-sensitive.

DR. SAGAN: A very important point is the great excess of energy in the visible region of the spectrum, compared with the ultraviolet. Any reasonable plant would cash in on this order of magnitude difference, and photosynthesize in the visible. But we might then expect plants to be black. Why are plants green?

DR. GAFFRON: They are so only in thin layers. You take many leaves and they look nearly black, like dense forests from an airplane. When you make a chlorophyll solution strong enough, you can't look through it. But after your eyes have been adapted to near infrared light, the apparently black chlorophyll solution becomes transparent. It is only in this near infrared region beyond λ 720 mμ where the chlorophyll ceases to absorb light efficiently. Otherwise this molecule is about the best active pigment nature has devised. In the green region the percentage absorption is least—but when green light is absorbed it is efficiently used.

DR. SAGAN: Adaptations toward saturation amounts of chlorophyll and the development of accessory pigments such as the carotenoids and the phycobilins suggests that at least some plants want to absorb photons where chlorophyll doesn't ordinarily absorb.

DR. GAFFRON: Particularly in the sea. When you go under the water, you begin to restrict the color of the light to spectral regions where the chlorophyll would not absorb much energy. As Dr. Sagan rightly points out, many plants contain so-called accessory pigments, the blue, red, and brown ones. They are not essential for the process as such, as I described it. There is only a physical coupling. The other pigments found in the chlorophyll apparatus in most cases transfer the energy in a physical way, exciton transfer, charge transfer, and sensitized fluores-cence.

DR. Fox: To follow Dr. Oró's lead, pigments are produced easily in the thermal experiments. In the summer of 1957 I polymerized amino acids thermally in the laboratory of Dr. Denis Fox at La Jolla. From this reaction mixture, particularly from the polymerization of glycine, Dr. Fox isolated some pigments.

DR. GAFFRON: In the literature there is a report that diacetyl can be produced with ultraviolet from acetate. The product, diacetyl, is colored. Thus some photochemistry with visible light absorbed by compounds like diacetyl was possible on the very morning of creation. In the same way porphyrins may have appeared as soon as plenty of acetate and glycine became available.

DR. SZUTKA: I think that Dr. Gaffron in his paper pointed out several important problems related to photosynthesis, and especially to the synthesis of porphines and porphine-like substances.

First of all, I agree that the first pigments that were formed and utilized in photosynthesis were somewhat similar to porphines. But they were not necessarily as elaborate as chlorophylls that we have right now.

In order to make the absorption of light more efficient, some of the compounds, similar to anthocyanins, could be active. In my work ten to fifteen compounds were formed in addition to the porphines.

All of these compounds are different since they move at different rates on the thin layer chromatogram.

Another problem that we are facing is what happens to those pigments when exposed to higher fluxes of energy. There is little work that I know of on the destruction of porphines. I can recall the work by Seely and Calvin as well as some other co-workers of Professor Calvin's. This work should be extended.

DR. SAGAN: The ozone concentration in a planetary atmosphere is proportional to the logarithm of the oxygen concentration. I believe you did your porphine synthesis under conditions of 20% oxygen, and one atmosphere pressure. It would be interesting to try a similar experiment with an oxygen concentration of, say, 10^{-5} by number the present value. With the oxygen abundance this small, there would have been essentially no ozone on the primitive Earth, and very likely high ultraviolet fluxes. You could have both ultraviolet light and small amounts of oxygen.

DR. SZUTKA: I just can guess what will happen. Since not much of the oxidizing agents are needed for the synthesis, I would guess that the synthesis of a porphine-like substance will occur. However, the yield will be reduced.

DR. GAFFRON: We should not look at these things as being present in pure substance. So when conditions are ready for the synthesis of porphyrin, there will be such metals as iron, vanadium, and best of all, cerium around. They will do all the oxidation you want.

DR. SAGAN: Without oxygen?

DR. GAFFRON: Yes. Cerium and light and water are equivalent to oxygen.

DR. BLOIS: I would like to say something about the ambivalence that has arisen in connection with the origin of pigments. A number of mechanisms have been proposed, wherein one obtains selective, monochromatically absorbing pigments, either on an inorganic basis, or through the synthesis of small organic molecules. On the other hand, people continue to pour the random polymers down the drain.

In considering the molecular evolution of pigments, I wonder if we shouldn't look for a moment, at least, at the kinds of syntheses which would very likely have occurred, the kinds of things that accidentally occur in the test tubes of otherwise very careful chemists. These would be the kinds of syntheses you might have expected nature to have conducted in rather early times. The development of a specific absorption property in a pigment might be expected to occur later when this more efficient process occurred as an evolutionary step forward.

But these inadvertent polymeric products that one finds, particularly those with a fair degree of aromaticity, have very interesting properties. They provide the first step in a mechanism providing escape from the destructive effects of UV or short wavelength light, and secondly, they offer a possibility for a primitive system which may convert absorbed light to a longer wavelength.

DR. GAFFRON: It would be helpful to find out which of your gunks does a good job of emitting light as fluorescence. Then you have a candidate for this type of work.

DR. BLOIS: Fluorescence has been detected in these polymers, but in an origin-of-life context, you don't have to ask for very much.

DR. GAFFRON: I would ask for as much as possible to increase the probability of success.

DR. PONNAMPERUMA: Dr. Gaffron, if the porphines existed before the evolution of photosynthesis, could they have had any function other than the one we assign them now?

DR. GAFFRON: Yes. You can get hydrogen transfer from one organic molecule to another, if the concentration is high enough. Again, we come to the question of high concentration. We cannot do it in the ocean, because the excited states of pigments that absorb light don't live long enough. They have to be in a concentrated brew of organic substances. Under these conditions you may photochemically transfer either electrons or hydrogen from one molecule to the other. The porphyrins could serve as catalysts for enrichment of new forms of organic molecules. It would not be a gain in free energy, but nevertheless a decrease in entropy, because of the creation of more improbable states, and this could go on in innumerable ways. With a little oxygen, such pigment-sensitized light could become either useful again or destructive. We know that such photoxidations may proceed with a quantum yield of one, or in case of chain reactions still better.

DR. SZUTKA: I was very impressed with Dr. Gaffron's work with intermittent turning off and on of light. This has a direct bearing to some work that I did in 1955–1956. I found that porphine-like substances undergo one and two electron oxidation states. And remarkably, in the presence of oxygen, here again, they are reduced when the source of energy is turned off. In our case we were using cobalt-60 gammas. But this turning on and off, which is similar to diurnal variations of the light intensity, might have a direct bearing. I do suspect—I don't have clear laboratory evidence—that chlorophylls will get "tired" whenever they are exposed over prolonged periods of time to high intensity, high energy, let's say light such as existed, for example, before the ozone layer was produced. And they would be not effective, their efficiency would drop down to zero, if that diurnal variation of light wouldn't be present.

I think that the work in that respect would prove to be quite useful for further studies.

DR. GAFFRON: Is this a statement or a question?

DR. SZUTKA: A statement.

DR. GAFFRON: Then please enlighten me as to what kind of work you refer to, which I am supposed to have done.

DR. SZUTKA: My work has been presented in 1957 at the American Chemical Society meeting in New York, and the second part was presented in 1958 at the Chicago meeting of the American Chemical Society and published in the *Journal of the American Chemical Society*.

CHAIRMAN QUIMBY: I would like to ask Dr. Gaffron a question. I wasn't sure whether you had "produced" or found an alga that did not release free oxygen.

DR. GAFFRON: Yes. This is Dr. Bishop's work.

DR. QUIMBY: Did you do this by mutation or did you find it somewhere?

DR. GAFFRON: Both. We first did it by mutation because we didn't know that another such alga existed. When I read that such an alga did exist, I hired the trainer of the alga, together with his beast. A young colleague, Dr. Wiessner, working with Professor E. G. Pringsheim at Göttingen, has discovered a green alga that uses light to assimilate acetate.

DR. SAGAN: Do you think that the production of a particular photosynthetic pigment is a forced process, during the early evolution of life, or is it possible that on some other planet, another pigment system could have developed?

DR. GAFFRON: This depends on how closely its geochemical history resembles ours. Any fluorescent dye may do, provided it has been stable enough to survive the particular geochemical processes on that particular planet. We have, besides green chlorophyll, many different photoactive pigments here on Earth. Not finding a chlorophyll spectrum on Mars does not preclude the evolution of photosynthetic organisms.

DR. SAGAN: Especially since it is difficult to detect the chlorophyll spectrum on Earth.

DR. GAFFRON: What evidence is there?

DR. SAGAN: There have been some reflection studies.

DR. GAFFRON: This is interesting. I did not know one could check it this way.

CONCLUDING REMARKS

CHAIRMAN QUIMBY: Before adjourning the meeting, I would like to make a formal statement. As a representative of the United States government, or as one of its employees, I would like to express my personal thanks, and the thanks of my country for the attendance at this meeting of Dr. Oparin, Dr. Haldane, Dr. Akabori, Dr. Pirie, Dr. Schramm—men who traveled great distances to contribute to our discussion.

I would also like to thank the others who traveled less distance but are very busy men, as all of us are, in this scientific age, for participating in this conference; and by all means Dr. Fox and associates for the tremendous work they have done in bringing us together for this productive and historic meeting, for your time, patience, and endurance. Thank you.

DR. OPARIN [through Mrs. Oparin]: In conclusion, I will express the opinion of the participants in this conference. It seems to me that this conference is a very important step on the way to the development of the question of the origin of life. I am quite sure that every participant will leave this place enriched by many facts and ideas which will stimulate him in his future work. I want to express all my thankfulness to the organizers of this conference for their brilliant management of this conference, and for their warm hospitality.

DR. QUIMBY: Thank you very much, Dr. and Mrs. Oparin.

SUBJECT INDEX

A

Abelson's syntheses, 374
Abiogenesis, 182
  concept of, 173
Absolute randomness, 403
Accessory pigments, 440
Accretion, gravitational potential energy
  of, 164
Acetaldehyde, 149, 159, 204, 211, 241
  302
Acetamide, 145
Acetate, 261, 450, 457
  photoassimilation of, 446, 447
Acetic acid, 175, 225, 226
Acetic anhydride, 276
Acetone, 231
Acetophenone, hydrogenation of, 132
Acetyl phosphate, 276
Acetylene, 149, 192, 249
Acidic proteinoid, 365
Acquired characteristics, inheritance of,82
Acrylonitrile, 155, 164, 200
Actin, 77, 79
Activation energy, 40, 284, 287
Adenine, 13, 56, 64, 102, 150, 152, 153,
  167, 170, 214, 215, 222, 223, 224,
  228, 229, 230, 233, 234, 235, 239,
  241, 242, 272, 303, 304, 318, 407,
  409, 450
  base catalyzed synthesis of, 229
  formation of, 62
  formation by electron irradiation, 224
  identification of, 151
  labeled, 231
  mechanism of formation of, 152
  rate of synthesis of, 150, 151
  synthesis of, 169, 191, 221
Adenine-C^{14}, 232
Adenine-8-C^{14}, 230
Adenosine, 17, 101, 214, 215, 231, 232,
  233, 234, 241, 266, 275, 303

labeled, 230–232
synthesis of, 303, 304
Adenosine diphosphate, 215, 230, 231,
  232, 233, 234, 235, 332, 338
Adenosine monophosphate, 215, 230,
  231, 232, 233, 234, 235
Adenosine phosphate, 241
Adenosine tetraphosphate, 230, 231, 232,
  233
Adenosine triphosphate, 2, 12, 13, 17, 45,
  103, 168, 214, 215, 230, 231, 232,
  233, 234, 235, 261, 265, 266, 269,
  270, 275, 276, 278, 279, 280, 289,
  296, 301, 314, 368, 370, 374, 377,
  381, 442, 447
  abiologically synthesized, 276
  autohydrolysis of, 374
  production of, 440
  production rate of, 275
  synthesized, biochemical activity of,
    234, 235
Adenosine triphosphate splitting ability,
  372, 374
Adenylic acid, 101, 264, 269, 318, 319
  labeled, 230, 231
Adenylyl 3′:5′-uridine-3′-phosphate, 41
ADP, see Adenosine diphosphate
Agar gel diffusion, 35
Agglutinin formation, 35
Alanine, 114, 118, 124, 143, 144, 149,
  170, 176, 178, 187, 190, 192, 204,
  291, 309
β-Alanine, 111, 112, 114, 115, 122, 145,
  155, 193
DL-Alanylglycylglycine, 309
Aldehydes, 244
Aldohexoses, acid-catalyzed polyconden-
  sation of, 287
Aldol condensation, 274
Algae, 442
  photoreducing mechanism of, 447
Aliphatic acids, 244